Math **Diagnosis** and **Intervention** System

W9-CNA-044

Booklet H

Fractions, Decimals, and Percents
in Grades 4–6

Scott Foresman·Addison Wesley

Overview of Math Diagnosis and Intervention System

The system can be used in a variety of situations:

- **During School** Use the system for intervention on prerequisite skills at the beginning of the year, the beginning of a topic, or the beginning of a lesson. Use for intervention during the Topic when more is needed beyond the resources already provide for the lesson.

- **After-school, Saturday school, summer-school (intersession) programs** Use the system for intervention offered in special programs.

The system provides resources for:

- **Assessment** Diagnostic Tests are provided. Each Diagnostic Test assesses the content for a grade. Use a test at the start of the year for entry-level assessment or anytime during the year as a summative evaluation.

- **Diagnosis** An item analysis identifies areas where intervention is needed.

- **Intervention** Booklets A–E in Part 1 and Booklets F–J in Part 2 identify specific concepts and assign a number to each concept, for example, A12 or E10. For each concept, there is a two-page Intervention Lesson that provides an instructional activity followed by practice. References for the Intervention Lessons are provided in teacher materials for *enVisionMATH*.

- **Monitoring** The Teacher's Guide provides both Individual Record Forms and Class Record Forms to monitor student progress.

Editorial Offices: Glenview, Illinois • Parsippany, New Jersey • New York, New York

Sales Offices: Boston, Massachusetts • Duluth, Georgia • Glenview, Illinois
Coppell, Texas • Sacramento, California • Mesa, Arizona

ISBN-13: 978-0-328-31123-1
ISBN-10: 0-328-31123-5

Copyright © Pearson Education, Inc.
All rights Reserved. Printed in the United States of America. All content in this publication is protected by Copyright.
Some pages in this publication are designed for use with appropriate equipment to reproduce copies for classroom use only.
Scott Foresman grants permission to classroom teachers to reproduce from these pages. Permission for other pages should
be obtained from the publisher prior to any prohibited preproduction, storage in a retrieval system, or transmission in any form
by any means, electronic, mechanical, photocopying, recording, or otherwise. For information regarding permission(s), write to:
Permissions Department, Scott Foresman, 1900 East Lake Avenue, Glenview, Illinois 60025.

16 V069 12 11

This work is protected by United States copyright laws and is provided *solely for the use of teachers and administrators* in teaching courses and assessing student learning in their classes and schools. Dissemination or sale of any part of this work (including the World Wide Web) will destroy the integrity of the work and is *not* permitted.

Table of Contents

Table of Contents continued

Equal Parts of a Whole

Worksheet (page 85)

Name _____

Equal Parts of a Whole

Materials rectangular sheets of paper, 3 for each student; crayons or markers

fold →

1. Fold a sheet of paper so the two shorter edges are on top of each other, as shown at the right.

2. Open up the piece of paper. Draw a line down the fold. Color each part a different color.

The table below shows special names for the equal parts. All parts must be **equal** before you can use these special names.

3. Are the parts you colored equal in size? **yes**

4. How many equal parts are there? **2**

5. What is the name for the parts you colored?
   halves

Number of Equal Parts	Name of Equal Parts
2	halves
3	thirds
4	fourths
5	fifths
6	sixths
8	eighths
10	tenths
12	twelfths

6. Fold another sheet of paper like above. Then fold it again so that it makes a long slender rectangle as shown below.

7. Open up the piece of paper. Draw lines down the folds. Color each part a different color.

8. Are the parts you colored equal in size? **yes**

9. How many equal parts are there? **4**

10. What is the name for the parts you colored?
    fourths

New fold →   ← Old fold

11. Fold another sheet of paper into 3 parts that are *not* equal. Open it and draw lines down the folds. In the space below, draw your rectangle and color each part a different color.

Check that students draw unequal parts.

© Pearson Education, Inc.

Worksheet (page 86)

Name _____

Equal Parts of a Whole (continued)

Tell if each shows parts that are equal or parts that are not equal. If the parts are equal, name them.

12. **equal** **fourths**

13. **not equal**

14. **equal** **thirds**

15. **equal** **eighths**

16. **equal** **twelfths**

17. **not equal**

18. **not equal**

19. **equal** **fifths**

20. **equal** **halves**

21. **not equal**

22. **equal** **sixths**

23. **not equal**

24. **Reasoning** If 5 children want to equally share a large pizza and each gets 2 pieces, will they need to cut the pizza into fifths, eighths, or tenths? **tenths**

© Pearson Education, Inc.

Teacher Notes

Ongoing Assessment

Ask: *Looking at the names for shapes divided into 4, 5, 6, 8, 10, and 12 equal parts, what might be the name of a shape divided into seven equal parts?* sevenths

Error Intervention

If children have trouble understanding the concept of equal parts,

then use A35: Equal parts.

If You Have More Time

Have students fold other rectangular sheets of paper and circular pieces of paper to find and name other equal parts.

Parts of a Region

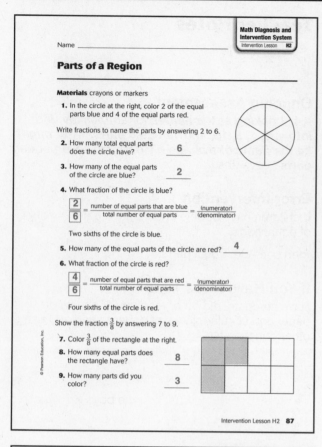

Name _____

Parts of a Region

Materials crayons or markers

1. In the circle at the right, color 2 of the equal parts blue and 4 of the equal parts red.

Write fractions to name the parts by answering 2 to 6.

2. How many total equal parts does the circle have? ___6___

3. How many of the equal parts of the circle are blue? ___2___

4. What fraction of the circle is blue?

$\dfrac{2}{6}$ = $\dfrac{\text{number of equal parts that are blue}}{\text{total number of equal parts}}$ = $\dfrac{\text{(numerator)}}{\text{(denominator)}}$

Two sixths of the circle is blue.

5. How many of the equal parts of the circle are red? ___4___

6. What fraction of the circle is red?

$\dfrac{4}{6}$ = $\dfrac{\text{number of equal parts that are red}}{\text{total number of equal parts}}$ = $\dfrac{\text{(numerator)}}{\text{(denominator)}}$

Four sixths of the circle is red.

Show the fraction $\frac{3}{8}$ by answering 7 to 9.

7. Color $\frac{3}{8}$ of the rectangle at the right.

8. How many equal parts does the rectangle have? ___8___

9. How many parts did you color? ___3___

Intervention Lesson H2 **87**

Teacher Notes

Ongoing Assessment

Ask: *Janet said she ate $\frac{4}{4}$ of an orange. Explain why Janet could have said she ate the whole orange.* Sample answer: The orange would be cut in 4 pieces and she ate 4 pieces, so she ate the whole thing.

Error Intervention

If children have trouble writing fractions for parts of a region,

then use A36: Understanding Fractions to Fourths and A38: Writing Fractions for Part of a Region.

If You Have More Time

Have students design a rectangular flag (or rug, placemat, etc.) that is divided into equal parts. Have them color their flag and then on the back write the fractional parts of each color.

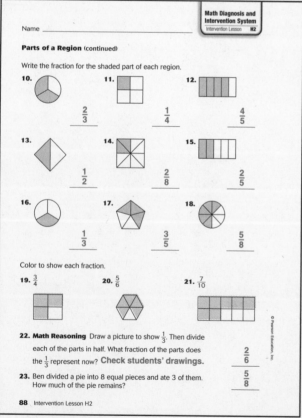

Name _____

Parts of a Region (continued)

Write the fraction for the shaded part of each region.

10. $\dfrac{2}{3}$

11. $\dfrac{1}{4}$

12. $\dfrac{4}{5}$

13. $\dfrac{1}{2}$

14. $\dfrac{2}{8}$

15. $\dfrac{2}{5}$

16. $\dfrac{1}{3}$

17. $\dfrac{3}{5}$

18. $\dfrac{5}{8}$

Color to show each fraction.

19. $\frac{3}{4}$

20. $\frac{5}{6}$

21. $\frac{7}{10}$

22. **Math Reasoning** Draw a picture to show $\frac{1}{3}$. Then divide each of the parts in half. What fraction of the parts does the $\frac{1}{3}$ represent now? **Check students' drawings.** $\dfrac{2}{6}$

23. Ben divided a pie into 8 equal pieces and ate 3 of them. How much of the pie remains? $\dfrac{5}{8}$

88 Intervention Lesson H2

© Pearson Education, Inc.

Parts of a Set

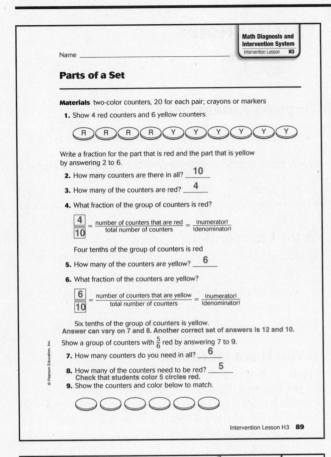

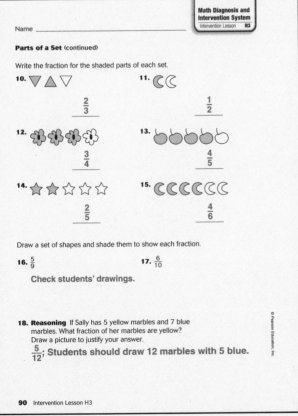

Teacher Notes

Ongoing Assessment

Ask: *What does it mean that $\frac{3}{12}$ of a group of marbles are green?* There are 3 green marbles out of a total of 12 marbles.

Error Intervention

If children have difficulty describing parts of a set, then use A37: Fractions of a Set and A39: Writing Fractions for Part of a Set.

If You Have More Time

Have students look around the classroom and name different fractions they see. For example: $\frac{6}{18}$ of the students have their math book out; $\frac{2}{5}$ of the computers are turned off; $\frac{5}{9}$ of the boys have on shorts.

Fractions and Length

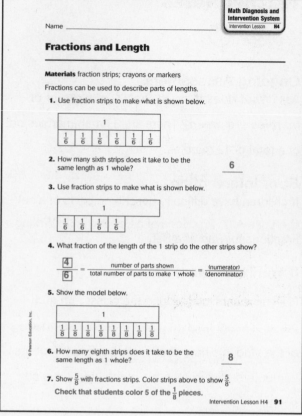

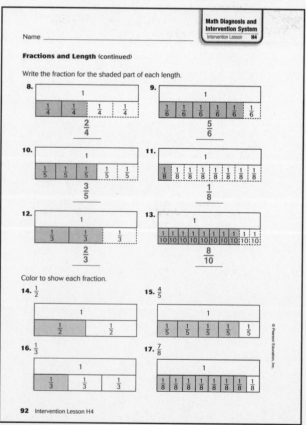

Teacher Notes

Ongoing Assessment

Ask: *If Nancy has walked $\frac{7}{10}$ of the length of the trail, how much more of the trail does she have left to walk?* $\frac{3}{10}$ of the trail

Error Intervention

If students have trouble identifying the denominator of the fraction,

then encourage them to use fraction strips to equal the length of the 1 strip to see how many total number of parts it takes to make 1 whole strip.

If You Have More Time

Have children name real-world situations which might use fractions of lengths. For example, fractions might be used to name the length of a pencil or the distance around a track in miles.

© Pearson Education, Inc.

Fractions on the Number Line

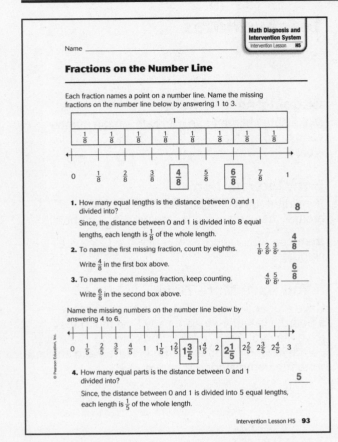

Name _____

Math Diagnosis and Intervention System
Intervention Lesson **H5**

Fractions on the Number Line

Each fraction names a point on a number line. Name the missing fractions on the number line below by answering 1 to 3.

1. How many equal lengths is the distance between 0 and 1 divided into?   **8**

Since, the distance between 0 and 1 is divided into 8 equal lengths, each length is $\frac{1}{8}$ of the whole length.

2. To name the first missing fraction, count by eighths. $\frac{1}{8}, \frac{2}{8}, \frac{3}{8}, \frac{4}{8}$

Write $\frac{4}{8}$ in the first box above.

3. To name the next missing fraction, keep counting. $\frac{4}{8}, \frac{5}{8}, \frac{6}{8}$

Write $\frac{6}{8}$ in the second box above.

Name the missing numbers on the number line below by answering 4 to 6.

4. How many equal parts is the distance between 0 and 1 divided into?   **5**

Since, the distance between 0 and 1 is divided into 5 equal lengths, each length is $\frac{1}{5}$ of the whole length.

Intervention Lesson H5   **93**

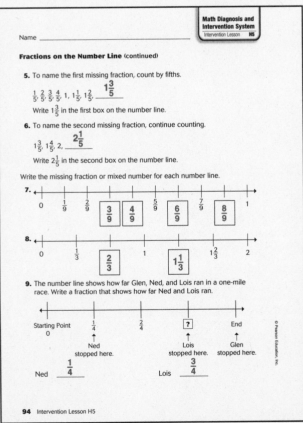

Name _____

Math Diagnosis and Intervention System
Intervention Lesson **H5**

Fractions on the Number Line (continued)

5. To name the first missing fraction, count by fifths.

$\frac{1}{5}, \frac{2}{5}, \frac{3}{5}, \frac{4}{5}, 1, 1\frac{1}{5}, 1\frac{2}{5}, \underline{1\frac{3}{5}}$

Write $1\frac{3}{5}$ in the first box on the number line.

6. To name the second missing fraction, continue counting.

$1\frac{3}{5}, 1\frac{4}{5}, 2, \underline{2\frac{1}{5}}$

Write $2\frac{1}{5}$ in the second box on the number line.

Write the missing fraction or mixed number for each number line.

7.

8.

9. The number line shows how far Glen, Ned, and Lois ran in a one-mile race. Write a fraction that shows how far Ned and Lois ran.

Ned ___ $\frac{1}{4}$ Lois ___ $\frac{3}{4}$

94   Intervention Lesson H5

Teacher Notes

Ongoing Assessment

Ask: ***How is finding a mixed number on a number line the same as finding a fraction on a number line?*** Sample answer: Find a mixed number like $1\frac{2}{5}$ between 1 and 2 the way you would find $\frac{2}{5}$ between 0 and 1.

Error Intervention

If students get confused when counting with fractions,

then have the students show a whole fraction strip and count as they put pieces below it. For example, they can count $\frac{1}{8}, \frac{2}{8}$, and so on as they put the eighths pieces below the one strip.

If You Have More Time

In pairs, have students practice counting from 0 to 5 using halves, thirds, fourths, fifths, sixths, eighths, tenths, and twelfths.

© Pearson Education, Inc.

Using Models to Compare Fractions

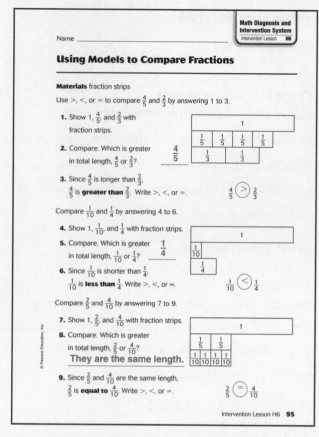

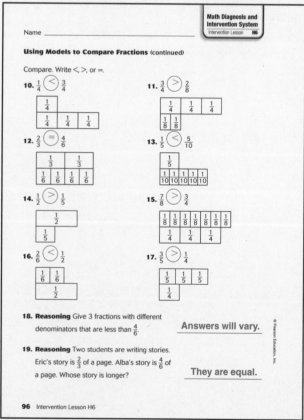

Teacher Notes

Ongoing Assessment
Make sure children can translate simple number sentences such as $7 < 8$, $4 > 2$, and $6 = 6$ into words.

Error Intervention
If children have difficulty with the concepts of greater than and less than, or with the symbols,

then use A27: Using $>$, $<$, and $=$ to Compare Numbers.

If You Have More Time
Have students pretend they are each painting a board. Have the students say how much they have stained. Then use fraction strips to show and compare who has stained more. Have each student write the comparison on paper.

© Pearson Education, Inc.

Using Models to Find Equivalent Fractions

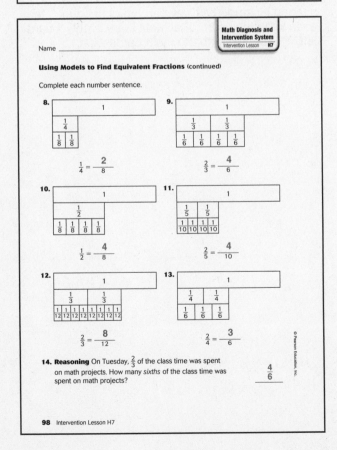

© Pearson Education, Inc.

Teacher Notes

Ongoing Assessment
Ask: *How many twelfths are equal to $\frac{1}{3}$?* $\frac{4}{12}$

Error Intervention
If students have trouble finding the equivalent fraction for Exercise 14,

then encourage them to use fraction strips.

If You Have More Time

Have students use fraction strips to find fractions equivalent to $\frac{1}{2}$. Have them record their findings. If time allows, do the same for $\frac{1}{4}$ and $\frac{3}{4}$.

Comparing Fractions on the Number Line

Name _____

Math Diagnosis and
Intervention System
Intervention Lesson   H8

Comparing Fractions on the Number Line

Materials 21 index cards for each pair; crayons or markers,
13 craft sticks for each pair; 1 yard of yarn for each pair

1. Write numbers on index cards, one number on each card.
   One partner writes the following numbers.

   $0, \frac{1}{3}, \frac{2}{3}, 1, 1\frac{1}{3}, 1\frac{2}{3}, 2, 2\frac{1}{3}, 2\frac{2}{3}, 3, 3\frac{1}{3}, 3\frac{2}{3},$ and 4

   The other partner writes the following numbers.

   $\frac{1}{3}, \frac{2}{3}, 1\frac{1}{3}, 1\frac{2}{3}, 2\frac{1}{3}, 2\frac{2}{3}, 3\frac{1}{3},$ and $3\frac{2}{3}$

2. Create a number line, like the one shown below, with the yarn,
   craft sticks, and the first set of index cards.

   ← | | | | | | | | | | | | | →
   0 $\frac{1}{3}$ $\frac{2}{3}$ 1 $1\frac{1}{3}$ $1\frac{2}{3}$ 2 $2\frac{1}{3}$ $2\frac{2}{3}$ 3 $3\frac{1}{3}$ $3\frac{2}{3}$ 4

3. Shuffle the other set of cards. Both you and your partner
   draw a card.

4. Match the numbers on the cards you drew
   with numbers on the number line you created.

   Which number is farther to the right?   **Answers will vary.**

   On the number line, fractions increase in value from
   left to right. So the fraction farther to the right is greater.

5. Write a comparison of your two numbers,
   such as $2\frac{2}{3} < 3\frac{1}{3}$.   **Answers will vary.**

   Set the first two cards aside. Continue drawing cards and writing
   comparisons until all the cards are gone.
   Answers will vary. Check comparisons.

6. _____   7. _____

8. _____   9. _____

Name _____

Math Diagnosis and
Intervention System
Intervention Lesson   H8

Comparing Fractions on the Number Line (continued)

For 10–18, use the number line below. Compare. Write <, >, or =.

← | | | | | | | | | | | | | →
0 $\frac{1}{4}$ $\frac{2}{4}$ or $\frac{1}{2}$ $\frac{3}{4}$ 1 $1\frac{1}{4}$ $1\frac{2}{4}$ or $1\frac{1}{2}$ $1\frac{3}{4}$ 2 $2\frac{1}{4}$ $2\frac{2}{4}$ or $2\frac{1}{2}$ $2\frac{3}{4}$ 3

10. $\frac{3}{4}$ ⊙> $\frac{1}{4}$ 11. $1\frac{1}{4}$ ⊙< $2\frac{1}{2}$ 12. $1\frac{1}{2}$ ⊙< $1\frac{3}{4}$

13. $1\frac{1}{4}$ ⊙> $\frac{1}{4}$ 14. $2\frac{3}{4}$ ⊙> $2\frac{1}{4}$ 15. $1\frac{1}{2}$ ⊙= $1\frac{1}{2}$

16. $\frac{1}{4}$ ⊙< $\frac{1}{2}$ 17. $1\frac{3}{4}$ ⊙= $1\frac{3}{4}$ 18. $\frac{3}{4}$ ⊙> $\frac{1}{2}$

For 19–24, use the number line below. Compare. Write <, >, or =.

← | | | | | | | | | | | | | →
0 1 2 3 4

19. $\frac{2}{3}$ ⊙> $\frac{1}{3}$ 20. $2\frac{1}{3}$ ⊙> $1\frac{2}{3}$ 21. $1\frac{1}{3}$ ⊙< $2\frac{1}{3}$

22. $\frac{3}{3}$ ⊙= 1 23. $2\frac{2}{3}$ ⊙> $2\frac{1}{3}$ 24. $\frac{2}{3}$ ⊙< $1\frac{1}{3}$

25. **Reasoning** Why is $2\frac{1}{8}$ greater than $1\frac{7}{8}$, even though $\frac{1}{8}$ is
    less than $\frac{7}{8}$?
    Sample answer: The whole number part of $2\frac{1}{8}$ is greater than the
    whole number part of $1\frac{7}{8}$. So, $2\frac{1}{8} > 1\frac{7}{8}$.

26. **Reasoning** Explain how you can use the number line above
    to compare $6\frac{1}{3}$ and $6\frac{2}{3}$.
    Sample answer: Since the whole number parts of the mixed
    numbers are the same, you can just compare the fractional parts.
    You can compare $\frac{1}{3}$ and $\frac{2}{3}$ on the number line above.

Teacher Notes

Ongoing Assessment
Ask: **Which is greater $4\frac{1}{4}$ or $4\frac{3}{4}$?** $4\frac{3}{4}$

Error Intervention
If students have trouble with comparing fractions
on a number line,

then have them use fraction strips to create a

number line where the length of a fraction piece,

like fifths, is the distance between 0 and $\frac{1}{5}$, $\frac{1}{5}$

and $\frac{2}{5}$, and so on, on the number line. Then,

students can line up fraction strips below the

number line to compare.

If You Have More Time
Have partners combine their cards from the activity.
Shuffle them and then each draw a card. The
student whose card is greater keeps both cards.
(Let them use the yarn to craft a number line if
needed.) If students draw cards that are equal, they
each keep their card. Play until there is only 1 card
left. The person with the most cards wins.

© Pearson Education, Inc.

Comparing Fractions

Math Diagnosis and
Intervention System
Intervention Lesson   H9

Name _____

Comparing Fractions

Materials fraction strips

Compare $\frac{3}{10}$ and $\frac{7}{8}$ by answering 1 to 3.

Compare each fraction to $\frac{1}{2}$. Write > or <.

1. $\frac{3}{10}$ $<$ $\frac{1}{2}$

2. $\frac{7}{8}$ $>$ $\frac{1}{2}$

3. Since $\frac{3}{10} < \frac{1}{2}$ and $\frac{7}{8} > \frac{1}{2}$, then $\frac{3}{10}$ $<$ $\frac{7}{8}$.

You can compare two fractions with the same denominator just by comparing the numerators.

Use equivalent fractions to compare $\frac{1}{4}$ and $\frac{5}{12}$ by answering 4 to 6.

4. $\frac{1}{4}$ is the same as how many twelfths? __3__

5. Since $\frac{1}{4} = \frac{3}{12}$, you can now compare $\frac{3}{12}$ and $\frac{5}{12}$. $\frac{5}{12}$
   Which fraction has the greater numerator?

6. Compare. Write > or <. $\frac{3}{12}$ $<$ $\frac{5}{12}$
   So, $\frac{1}{4}$ $<$ $\frac{5}{12}$.

7. Use fraction strips to compare $\frac{1}{8}$ and $\frac{1}{4}$. Write > or <.
   $\frac{1}{8}$ $<$ $\frac{1}{4}$

8. Which fraction has the greater denominator $\frac{1}{8}$ or $\frac{1}{4}$? $\frac{1}{8}$

When both fractions have the same numerator, the fraction with the greater denominator is **less than** the other fraction.

© Pearson Education, Inc.

Intervention Lesson H9   **101**

Math Diagnosis and
Intervention System
Intervention Lesson   H9

Name _____

Comparing Fractions (continued)

Compare. Write >, <, or = for each.

9. $\frac{1}{4}$ $<$ $\frac{3}{4}$

10. $\frac{5}{10}$ $>$ $\frac{3}{10}$

11. $\frac{1}{5}$ $<$ $\frac{5}{8}$

12. $\frac{7}{10}$ $<$ $\frac{9}{10}$

13. $\frac{2}{8}$ $=$ $\frac{1}{4}$

14. $\frac{8}{12}$ $<$ $\frac{5}{6}$

15. $\frac{6}{8}$ $>$ $\frac{6}{10}$

16. $\frac{3}{6}$ $=$ $\frac{6}{12}$

17. $\frac{3}{5}$ $>$ $\frac{7}{12}$

18. $\frac{1}{2}$ $>$ $\frac{3}{8}$

19. $\frac{3}{5}$ $=$ $\frac{6}{10}$

20. $\frac{1}{5}$ $>$ $\frac{1}{8}$

21. **Reasoning** Two students are timed on a math facts test.
    Nathan finished $\frac{5}{6}$ of the problems. Terrell finished $\frac{5}{8}$
    of the problems. Which student finished a greater part?   **Nathan**

© Pearson Education, Inc.

102 Intervention Lesson H9

Teacher Notes

Ongoing Assessment

Ask: *How can you compare $\frac{1}{3}$ and $\frac{1}{5}$ without fraction strips and without finding a common denominator?* Sample answer: Both of the numerators are 1, so the fraction with the greater denominator is less. So, $\frac{1}{5}$ is less than $\frac{1}{3}$.

Error Intervention

If students have trouble comparing fractions,

then use H6: Using Models to Compare Fractions.

If You Have More Time

Have students use fraction strips to find fractions less than $\frac{1}{2}$. Have them record their findings. If time allows, do the same for fractions greater than $\frac{1}{2}$.

Fractions and Decimals

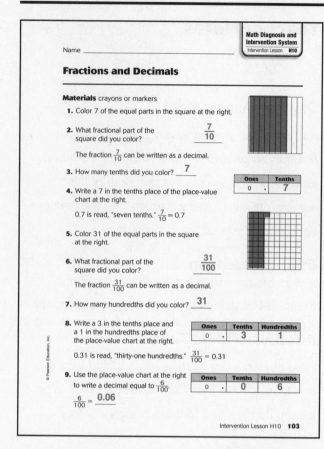

Name _____

Math Diagnosis and
Intervention System
Intervention Lesson   H10

Fractions and Decimals

Materials crayons or markers

1. Color 7 of the equal parts in the square at the right.

2. What fractional part of the square did you color? $\frac{7}{10}$

The fraction $\frac{7}{10}$ can be written as a decimal.

3. How many tenths did you color?   7

4. Write a 7 in the tenths place of the place-value chart at the right.

Ones		Tenths
0	.	7

0.7 is read, "seven tenths." $\frac{7}{10} = 0.7$

5. Color 31 of the equal parts in the square at the right.

6. What fractional part of the square did you color? $\frac{31}{100}$

The fraction $\frac{31}{100}$ can be written as a decimal.

7. How many hundredths did you color?   31

8. Write a 3 in the tenths place and a 1 in the hundredths place of the place-value chart at the right.

Ones		Tenths	Hundredths
0	.	3	1

0.31 is read, "thirty-one hundredths." $\frac{31}{100} = 0.31$

9. Use the place-value chart at the right to write a decimal equal to $\frac{6}{100}$.

Ones		Tenths	Hundredths
0	.	0	6

$\frac{6}{100} = $ 0.06

© Pearson Education, Inc.

Intervention Lesson H10   **103**

Teacher Notes

Ongoing Assessment

Ask: **Why is $\frac{9}{100}$ written as 0.09 and not 0.9 in decimal form?** Sample answer: The 9 needs to be in the hundredths place to show 9 hundredths instead of 9 tenths.

Error Intervention

If students have trouble remembering how many decimal places a tenth or hundredth has,

then explain that a 10 has **one** zero, so a fraction with a denominator of 10 will only have **one** digit to the right of the decimal point. Since a 100 has **two** zeros, a fraction with a denominator of 100 will have **two** digits to the right of the decimal point.

If You Have More Time

Have students work in pairs. Have each student write a fraction and then give the paper to the partner. Have the partner write the fraction in decimal form and in word form.

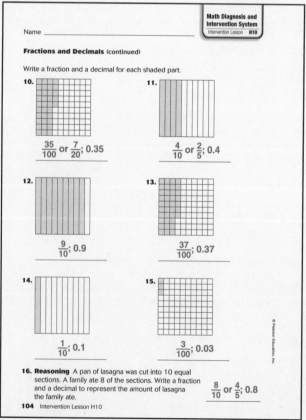

Name _____

Math Diagnosis and
Intervention System
Intervention Lesson   H10

Fractions and Decimals (continued)

Write a fraction and a decimal for each shaded part.

10.

$\frac{35}{100}$ or $\frac{7}{20}$; 0.35

11.

$\frac{4}{10}$ or $\frac{2}{5}$; 0.4

12.

$\frac{9}{10}$; 0.9

13.

$\frac{37}{100}$; 0.37

14.

$\frac{1}{10}$; 0.1

15.

$\frac{3}{100}$; 0.03

16. Reasoning A pan of lasagna was cut into 10 equal sections. A family ate 8 of the sections. Write a fraction and a decimal to represent the amount of lasagna the family ate.

$\frac{8}{10}$ or $\frac{4}{5}$; 0.8

© Pearson Education, Inc.

104   Intervention Lesson H10

© Pearson Education, Inc.

Counting Money

Name _____

Counting Money

Gary has a $1 bill, a quarter, 2 dimes, a nickel, and a penny.

When you count money, start with the bill or coin of greatest value. Then count on to find the total.

1. Count Gary's money.

$1.00 $1.25 $1.35 $1.45 $1.50 $1.51

2. How much money does Gary have? __$1.51__

3. Write $1.51 in words.   one dollar and __fifty-one__ cents

4. Ty has a $1 bill, a half-dollar, 2 quarters, and 3 dimes. Count Ty's money.

$1.00 $1.50 $1.75 $2.00 $2.10 $2.20 $2.30

5. How much money does Ty have? __$2.30__

6. Who had more money, Gary or Ty? __Ty__

Intervention Lesson H11   **105**

© Pearson Education, Inc.

Teacher Notes

Ongoing Assessment

Ask: *Suri has a $1 bill, 2 quarters, 3 dimes, 5 nickels, and 15 pennies. How much money does she have?* $2.20

Error Intervention

If children have difficulty counting the value of the bills and coins,

then let them use play money and use A63: Dollars.

If children have trouble with the < and > signs,

then use A27: Using <, >, and = to Compare Numbers.

If You Have More Time

Have students work in pairs. Give partners a variety of bills and coins. Have partners sell and buy items in the classroom. The "seller" gives the price of the item. The "buyer" counts the correct amount of money out to the seller. Switch roles and repeat as time allows.

Name _____

Counting Money (continued)

Write the total value in dollars and cents.

7.

__$1.83__

8. 1 five-dollar bill, 3 quarters, 1 nickel, 2 pennies

__$5.82__

9. 1 one-dollar bill, 1 half-dollar, 4 nickels, 8 pennies

__$1.78__

10. 1 one-dollar bill, 2 quarters, 4 dimes, 3 nickels, 1 penny

__$2.06__

11. 1 five-dollar bill, 1 one-dollar bill, 1 quarter, 4 dimes, 3 nickels

__$6.80__

Compare the amounts. Write <, >, or =.

12. $1.17 ⟨<⟩ 4 quarters, 2 dimes   **13.** $0.49 ⟨>⟩ 4 dimes, 1 nickel

14. 2 quarters, 6 dimes ⟨=⟩ $1.10   **15.** 3 half-dollars, 3 nickels ⟨<⟩ $1.70

16. Reasoning Anita and Ted both have $1.49, but each have different coins. What coins could each have?

Check that students have two different ways to show $1.49.

106 Intervention Lesson H11

© Pearson Education, Inc.

Making Change

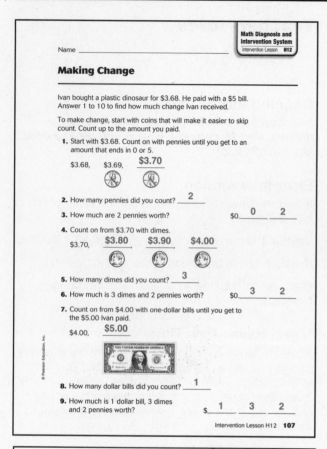

Name _____

Making Change

Ivan bought a plastic dinosaur for $3.68. He paid with a $5 bill. Answer 1 to 10 to find how much change Ivan received.

To make change, start with coins that will make it easier to skip count. Count up to the amount you paid.

1. Start with $3.68. Count on with pennies until you get to an amount that ends in 0 or 5.

$3.68, $3.69,   **$3.70**

2. How many pennies did you count?   **2**

3. How much are 2 pennies worth? $0. **0** **2**

4. Count on from $3.70 with dimes.

$3.70,   **$3.80**   **$3.90**   **$4.00**

5. How many dimes did you count?   **3**

6. How much is 3 dimes and 2 pennies worth? $0. **3** **2**

7. Count on from $4.00 with one-dollar bills until you get to the $5.00 Ivan paid.

$4.00,   **$5.00**

8. How many dollar bills did you count?   **1**

9. How much is 1 dollar bill, 3 dimes and 2 pennies worth? $ **1** **3** **2**

Intervention Lesson H12   **107**

© Pearson Education, Inc.

Name _____

Making Change (continued)

10. How much change did Ivan receive?   **$1.32**

List the coins and bills you would use to make change. Then write the change in dollars and cents.

11. Cost: $1.40
Amount paid: $2.00
Possible answer: 1 dime, 2 quarters

$0.60

12. Cost: $3.17
Amount paid: $4.00
Possible answer: 3 pennies, 1 nickel, 3 quarters

$0.83

13. Cost: $0.76
Amount paid: $5.00
Possible answer: 4 pennies, 2 dimes, 4 one-dollar bills

$4.24

14. Cost: $1.33
Amount paid: $5.00
Possible answer: 2 pennies, 1 nickel, 1 dime,
2 quarters, 3 one-dollar bills

$3.67

15. Reasoning Beverly bought a gallon of juice for $2.69. She used three $1 bills. Give two ways to show the change. Circle the one that uses the fewest coins.
Coins will vary. Check that total value is $0.31.
Fewest possible coins: 1 penny, 1 nickel, 1 quarter

© Pearson Education, Inc.

Teacher Notes

Ongoing Assessment

Ask: *Meg bought a pencil that cost $0.35. She paid with a $5 bill. Explain how to count on to find how much change she received.* 35 cents, 40 cents, 50 cents, 75 cents, 1 dollar, 2 dollars, 3 dollars, 4 dollars, 5 dollars. She received $4.65 in change.

Error Intervention

If students have trouble counting money,

then use H11: Counting Money and allow them to use play money to help visualize the change while counting.

If You Have More Time

Have students work in pairs. Give partners four $1 bills, one $5 bill, 1 half-dollar, 4 quarters, 10 dimes, 10 nickels, and 10 pennies. Have partners sell and buy items in the classroom. The "seller" gives the price of the item (between $0.01 and $9.00). The "buyer" can only pay with bills. The seller then counts out the "buyer's" change. Switch roles and repeat as time allows. Instead of classroom items, grocery ads can be used if available. Make sure items are available for the $0.01 to $9.00 price range in the ad.

© Pearson Education, Inc.

Using Money to Understand Decimals

Using Money to Understand Decimals

1. How many dimes are equal to one dollar? **10**

2. What fraction of a dollar is each dime? $\frac{1}{10}$

3. What decimal shows what part of a dollar each dime is? **0.1**

4. How many pennies are equal to one dollar? **100**

5. What fraction of a dollar is each penny? $\frac{1}{100}$

6. What decimal shows what part of a dollar each penny is? **0.01**

7. Show $1.32 in the place-value chart at the right.

dollars (ones)		dimes (tenths)	pennies (hundredths)
$1	.	3	2

8. $1.32 = **1** dollar + 3 dimes + **2** pennies

1.32 = **1** one + **3** tenths + 2 hundredths

9. $1.32 = **1** dollar + 32 pennies

1.32 = **1** one + **32** hundredths

Reading decimals and money are very similar.
$1.32 is read "one dollar and thirty-two cents."
1.32 is read "one and thirty-two hundredths."

10. Show two dollars and sixty four cents in the chart at the right.

dollars (ones)		dimes (tenths)	pennies (hundredths)
$2	.	6	4

11. Write two and sixty-four hundredths with a decimal point. **2.64**

© Pearson Education, Inc.

Using Money to Understand Decimals (continued)

Write the values for the money amounts and the decimal numbers.

12. $4.62 = **4** dollars + **6** dimes + **2** pennies

4.62 = **4** ones + **6** tenths + **2** hundredths

13. $7.31 = **7** dollars + **3** dimes + **1** penny

7.31 = **7** ones + **3** tenths + **1** hundredth

14. $1.04 = **1** dollar + **0** dimes + **4** pennies

1.04 = **1** one + **0** tenths + **4** hundredths

15. $2.87 = **2** dollars + **87** pennies

2.87 = **2** ones + **87** hundredths

16. $9.16 = **9** dollars + **16** pennies

9.16 = **9** ones + **16** hundredths

17. $7.39 = **7** dollars + **39** pennies

7.39 = **7** ones + **39** hundredths

18. Write three and ninety-one hundredths with a decimal point. **3.91**

19. Write seven and twenty-six hundredths with a decimal point. **7.26**

20. Lisabeth wants to buy school supplies for $5.25. How can she pay for them using only dollars, dimes, and pennies?
5 dollars, 2 dimes, and 5 pennies

21. Reasoning Explain why the 2 in $6.27 represents tenths of a dollar.
Sample answer: The 2 is in the dimes, or tenths, place.

© Pearson Education, Inc.

Teacher Notes

Ongoing Assessment

Ask: *Explain why the 4 in $3.24 represents hundredths of a dollar.* Sample answer: The 4 is in the pennies, or hundredths, place.

Error Intervention

If students have trouble with the tenths and hundredths concept,

then use H10: Fractions and Decimals.

If students have difficulty figuring out how many dimes and/or pennies there are in the money amount,

then use A57: Counting Pennies, Nickels, and Dimes and allow them to use play money while they count out the money amount.

If You Have More Time

Have students work in pairs and write 0 through 9, a decimal point, and a dollar sign on 12 index cards (one number or symbol on each card). Have one partner display 5 cards to show an amount in dollars and cents, like $5.47. Have the other partner read the amount and then say how many dollars, dimes, and pennies. Have the student remove the dollar sign, say the decimal amount, and then say how many ones, tenths, and hundredths. Have students take turns in each role with different amounts.

Equivalent Fractions

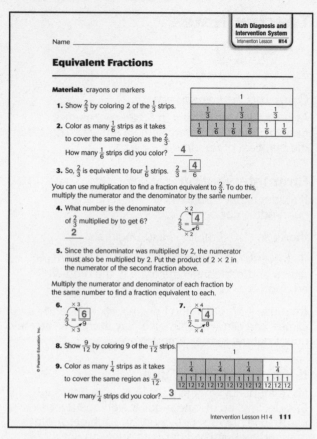

Name _____

Equivalent Fractions

Materials crayons or markers

1. Show $\frac{2}{3}$ by coloring 2 of the $\frac{1}{3}$ strips.

2. Color as many $\frac{1}{6}$ strips as it takes to cover the same region as the $\frac{2}{3}$. How many $\frac{1}{6}$ strips did you color? __4__

3. So, $\frac{2}{3}$ is equivalent to four $\frac{1}{6}$ strips. $\frac{2}{3} = \frac{4}{6}$

You can use multiplication to find a fraction equivalent to $\frac{2}{3}$. To do this, multiply the numerator and the denominator by the same number.

4. What number is the denominator of $\frac{2}{3}$ multiplied by to get 6? __2__

5. Since the denominator was multiplied by 2, the numerator must also be multiplied by 2. Put the product of 2×2 in the numerator of the second fraction above.

Multiply the numerator and denominator of each fraction by the same number to find a fraction equivalent to each.

6. $\frac{2}{3} = \frac{6}{9}$ ($\times 3$)

7. $\frac{2}{2} = \frac{4}{8}$ ($\times 4$)

8. Show $\frac{9}{12}$ by coloring 9 of the $\frac{1}{12}$ strips.

9. Color as many $\frac{1}{4}$ strips as it takes to cover the same region as $\frac{9}{12}$. How many $\frac{1}{4}$ strips did you color? __3__

Intervention Lesson H14 **111**

Name _____

Equivalent Fractions (continued)

10. So, $\frac{9}{12}$ is equivalent to three $\frac{1}{4}$ strips. $\frac{9}{12} = \frac{3}{4}$

You can use division to find a fraction equivalent to $\frac{9}{12}$. To do this, divide the numerator and the denominator by the same number.

11. What number is the denominator of $\frac{9}{12}$ divided by to get 4? __3__ $\frac{9}{12} = \frac{3}{4}$ ($\div 3$)

12. Since the denominator was divided by 3, the numerator must also be divided by 3. Put the quotient of $9 \div 3$ in the numerator of the second fraction above.

Divide the numerator and denominator of each fraction by the same number to find a fraction equivalent to each.

13. $\frac{8}{10} = \frac{4}{5}$ ($\div 2$)

14. $\frac{10}{15} = \frac{2}{3}$ ($\div 5$)

If the numerator and denominator cannot be divided by anything else, then the fraction is in simplest form.

15. Is $\frac{5}{12}$ in simplest form? __yes__

16. Is $\frac{6}{8}$ in simplest form? __no__

Find each equivalent fraction.

17. $\frac{1}{5} = \frac{3}{15}$

18. $\frac{8}{10} = \frac{4}{5}$

19. $\frac{2}{8} = \frac{1}{4}$

20. $\frac{7}{10} = \frac{14}{20}$

21. $\frac{6}{14} = \frac{3}{7}$

22. $\frac{8}{11} = \frac{16}{22}$

Write each fraction in simplest form.

23. $\frac{6}{8}$ __$\frac{3}{4}$__

24. $\frac{8}{12}$ __$\frac{2}{3}$__

25. $\frac{7}{35}$ __$\frac{1}{5}$__

26. $\frac{16}{24}$ __$\frac{2}{3}$__

27. **Reasoning** Explain why $\frac{4}{6}$ is not in simplest form.
   Sample answer: 4 and 6 have a common factor of 2.

112 Intervention Lesson H14

Teacher Notes

Ongoing Assessment

Ask: *Explain how you can tell $\frac{3}{7}$ is in simplest form.* 3 and 7 have only 1 as a common factor.

Error Intervention

If students do not understand how two fractions can be equivalent,

then use H7: Using Models to Find Equivalent Fractions.

If You Have More Time

Have students create and number a cube 2, 2, 3, 3, 6, and 6. Label 8 index cards: $\frac{1}{2}$, $\frac{2}{3}$, $\frac{4}{6}$, $\frac{6}{18}$, $\frac{6}{24}$, $\frac{6}{10}$, $\frac{6}{12}$, and $\frac{3}{4}$. Shuffle the index cards. One student rolls the number cube and the other draws an index card. Both students find a fraction equivalent to the one on the index card by either multiplying or dividing by the number rolled. Have students check each others' work. Sometimes either operation can be done, sometimes only one can be used.

© Pearson Education, Inc.

Fractions and Division

Name _____

Math Diagnosis and
Intervention System
Intervention Lesson H15

Fractions and Division

Reg, Sal, Mac, and Ned shared 3 granola bars equally.
What fraction of a granola bar did each boy get?

Find 3 ÷ 4 by answering 1 to 5.

1. Since 4 friends shared the bars equally, divide each bar into 4 equal sections.

| Reg | Sal | Mac | Ned |

2. Each boy got 1 section from each granola bar. Write Reg in the first section of each granola bar, Sal in the second section, Mac in the third section, and Ned in the fourth section.

| Reg | Sal | Mac | Ned |

| Reg | Sal | Mac | Ned |

3. How many sections total did each boy get? ___ 3

4. Each boy got a total of 3 sections. Each granola bar was divided into 4 sections. What part of a granola bar did each boy get? $\frac{3}{4}$

5. So, 3 ÷ 4 = $\frac{3}{4}$.

Mia, Val, Bea, Dee, and Kim shared 4 granola bars equally. What fraction of a granola bar did each girl get?

Find 4 ÷ 5 by answering 6 to 10.

6. Since 5 friends shared the bars equally, divide each bar into 5 equal sections.

| Mia | Val | Bea | Dee | Kim |

7. Each girl got 1 section from each granola bar. Write each of the girls names in 1 section of each of the granola bars.

Mia	Val	Bea	Dee	Kim
Mia	Val	Bea	Dee	Kim
Mia	Val	Bea	Dee	Kim

8. How many sections total did each girl get? ___ 4

9. What part of a granola bar did each girl get? $\frac{4}{5}$

10. So, 4 ÷ 5 = $\frac{4}{5}$.

© Pearson Education, Inc.

Intervention Lesson H15   **113**

Name _____

Math Diagnosis and
Intervention System
Intervention Lesson H15

Fractions and Division (continued)

11. Reasoning You found that 3 ÷ 4 = $\frac{3}{4}$ and 4 ÷ 5 = $\frac{4}{5}$.

What is 2 ÷ 9? How do you know?

$\frac{2}{9}$; Sample answer: The 2 goes in the numerator and the 9 goes in the denominator.

Tell what fraction each person gets when they share equally.

12. Three students share 2 packs of paper. — $\frac{2}{3}$ pack of paper

13. Eight girls share 3 bags of balloons. — $\frac{3}{8}$ bag of balloons

14. Two sisters share 1 bag of popcorn. — $\frac{1}{2}$ bag of popcorn

15. Seven family members share 3 pounds of meat. — $\frac{3}{7}$ pound of meat

16. Five brothers pay for a $3 card. — $\frac{3}{5}$ of a dollar

Give each answer as a fraction.

17. 7 ÷ 8 = $\frac{7}{8}$ **18.** 2 ÷ 5 = $\frac{2}{5}$ **19.** 1 ÷ 9 = $\frac{1}{9}$

20. 2 ÷ 6 = $\frac{2}{6}$ **21.** 7 ÷ 9 = $\frac{7}{9}$ **22.** 1 ÷ 5 = $\frac{1}{5}$

23. 8 ÷ 9 = $\frac{8}{9}$ **24.** 2 ÷ 8 = $\frac{2}{8}$ **25.** 7 ÷ 10 = $\frac{7}{10}$

26. Reasoning Mrs. Savagae baked 5 loaves of banana bread and used 2 bananas to make each loaf. She is dividing the loaves equally among 7 different friends. What fraction of a loaf does each friend get? — $\frac{5}{7}$ of a loaf

© Pearson Education, Inc.

114 Intervention Lesson H15

Teacher Notes

Ongoing Assessment

Ask: **What is 5 ÷ 8?** $\frac{5}{8}$

Error Intervention

If students do not understand why each boy gets $\frac{3}{4}$ and each girl gets $\frac{4}{5}$,

then have them draw the same number of granola bars for each problem and divide each bar into 4 sections. Then label Reg in 3 of the 4 sections of the first bar, Sal in 3 of the 4 sections of the second bar, Mac in 3 of the 4 sections of the third bar, and Ned in the 3 remaining sections. Do the same for the other problem.

If You Have More Time

Write $\frac{3}{10}$, $\frac{4}{9}$, $\frac{1}{3}$, $\frac{2}{3}$, and $\frac{5}{9}$ on the board. Have students write situations where people are sharing and each person gets each fraction listed.

Estimating Fractional Amounts

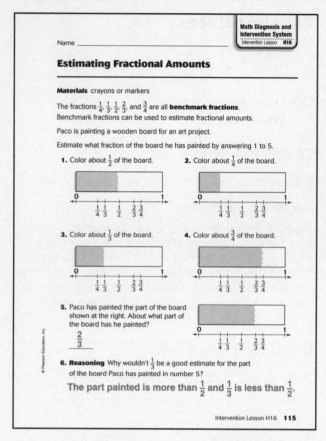

Teacher Notes

Ongoing Assessment

Ask: *Which benchmark fractions are greater than $\frac{1}{2}$? $\frac{2}{3}$ and $\frac{3}{4}$ Which benchmark fractions are less than $\frac{1}{2}$? $\frac{1}{3}$ and $\frac{1}{4}$*

Error Intervention

If students have trouble visualizing fractional amounts, for example, $\frac{2}{3}$ and $\frac{3}{4}$ of a pizza,

then have them draw two pictures the same size of a whole pizza. Have students shade $\frac{3}{4}$ of one and $\frac{2}{3}$ of the other. Then, they can compare the pizza they are estimating to the pictures they drew.

If You Have More Time

Give each student two rectangles. Have each student color a part of each rectangle. Then have the students exchange the rectangles with a partner. Have the partner estimate which fractional amount of the rectangle is colored.

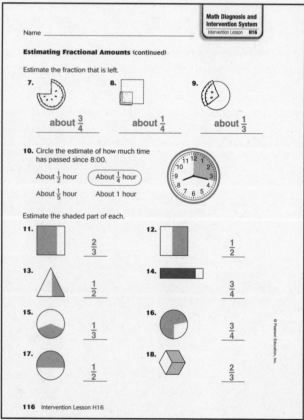

© Pearson Education, Inc.

Simplest Form

Name _____

Simplest Form

Anita saw that $\frac{12}{30}$ of the students in her class wore t-shirts one day.

Write $\frac{12}{30}$ in simplest form by answering 1 to 5.

To write a fraction in simplest form, you need to use the greatest common factor (GCF) for the numerator and the denominator.

1. What is the GCF of 12 and 30? ____**6**____

2. Divide both the numerator and the denominator by the GCF to find an equivalent fraction. $\frac{12 \div 6}{30 \div 6} = \frac{\boxed{2}}{5}$

3. What is the fraction that you found that is equivalent to $\frac{12}{30}$? $\frac{2}{5}$

A fraction is in simplest form when the GCF of the numerator and the denominator is 1.

4. Is the GCF of the numerator and the denominator of the fraction you found 1?   **yes**

5. What is $\frac{12}{30}$ in simplest form? $\frac{2}{5}$

Nine out of 24 girls on the cross county team went to the state finals.

6. What fraction of the girls went to the state final? $\frac{9}{24}$

Write $\frac{9}{24}$ in simplest form by answering 7 to 11.

7. What is the GCF of 9 and 24?   **3**

8. Divide both the numerator and the denominator by the GCF to find an equivalent fraction. $\frac{9 \div 3}{24 \div 3} = \frac{\boxed{3}}{\boxed{8}}$

9. What is the GCF of the numerator and the denominator of the fraction you found?   **1**

10. Is this fraction written in simplest form?   **yes**

11. What fraction in simplest form represents the part of girls on the cross country team that went to the state finals? $\frac{3}{8}$

Intervention Lesson H17   **117**

Name _____

Simplest Form (continued)

Write each fraction in simplest form. If it is in simplest form, write simplest form.

12. $\frac{5}{10}$ $\frac{1}{2}$

13. $\frac{14}{16}$ $\frac{7}{8}$

14. $\frac{27}{45}$ $\frac{3}{5}$

15. $\frac{10}{15}$ $\frac{2}{3}$

16. $\frac{5}{20}$ $\frac{1}{4}$

17. $\frac{14}{18}$ $\frac{7}{9}$

18. $\frac{5}{11}$ simplest form

19. $\frac{1}{15}$ simplest form

20. $\frac{6}{20}$ $\frac{3}{10}$

21. $\frac{36}{45}$ $\frac{4}{5}$

22. $\frac{11}{33}$ $\frac{1}{3}$

23. $\frac{24}{60}$ $\frac{2}{5}$

24. $\frac{18}{24}$ $\frac{3}{4}$

25. $\frac{12}{160}$ $\frac{3}{40}$

26. $\frac{6}{12}$ $\frac{1}{2}$

27. $\frac{9}{81}$ $\frac{1}{9}$

28. $\frac{16}{48}$ $\frac{1}{3}$

29. $\frac{7}{13}$ simplest form

30. $\frac{21}{25}$ simplest form

31. $\frac{14}{35}$ $\frac{2}{5}$

32. Reasoning Explain how to tell $\frac{100}{105}$ is not in simplest form without finding all the factors.

Since each number ends in 0 or 5, each is divisible by 5. Simplify $\frac{100}{105}$ by dividing the numerator and denominator by 5.

118   Intervention Lesson H17

Teacher Notes

Ongoing Assessment

Ask: **What is $\frac{6}{8}$ written in simplest form?** $\frac{3}{4}$ **How do you know it is in simplest form?** The GCF of 3 and 4 is one.

Error Intervention

If students can not find the greatest common factor,

then use G64: Greatest Common Factor.

If students do not know how to find equivalent fractions,

then use H14: Equivalent Fractions.

If You Have More Time

Have students work in pairs. Have partners write each of the following numbers on index cards, shuffle the cards, and place them in a stack face down.

1, 2, 3, 4, 5, 6, 8, 9, 10, 12, 24

Each partner draws a card. The students write a fraction with the smaller number as the numerator and the greater number as the denominator. The pair decides if the fraction is in simplest form. If the fractions is not in simplest form, the pair works together to rewrite the fraction in simplest form. Have pairs shuffle the two cards back into the deck and repeat, at least 7 more times. Have the students share with the class what fractions can be simplified to $\frac{1}{2}$, $\frac{1}{3}$, and $\frac{1}{4}$.

© Pearson Education, Inc.

Mixed Numbers

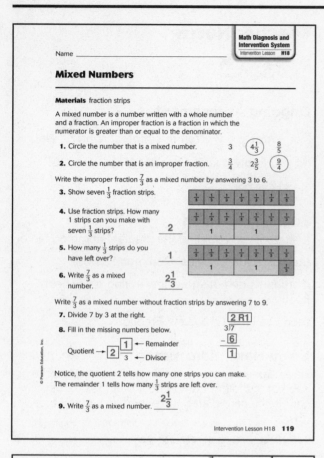

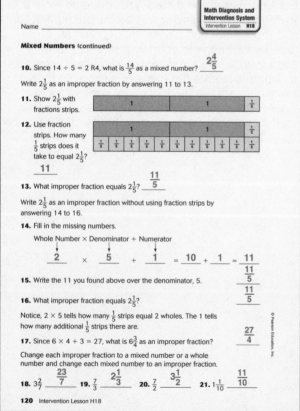

Teacher Notes

Ongoing Assessment

Ask: **What is $\frac{15}{4}$ written as a mixed number?** $3\frac{3}{4}$

Error Intervention

If students have difficulty dividing when converting from an improper fraction to a mixed number,

then use G42: Dividing with Objects and H15: Fractions and Division.

If students are changing a mixed number to an improper fraction and the students multiply the whole number and the numerator,

then, have the students write the word DoWN on their paper to remind them of the correct procedure: (D × W) + N.

If You Have More Time

Have students work in pairs. Have each student write 5 mixed numbers on index cards, one number per card. Then have students each write an improper fraction on an index card to match each mixed number written by the partner. Then the pair can play a memory game. Have the students shuffle the cards and lay them face down in an array. Have one student flip over two cards. If the cards are a match, then that player keeps the cards and can take another turn. If the cards are not a match, then the cards are turned back over and the other student has a chance to find a match. The game continues until all of the matches are found. The player with the most matches wins.

© Pearson Education, Inc.

Comparing and Ordering Fractions

Worksheet (page 121)

Name _____

Comparing and Ordering Fractions

Jen ate $\frac{7}{9}$ of a salad. Jack ate $\frac{5}{9}$ of a salad. Find out who ate the greater part of a salad by answering 1–3.

Compare $\frac{7}{9}$ and $\frac{5}{9}$.

1. Are the denominators the same? **yes**

If the denominators are the same, then compare the numerators. The fraction with the **greater** numerator is **greater than** the other fraction.

2. Compare. Write >, <, or =. 7 $>$ 5

$\frac{7}{9}$ $>$ $\frac{5}{9}$

3. Who ate the greater part of a salad, Jen or Jack? **Jen**

Compare $\frac{3}{5}$ and $\frac{3}{4}$ by answering 4 to 6

4. Are the denominators the same? **no**

5. Are the numerators the same? **yes**

If the numerators are the same, compare the denominators. The fraction with the **greater** denominator is **less than** the other fraction.

6. Compare. Write >, <, or =. 5 $>$ 4

$\frac{3}{5}$ $<$ $\frac{3}{4}$

Compare $\frac{3}{4}$ and $\frac{2}{3}$ by answering 7 to 11.

7. Are the denominators the same? **no**

8. Are the numerators the same? **no**

If neither the numerators or the denominators are the same, change to equivalent fractions with the same denominator.

9. What is the LCM of 3 and 4? **12**

Intervention Lesson H19   **121**

Worksheet (page 122)

Name _____

Comparing and Ordering Fractions (continued)

10. Rewrite $\frac{2}{3}$ and $\frac{3}{4}$ as equivalent fractions with a denominator of 12.

$\frac{3}{4} = \frac{\boxed{9}}{12}$ $\frac{2}{3} = \frac{\boxed{8}}{12}$

11. Compare. Write >, <, or =. $\frac{9}{12}$ $>$ $\frac{8}{12}$

$\frac{3}{4}$ $>$ $\frac{2}{3}$

Write $\frac{5}{6}, \frac{5}{9},$ and $\frac{1}{3}$ in order from least to greatest by answering 12 to 15.

12. Use the denominators to compare. Write >, <, or =. $\frac{5}{6}$ $>$ $\frac{5}{9}$

13. Rewrite $\frac{1}{3}$ so that it has a denominator common with $\frac{5}{9}$. $\frac{1}{3} = \frac{\boxed{3}}{9}$

14. Compare the numerators. Write >, <, or =. $\frac{5}{9}$ $>$ $\frac{3}{9}$

$\frac{5}{9}$ $>$ $\frac{1}{3}$

15. Use the comparisons to write $\frac{5}{9}, \frac{5}{6},$ and $\frac{1}{3}$ in order from least to greatest.

$\frac{1}{3}$ $<$ $\frac{5}{9}$ $<$ $\frac{5}{6}$

Compare. Write >, <, or =.

16. $\frac{3}{7}$ $>$ $\frac{1}{7}$ **17.** $\frac{5}{8}$ $=$ $\frac{10}{16}$ **18.** $\frac{3}{11}$ $<$ $\frac{4}{10}$ **19.** $\frac{3}{4}$ $>$ $\frac{2}{3}$

20. $\frac{3}{5}$ $=$ $\frac{9}{15}$ **21.** $\frac{5}{6}$ $>$ $\frac{5}{8}$ **22.** $\frac{5}{8}$ $>$ $\frac{7}{12}$ **23.** $\frac{7}{9}$ $>$ $\frac{4}{9}$

24. $\frac{1}{4}, \frac{6}{5}, \frac{3}{7}$ **25.** $\frac{5}{8}, \frac{8}{10}, \frac{2}{7}$ **26.** $\frac{5}{9}, \frac{10}{12}, \frac{5}{7}$ **27.** $\frac{3}{9}, \frac{12}{15}, \frac{5}{6}$

$\frac{1}{4}, \frac{3}{5}, \frac{6}{7}$ $\frac{2}{7}, \frac{5}{8}, \frac{8}{10}$ $\frac{5}{9}, \frac{5}{7}, \frac{10}{12}$ $\frac{3}{9}, \frac{12}{15}, \frac{5}{6}$

28. Reasoning Mario has two pizzas the same size. He cuts one into 4 equal pieces and the other into 5 equal pieces. Which pizza has larger pieces? Explain.

If there are fewer pieces, then each piece is larger. The pizza with 4 pieces has larger pieces.

122   Intervention Lesson H19

Teacher Notes

Ongoing Assessment

Ask: **Which is larger $\frac{1}{4}$ or $\frac{1}{3}$? How can you tell?**
$\frac{1}{3}$ is larger than $\frac{1}{4}$ because when the numerators are the same, you just compare the denominators. The fraction with the smaller denominator is the larger of the two fractions.

Error Intervention

If students can not find the LCD,

then use G65: Least Common Multiple.

If students are having problems writing equivalent fractions,

then use H7: Using Models to Find Equivalent Fractions or H14: Equivalent Fractions.

If You Have More Time

Write a fraction, such as $\frac{5}{6}$, on the board. Ask students to write 5 fractions that are greater than the fraction and 5 fractions that are less. Encourage students to use different denominators and numerators as they create different fractions. Share findings as a class.

© Pearson Education, Inc.

Comparing and Ordering Mixed Numbers

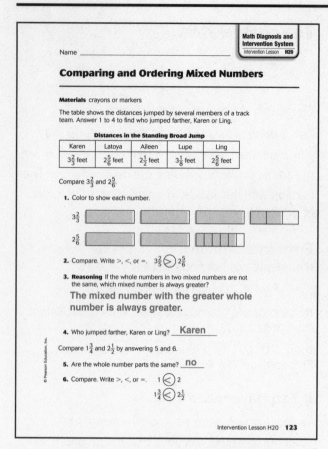

Name _____

Math Diagnosis and Intervention System
Intervention Lesson **H20**

Comparing and Ordering Mixed Numbers

Materials crayons or markers

The table shows the distances jumped by several members of a track team. Answer 1 to 4 to find who jumped farther, Karen or Ling.

Distances in the Standing Broad Jump

Karen	Latoya	Aileen	Lupe	Ling
$3\frac{2}{3}$ feet	$2\frac{5}{6}$ feet	$2\frac{1}{2}$ feet	$3\frac{1}{8}$ feet	$2\frac{5}{6}$ feet

Compare $3\frac{2}{3}$ and $2\frac{5}{6}$.

1. Color to show each number.

$3\frac{2}{3}$

$2\frac{5}{6}$

2. Compare. Write >, <, or =. $3\frac{2}{3}$ ⊙ $2\frac{5}{6}$

3. Reasoning If the whole numbers in two mixed numbers are not the same, which mixed number is always greater?

The mixed number with the greater whole number is always greater.

4. Who jumped farther, Karen or Ling? **Karen**

Compare $1\frac{3}{4}$ and $2\frac{1}{2}$ by answering 5 and 6.

5. Are the whole number parts the same? **no**

6. Compare. Write >, <, or =. 1 ⊙ 2

$1\frac{3}{4}$ ⊙ $2\frac{1}{2}$

Intervention Lesson H20 **123**

Teacher Notes

Ongoing Assessment

Ask: **Which is greater $\frac{10}{3}$ or $2\frac{1}{2}$? $\frac{10}{3}$ How do you know?** $\frac{10}{3} = 3\frac{1}{3}$. Since $3 > 2$, $3\frac{1}{3} > 2\frac{1}{2}$.

Error Intervention

If students have trouble rewriting fractions so that there is a common denominator,

then use G65: Least Common Multiple and H14: Equivalent Fractions.

If You Have More Time

Give each student a sheet of paper displaying a mixed number or an improper fraction. Have 5 students come to the front of the class and line up in order of their numbers, from least to greatest. Then, have another group of students line up from greatest to least. Continue until all students have had a chance to line up.

Name _____

Math Diagnosis and Intervention System
Intervention Lesson **H20**

Comparing and Ordering Mixed Numbers (continued)

Use the Standing Broad Jump table on the previous page. Who jumped farther Aileen or Latoya?

Compare $2\frac{1}{2}$ and $2\frac{5}{6}$ by answering 7 to 8.

7. Color to show each number.

$2\frac{1}{2}$

$2\frac{5}{6}$

8. Compare. Write >, <, or =. $2\frac{5}{6}$ ⊙ $2\frac{1}{2}$

9. Reasoning If the whole number parts of two mixed numbers are the same, which mixed number is greater?

The mixed number with the greater fraction part is greater.

Compare. Write >, <, or =.

10. $4\frac{5}{15}$ ⊙ $3\frac{4}{7}$ **11.** $3\frac{3}{4}$ ⊙ $3\frac{2}{15}$ **12.** $3\frac{2}{8}$ ⊙ $3\frac{1}{4}$

13. $5\frac{4}{9}$ ⊙ $5\frac{2}{7}$ **14.** $2\frac{8}{12}$ ⊙ $2\frac{3}{4}$ **15.** $8\frac{1}{7}$ ⊙ $8\frac{1}{5}$

Write each set of numbers in order from least to greatest.

16. $\frac{14}{9}$, $\frac{10}{12}$, $\frac{5}{3}$

$\frac{10}{12}$, $\frac{14}{9}$, $\frac{5}{3}$

17. $1\frac{3}{7}$, $1\frac{12}{15}$, $1\frac{5}{6}$

$1\frac{3}{7}$, $1\frac{12}{15}$, $1\frac{5}{6}$

18. $8\frac{4}{5}$, $8\frac{1}{2}$, $8\frac{7}{10}$

$8\frac{1}{2}$, $8\frac{7}{10}$, $8\frac{4}{5}$

19. Jim's height is 4 feet, $3\frac{3}{4}$ inches. Rex's height is 4 feet, $3\frac{3}{8}$ inches. Joan's height is 4 feet, $3\frac{7}{16}$ inches. Who is the tallest? Who is the shortest?

Tallest: Jim; Shortest: Rex

124 Intervention Lesson H20

© Pearson Education, Inc.

Fractions and Mixed Numbers on the Number Line

Math Diagnosis and Intervention System
Intervention Lesson **H21**

Name _____

Fractions and Mixed Numbers on the Number Line

Each fraction names a point on the number line below. Use the number line to answer 1 to 7.

1. How many equal lengths is the distance between 0 and 1 divided into?   **10**

2. How many equal lengths is the distance between 1 and 2 divided into?   **10**

Since the distance between 0 and 1 and the distance between 1 and 2 are each divided into 10 equal lengths, each length is $\frac{1}{10}$ of the whole length.

3. To name point A, count by tenths. $\frac{1}{10}, \frac{2}{10}, \boxed{\frac{3}{10}}$

4. What fraction is represented by point A on the number line above? $\boxed{\frac{3}{10}}$

5. To name point B, continue counting.
$\frac{4}{10}, \frac{5}{10}, \frac{6}{10}, \frac{7}{10}, \frac{8}{10}, \frac{9}{10}, \boxed{\frac{11}{10}}\ \boxed{\frac{12}{10}}\ \boxed{\frac{13}{10}}\ \boxed{\frac{14}{10}}\ \boxed{\frac{15}{10}}$

6. What improper fraction is represented by point B? $\boxed{\frac{15}{10}}$

7. Write point B as a mixed number. $\boxed{1\frac{1}{2}}$

Plot point C at $\frac{3}{5}$ on the number line above by answering 8 and 9.

8. What fraction with a denominator of 10 is equivalent to $\frac{3}{5}$? $\frac{3}{5} = \frac{\boxed{6}}{10}$

9. Plot point C at $\frac{6}{10}$. This point represents $\frac{3}{5}$.

Plot point D at $1\frac{4}{5}$ on the number line above by answering 10 and 11.

10. What improper fraction with a denominator of 10 is equivalent to $1\frac{4}{5}$?

$1\frac{4}{5} = 1\frac{\boxed{8}}{10} = \frac{\boxed{18}}{10}$

Intervention Lesson H21   **125**

© Pearson Education, Inc.

Teacher Notes

Ongoing Assessment

Ask: *Which fraction comes before $1\frac{1}{10}$ on a number line: $\frac{9}{10}$ or $\frac{12}{10}$?* $\frac{9}{10}$

Error Intervention

If students have trouble locating proper fractions on the number line,

then use H5: Fractions on the Number Line.

If You Have More Time

Have students work in pairs. Have each student write 3 different mixed numbers, with an agreed upon denominator. The numbers must be less than 5. Have partners work together to draw and label a number line from 0 to 5 and plot a point for each mixed number they wrote.

Math Diagnosis and Intervention System
Intervention Lesson **H21**

Name _____

Fractions and Mixed Numbers on the Number Line (continued)

11. Plot point D at $\frac{18}{10}$. This point represents $1\frac{4}{5}$.

12. **Reasoning** On a number line, numbers increase in value from left to right. Use the number line on the previous page to help you order $\frac{3}{10}, 1\frac{1}{2}, \frac{3}{5},$ and $1\frac{4}{5}$ from least to greatest.

$\boxed{\frac{3}{10}}\ \boxed{\frac{3}{5}}\ \boxed{1\frac{1}{2}}\ \boxed{1\frac{4}{5}}$

Plot each point on the number line below.

13. Point A at $\frac{3}{4}$ 14. Point B at $1\frac{1}{4}$ 15. Point C at $2\frac{1}{2}$ 16. Point D at $3\frac{1}{2}$

Use the number lines below. What fraction or mixed number represents each point?

17. Point A $\boxed{\frac{1}{2}}$ 18. Point B $\boxed{2\frac{1}{2}}$ 19. Point C $\boxed{3\frac{1}{2}}$

20. Point D $\boxed{\frac{1}{5}}$ 21. Point E $\boxed{\frac{4}{5}}$ 22. Point F $\boxed{1\frac{2}{5}}$

Use the number lines below. What number represents each point? If a point can be represented by both an improper fraction and a mixed number, give both.

23. Point A $\boxed{\frac{5}{6}}$ 24. Point B $\boxed{\frac{8}{6} \text{ or } 1\frac{2}{6}}$ 25. Point C $\boxed{\frac{16}{6} \text{ or } 2\frac{4}{6}}$

26. Point D $\boxed{\frac{3}{8}}$ 27. Point E $\boxed{\frac{9}{8} \text{ or } 1\frac{1}{8}}$ 28. Point F $\boxed{\frac{14}{8} \text{ or } 1\frac{6}{8}}$

126 Intervention Lesson H21

© Pearson Education, Inc.

Place Value Through Hundredths

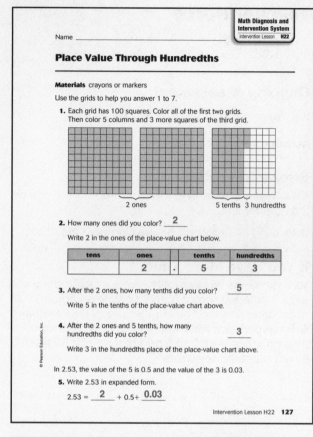

Name _____

Math Diagnosis and
Intervention System
Intervention Lesson   H22

Place Value Through Hundredths

Materials crayons or markers

Use the grids to help you answer 1 to 7.

1. Each grid has 100 squares. Color all of the first two grids.
Then color 5 columns and 3 more squares of the third grid.

2 ones   5 tenths 3 hundredths

2. How many ones did you color? __2__

Write 2 in the ones of the place-value chart below.

tens	ones	tenths	hundredths
	2 .	5	3

3. After the 2 ones, how many tenths did you color? __5__

Write 5 in the tenths of the place-value chart above.

4. After the 2 ones and 5 tenths, how many
hundredths did you color? __3__

Write 3 in the hundredths place of the place-value chart above.

In 2.53, the value of the 5 is 0.5 and the value of the 3 is 0.03.

5. Write 2.53 in expanded form.

2.53 = __2__ + 0.5+ __0.03__

Intervention Lesson H22 **127**

Name _____

Math Diagnosis and
Intervention System
Intervention Lesson   H22

Place Value Through Hundredths (continued)

6. If 1 tenth = 10 hundredths, how many
hundredths are in 5 tenths + 3 hundredths? **53 hundredths**

So, the grids show 2 ones + 53 hundredths or 2.53.

7. Write 2.53 in words. ____two____ and fifty-__three__ hundredths

Answer 8 to 11 to examine the number 25.09.

8. Write 25.09 in the place-value chart below.

tens	ones	tenths	hundredths
2	5 .	0	9

9. What is the value of the 9 in 25.09? 0.09

10. Write 25.09 in expanded form. __20__ + __5__ + __0.09__

11. Write 25.09 in words. __twenty-five__ and __nine__ hundredths

Write the value of the underlined digit.

12. 14.7<u>5</u>   **13.** <u>4</u>.29   **14.** 26.<u>4</u>6   **15.** 3.6<u>8</u>

  __0.05__   __4__   __0.4__   __0.08__

Write each decimal in expanded form.

16. 21.97   **17.** 3.05

  __20 + 1 + 0.9 + 0.07__   __3 + 0.05__

Write each decimal in words.

18. 17.81 __seventeen and eighty-one hundredths__

19. 0.03 __three hundredths__

20. Reasoning What missing number makes the
number sentence, 28.02 = 20 + 8 = ☐ true? __0.02__

128 Intervention Lesson H22

Teacher Notes

Ongoing Assessment

Ask: *What is twenty and two hundredths written in standard form?* 20.02

Error Intervention

If students are having trouble with the concept of tenths and hundredths,

then use H11: Using Money to Understand Decimals.

If You Have More Time

Have students research the periodic table of chemical elements. Have them choose an element in the 4th row of the table and write the weight of the element in expanded form and word form.

© Pearson Education, Inc.

Decimals on the Number Line

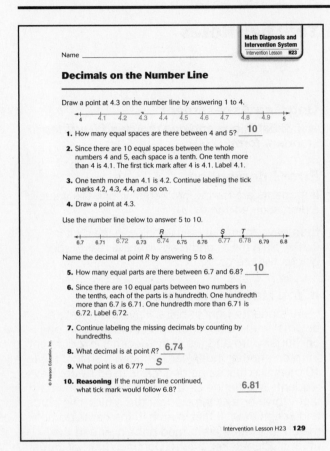

Teacher Notes

Ongoing Assessment

Ask: *If you drew a number line from 1 to 2 and wanted to label 1.65, how many equal parts would you need to make between 1 and 2?* 100

Error Intervention

If students have trouble with the hundredths number line,

then remind them that decimals in the tenths, like 4.3, are equal to a decimal to hundredths, like 4.30. Have students add a zero to the numbers written as tenths.

If You Have More Time

Have students work in pairs and practice counting from 3.4 to 3.9 using tenths and hundredths.

Place Value Through Thousandths

Place Value Through Thousandths

1. Write 5.739 in the place-value chart below.

ones		tenths	hundredths	thousandths
5	.	7	3	9

2. What is the value of the 5 in 5.739? __5__

3. What is the value of the 7 in 5.739? __0.7__

4. What is the value of the 3 in 5.739? __0.03__

5. What is the value of the 9 in 5.739? __0.009__

6. Write 5.739 in expanded form. __5__ + 0.7 + __0.03__ + 0.009

7. Write 5.739 in words.

__five__ and seven hundred __thirty-nine__ thousandths

Write seven and two hundred four thousandths in standard from by answering 8 to 14.

8. How many ones are in seven and two hundred four thousandths? __7__

Write 7 in the ones place of the place-value chart below.

ones		tenths	hundredths	thousandths
7	.	2	0	4

9. Write two hundred, thousandths as a fraction. $\frac{200}{1,000}$

10. Write an equivalent fraction. $\frac{200}{1,000} = \frac{2}{10}$

11. How many tenths are in seven and two hundred four thousandths? __2__

Write 2 in the tenths place of the place-value chart above.

12. How many hundredths are in seven and two hundred four thousandths? __0__

Write 0 in the hundredths place of the place-value chart above.

Intervention Lesson H24   **131**

© Pearson Education, Inc.

Place Value Through Thousandths (continued)

13. How many thousandths are in seven and two hundred four thousandths? __4__

Write 4 in the thousandths place of the place-value chart.

14. Write 7.204 in expanded form. __7__ + __0.2__ + __0.004__

15. Reasoning What is 1 thousandth less than 7.204? __7.203__

Write each value in standard form.

16. 507 thousandths
__0.507__

17. 5 and 6 thousandths
__5.006__

18. 9 and 62 thousandths
__9.062__

Write the value of the underlined digit.

19. 2.5<u>5</u>3
__0.05__

20. 0.38<u>1</u>
__0.001__

21. <u>6</u>.647
__0.6__

22. 9.0<u>9</u>7
__0.09__

Write each decimal in expanded form.

23. 4.685
__4 + 0.6 + 0.08 + 0.005__

24. 3.056
__3 + 0.05 + 0.006__

25. 0.735
__0.7 + 0.03 + 0.005__

26. 4.004
__4 + 0.004__

Write each decimal in word form.

27. 2.598
__two and five hundred ninety-eight thousandths__

28. 0.008
__eight thousandths__

29. 0.250
__two hundred and fifty thousandths__

© Pearson Education, Inc.

132   Intervention Lesson H24

Teacher Notes

Ongoing Assessment

Ask: *What is one and one thousandth written in standard form?* 1.001

Error Intervention

If students are having problems writing the value of a digit such as 1 in 0.381,

then have them put blanks below each digit in 0.381, fill in the 1, and then fill in the rest of the places with zeros.

If You Have More Time

Have students work in pairs. Have them write a decimal in the thousandths in standard form on one index card and the same decimal in a different form on another index card. Students should make 10 pairs like this so no decimal is used twice. Have students shuffle the cards and arrange them in a face-down array. One student turns over two cards and keeps them if they match. If the cards do not match, the cards are turned back over and the other student takes a turn. Continue until all cards are matched.

© Pearson Education, Inc.

Place Value Through Millionths

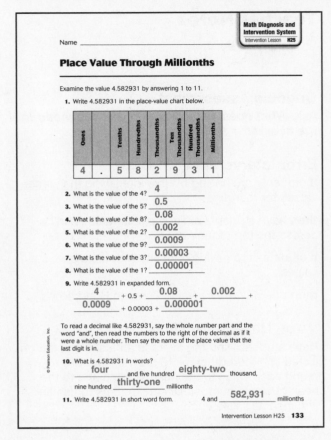

Name _____

Place Value Through Millionths

Examine the value 4.582931 by answering 1 to 11.

1. Write 4.582931 in the place-value chart below.

Ones		Tenths	Hundredths	Thousandths	Ten Thousandths	Hundred Thousandths	Millionths
4	.	5	8	2	9	3	1

2. What is the value of the 4? _4_

3. What is the value of the 5? _0.5_

4. What is the value of the 8? _0.08_

5. What is the value of the 2? _0.002_

6. What is the value of the 9? _0.0009_

7. What is the value of the 3? _0.00003_

8. What is the value of the 1? _0.000001_

9. Write 4.582931 in expanded form.

_4_ + 0.5 + _0.08_ + _0.002_ + _0.0009_ + _0.00003_ + _0.000001_

To read a decimal like 4.582931, say the whole number part and the word "and", then read the numbers to the right of the decimal as if it were a whole number. Then say the name of the place value that the last digit is in.

10. What is 4.582931 in words?

four and five hundred _eighty-two_ thousand, nine hundred _thirty-one_ millionths

11. Write 4.582931 in short word form. 4 and _582,931_ millionths

Intervention Lesson H25 **133**

Name _____

Place Value Through Millionths (continued)

Write each value in standard form.

12. 35 ten thousandths   **13.** 5 and 3,759 millionths   **14.** 65,983 millionths

_0.0035_   _5.003759_   _0.065983_

Write the value of the underlined digit.

15. 0.475823   **16.** 2.652004   **17.** 1.883926   **18.** 0.000349

_0.0008_   _0.000004_   _0.00002_   _0.0003_

19. 2.909095   **20.** 1.003045   **21.** 0.650007   **22.** 0.123608

_0.009_   _0.00004_   _0.000007_   _0.02_

Write each decimal in expanded form.

23. 1.009671   _1 + 0.009 + 0.0006 + 0.00007 + 0.000001_

24. 0.050076   _0.05 + 0.00007 + 0.000006_

25. 0.500429   _0.5 + 0.0004 + 0.00002 + 0.000009_

Write each decimal in word form.

26. 0.125456

one hundred twenty-five thousand, four hundred fifty-six millionths

27. 1.00058

one and fifty-eight hundred thousandths

28. Reasoning What is 1 ten thousandths more than 0.347568? _0.347668_

29. Reasoning What is 1 hundred thousandths more than 0.347568? _0.347578_

30. Reasoning What is 1 millionth more than 0.347598? _0.347599_

134 Intervention Lesson H25

© Pearson Education, Inc.

Teacher Notes

Ongoing Assessment

Ask: *What is the difference between the number 3 thousand and 2 millionths and the number 3 thousand 2 millionths?* The *and* indicates the decimal point. So in 3 thousand and 2 millionths, the 3 thousand is a whole number. The number is 3000.000002. In 3 thousand 2 millionths, the 3 thousand is part of the number of millionths. The number is 0.003002.

Error Intervention

If students are having trouble remembering the number of zeros each value has,

then encourage students to write 0.# above the heading tenths, 0.0# above the heading hundredths, 0.00# above the heading thousandths, and so on. That way they know to place the appropriate number of zeros and then the digit.

If You Have More Time

Have students write a number in the ten thousandths, hundred thousandths, and millionths in standard, expanded, short word, and word forms.

Rounding Decimals Through Hundredths

Name _____

Math Diagnosis and Intervention System
Intervention Lesson **H26**

Rounding Decimals Through Hundredths

Round 58.21 to the nearest whole number by answering 1 to 5.

1. What digit is in the ones place? __8__

2. What digit is to the right of the 8? __2__

3. Is the digit to the right of the 8 less than 5, or is it 5 or greater?
   __less than 5__

If the digit to the right of the 8 is 5 or more, the number rounds up. If the digit is less than 5, the number rounds down.

4. Do you need to round up or down? __down__

5. So, keep the 8. Since you are rounding to a whole number, you do not need to keep the decimal point or any digits to the right of the decimal point.

   What is 58.21 rounded to the nearest whole number? __58__

6. What is 82.62 rounded to the nearest whole number? __83__

Round 27.35 to the nearest tenth by answering 7 to 11.

7. Which digit is in the tenths place? __3__

8. What digit is to the right of the 3? __5__

9. Is the digit to the right of the 3 less than 5, or is it 5 or greater?
   __5 or greater__

10. Do you need to round up or down? __up__

11. So, change the 3 to the next highest digit. Since you are rounding to the tenths, you do not need a digit in hundredths place.

    What is 27.35 rounded to the nearest tenth? __27.4__

12. What is 36.82 rounded the nearest tenth? __36.8__

© Pearson Education, Inc.

Intervention Lesson H26   **135**

Name _____

Math Diagnosis and Intervention System
Intervention Lesson **H26**

Rounding Decimals Through Hundredths (continued)

Round each decimal to the nearest whole number.

13. 41.4	14. 5.63	15. 5.8	16. 78.78	17. 0.96
41	6	6	79	1

18. 47.05	19. 1.75	20. 0.5	21. 83.41	22. 6.70
47	2	1	83	7

Round each decimal to the nearest tenth.

23. 22.79	24. 59.34	25. 0.85	26. 2.55	27. 12.86
22.8	59.3	0.9	2.6	12.9

28. 38.35	29. 91.05	30. 0.62	31. 17.96	32. 28.11
38.4	91.1	0.6	18.0	28.1

33. When rounded to the nearest whole number, which of these decimals round to 18?

    18.5, 17.8, 18.43, 18.07, 17.58, 17.4, 17.63, 18.25, 17.49

    __17.8, 18.43, 18.07, 17.58, 17.63, 18.25__

34. When rounded to the nearest tenth, which of these decimals round to 7.5?

    6.9, 7.48, 7.59, 7.51, 7.43, 8.1, 7.53, 7.45, 7.65

    __7.48, 7.51, 7.53, 7.45__

35. **Reasoning** When rounding to the nearest whole number, why do 5.43 and 4.68 both round to 5?

    5.43 rounds down to 5 because the 4 in the tenths place is less than 5; 4.68 rounds up because the 6 in the tenths place is greater than 5.

© Pearson Education, Inc.

136 Intervention Lesson H26

Teacher Notes

Ongoing Assessment

Ask: *What does 19.92 round to when rounded to the nearest tenth?* 19.9

Error Intervention

If students are having trouble identifying the place values for rounding,

then have students make a place-value chart across the top of their page.

If students are having difficulty with the place values,

then use H22: Place Value Through Hundredths.

If You Have More Time

Have students find the average annual precipitation (listed in hundredths) for 10 states. Have them round each value to the nearest tenth and to the nearest whole number. Direct students to use an almanac as a reference.

© Pearson Education, Inc.

Rounding Decimals Through Thousandths

Name _____

Rounding Decimals Through Thousandths

Round 24.683 to the nearest tenth by answering 1 to 5.

1. What digit is in the tenths place? __6__

2. What digit is to the right of the 6? __8__

3. Is the digit to the right of the 6 less than 5, or is it 5 or greater?
   __5 or greater__

If the digit to the right of the 6 is 5 or more, the number rounds up. If the digit is less than 5, the number rounds down.

4. Do you need to round up or down? __up__

5. So, change the 6 to the next highest digit. Since you are rounding to the tenths, you do not need any digits to the right of the tenths.
   What is 24.683 rounded to the nearest tenth? __24.7__

Round 0.973 to the nearest hundredth by answering 6 to 10.

6. Which digit is in the hundredths place? __7__

7. What digit is to the right of the 7? __3__

8. Is the digit to the right of the 7 less than 5, or is it 5 or greater?
   __less than 5__

9. Do you need to round up or down? __down__

10. So, keep the 7. Since you are rounding to the hundredths, you do not need any digits to the right of the hundredths.
    What is 0.973 rounded to the nearest hundredth? __0.97__

Round 15.136 to the nearest whole number by answering 11 to 14.

11. Which digit is in the ones place? __5__

12. What digit is to the right of the 5? __1__

13. Do you need to round up or down? __down__

14. So, keep the 5. What is 15.136 rounded to the nearest whole number? __15__

© Pearson Education, Inc.

Intervention Lesson H27   **137**

Name _____

Rounding Decimals Through Thousandths (continued)

Round 82.946 to the given place.

15. Nearest hundredth	16. Nearest tenth	17. Nearest one	18. Nearest ten
82.95	82.9	83	80

Round 37.054 to the given place.

19. Nearest hundredth	20. Nearest tenth	21. Nearest one	22. Nearest ten
37.05	37.1	37	40

Round each number to the nearest hundredth.

23. 0.873   __0.87__   24. 23.892   __23.89__

25. 456.134   __456.13__   26. 1.006   __1.01__

Round each number to the nearest tenth.

27. 34.276   __34.3__   28. 729.35   __729.4__

29. 0.524   __0.5__   30. 10.478   __10.5__

Round each number to the nearest whole number.

31. 184.535   __185__   32. 50.345   __50__

33. 23.297   __23__   34. 6.767   __7__

Round each number to the nearest ten.

35. 345.893   __350__   36. 19.34   __20__

37. 1,784.34   __1,780__   38. 9.457   __10__

39. When rounded to the nearest hundredth, which of these decimals round to 5.43?

   5.44, 5.431, 5.425, 5.435, 5.434, 5.428, 5.438, 5.437, 5.429
   __5.431, 5.425, 5.434, 5.428, 5.429__

40. **Reasoning** When rounding to the nearest tenth, why do 8.783 and 8.839 both round to 8.8?

   8.783 rounds up because the 8 in the hundredths place is greater than 5; 8.839 rounds down because the 3 in the hundredths place is less than 5.

© Pearson Education, Inc.

138   Intervention Lesson H27

Teacher Notes

Ongoing Assessment

Ask: ***What is 345.846 rounded to the nearest hundredth?*** 345.85

Error Intervention

If students do not know the place values,

then use H24: Place Value Through Thousandths.

If You Have More Time

Have students find batting averages for 10 baseball players. Have them round each value to the nearest hundredth and to the nearest tenth.

Comparing and Ordering Decimals Through Hundredths

Name _____

Math Diagnosis and
Intervention System
Intervention Lesson   H28

Comparing and Ordering Decimals Through Hundredths

Jackson's puppy weighs 8.42 pounds. Benjamin's puppy weighs 8.48 pounds. Find whose puppy weighs more by answering 1 to 6.

1. Write 8.42 and 8.48 in the place-value chart.

ones		tenths	hundredths
8	.	4	2
8	.	4	8

For Exercises 2–5, write <, >, or =.

2. Start on the left. Compare the ones.   8 __=__ 8

3. Since the ones are equal, compare the tenths.   0.4 __=__ 0.4

4. Since the tenths are equal, compare the hundredths.   0.02 __<__ 0.08

5. Since 0.02 < 0.08, 8.42 __<__ 8.48.

6. Whose dog weighs more? __Benjamin's__

Order 3.56; 3.67; and 2.59 from least to greatest by answering 7 to 12.

7. Write the decimals so the decimal points line up.

3	.	5	6
3	.	6	7
2	.	5	9

8. Start on the left. Compare the ones. 2 __<__ 3

9. Since 2 < 3, which decimal is the least? __2.59__

10. Compare the tenths of the two other decimals. 0.5 __<__ 0.6

Intervention Lesson H28   **139**

Name _____

Math Diagnosis and
Intervention System
Intervention Lesson   H28

Comparing and Ordering Decimals Through Hundredths (continued)

11. Since 0.5 < 0.6, which decimal is the least? __3.56__

12. Write the decimals in order from least to greatest. __2.59   3.56   3.67__

Compare. Write >, <, or = for each.

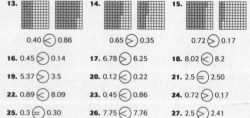

13. 0.40 (<) 0.86

14. 0.65 (>) 0.35

15. 0.72 (>) 0.17

16. 0.45 (>) 0.14

17. 6.78 (>) 6.25

18. 8.02 (<) 8.2

19. 5.37 (>) 3.5

20. 0.12 (<) 0.22

21. 2.5 (=) 2.50

22. 0.89 (<) 8.09

23. 0.45 (<) 0.86

24. 0.72 (>) 0.17

25. 0.3 (=) 0.30

26. 7.75 (<) 7.76

27. 2.5 (>) 2.41

Order the numbers from least to greatest.

28. 0.45, 0.30, 0.40
__0.30, 0.40, 0.45__

29. 0.05, 0.50, 0.15
__0.05, 0.15, 0.50__

30. 8.45, 9.56, 8.42
__8.42, 8.45, 9.56__

31. 3.56, 3.21, 3.72
__3.21, 3.56, 3.72__

32. 9.34, 9.25, 9.37, 9.3
__9.25, 9.3, 9.34, 9.37__

33. 0.67, 6.77, 6.67, 0.76
__0.67, 0.76, 6.67, 6.77__

34. Reasoning A green parakeet weighs 0.74 pound. A blue parakeet weighs 0.69 pound. Which parakeet weighs more?
__green parakeet__

140   Intervention Lesson H28

Teacher Notes

Ongoing Assessment

Ask: *Why is it important to line the numbers up by their decimal point when comparing and ordering numbers?* When the decimal points are lined up, the place values are also lined up.

Error Intervention

If students have trouble comparing decimals like 0.53 and 0.5,

then remind them that they can add zeros to the right of the last digit of a decimal and the value will not change. So 0.5 and 0.50 are equal. They then can compare 0.53 and 0.50.

If You Have More Time

Have students write comparison problems using real-world data, for a partner to solve.

© Pearson Education, Inc.

Comparing and Ordering Decimals Through Thousandths

Math Diagnosis and
Intervention System
Intervention Lesson **H29**

Name _____

Comparing and Ordering Decimals Through Thousandths

Compare 3.761 and 3.766 by answering 1 to 6.

1. Write the decimals so the decimal points line up.

3	.	7	6	1
3	.	7	6	6

For Exercises 2–6, write <, >, or =.

2. Start on the left. Compare the ones.   3 __=__ 3

3. Since the ones are equal, compare the tenths.   0.7 __=__ 0.7

4. Since the tenths are equal, compare the hundredths.   0.06 __=__ 0.06

5. Since the hundredths are equal, compare the thousandths.   0.001 __<__ 0.006

6. So, 3.761 __<__ 3.766.

Order these numbers from least to greatest by answering 7 to 13.

    5.432; 5.45; 5.437

7. Write the decimals so the decimal points are lined up. You can place zeros so that all of the decimals have digits to the same place value.

5	.	4	3	2
5	.	4	5	0
5	.	4	3	7

8. Starting on the left, in the ones place, compare the digits in each place. In what place do the digits become different?   **hundredths**

9. Compare the hundredths.   0.03 __<__ 0.05

10. Since 0.03 < 0.05, which decimal is the greatest? __5.453__

© Pearson Education, Inc.

Math Diagnosis and
Intervention System
Intervention Lesson **H29**

Name _____

Comparing and Ordering Decimals Through Thousandths (continued)

11. Compare the thousandths of the two other decimals.   0.002 __<__ 0.007

12. Since 0.002 < 0.007, which decimal is the least? __5.432__

13. Write the numbers in order from least to greatest.

    __5.432__   __5.437__   __5.45__

Compare, use >, <, or = for each .

14. 3.75 (=) 3.750   **15.** 79.6 (>) 79.06   **16.** 48.97 (<) 49.87

17. 0.287 (>) 0.278   **18.** 1.382 (<) 1.823   **19.** 85.271 (>) 85.27

20. 29.699 (<) 29.700   **21.** 8.95 (=) 8.950   **22.** 16.050 (>) 16.005

23. 0.54 (<) 0.549   **24.** 21.603 (<) 21.63   **25.** 7.93 (>) 7.9

Write the numbers in each set from least to greatest.

26. 84.44, 84.444, 84.4
    84.4; 84.44; 84.444

27. 4.05, 4.005, 4.500
    4.005; 4.05; 4.500

28. 10.56, 10.165, 10.156, 10.615
    10.156; 10.165; 10.56; 10.615

29. 7.29, 7.199, 7.129, 7.219
    7.129; 7.199; 7.219; 7.29

30. If a table tennis ball weighs 0.085 ounce and a squash ball weighs 0.821 ounce, which ball weighs more?   **squash ball**

31. If a northern elephant seal weighs 3.35 tons and a southern elephant seal weighs 3.54 tons, which seal weighs less?
    The northern elephant seal

32. Reasoning Write three numbers between 50.1 and 50.2.
    Answers may vary. Possible answer: 50.13, 50.14, 50.15

© Pearson Education, Inc.

Teacher Notes

Ongoing Assessment

Ask: *How can you tell that 4.876 is greater than 4.834?* Since the ones and tenths are the same, I compare the hundredths. 7 is greater than 3, so 4.876 is greater than 4.834.

Error Intervention

If students have trouble ordering decimals that are written horizontally,

then encourage them to write one decimal above the other, making sure they line up decimal points. Then compare the decimals by the columns.

If You Have More Time

Have students write ordering problems using real-world data, for a partner to solve.

Relating Fractions and Decimals

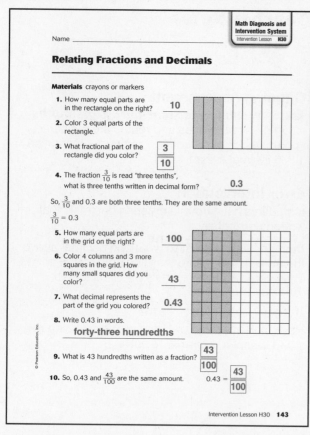

**Math Diagnosis and
Intervention System**
Intervention Lesson   **H30**

Name _____

Relating Fractions and Decimals

Materials crayons or markers

1. How many equal parts are in the rectangle on the right?   **10**

2. Color 3 equal parts of the rectangle.

3. What fractional part of the rectangle did you color?   **3/10**

4. The fraction $\frac{3}{10}$ is read "three tenths", what is three tenths written in decimal form?   **0.3**

So, $\frac{3}{10}$ and 0.3 are both three tenths. They are the same amount.

$\frac{3}{10} = 0.3$

5. How many equal parts are in the grid on the right?   **100**

6. Color 4 columns and 3 more squares in the grid. How many small squares did you color?   **43**

7. What decimal represents the part of the grid you colored?   **0.43**

8. Write 0.43 in words.
   forty-three hundredths

9. What is 43 hundredths written as a fraction?   **43/100**

10. So, 0.43 and $\frac{43}{100}$ are the same amount. $0.43 = $ **43/100**

Intervention Lesson H30   **143**

© Pearson Education, Inc.

Teacher Notes

Ongoing Assessment
Ask: **What is 5.7 written as a fraction?** $5\frac{7}{10}$

Error Intervention
If students have trouble with the concept of tenths and hundredths,

then use H10: Fractions and Decimals.

If You Have More Time
Have students work in pairs. Have one student write a fraction with a denominator of 10 or 100 and have the partner write the related decimal. Then have one student write a decimal to tenths or hundredths and have the partner write the related fraction. Have students change roles and repeat.

Name _____

**Math Diagnosis and
Intervention System**
Intervention Lesson   **H30**

Relating Fractions and Decimals (continued)

Write a fraction and a decimal for each shaded part.

11.

12.

13.

$\frac{7}{10}$; 0.7 $\frac{39}{100}$; 0.39 $\frac{54}{100}$; 0.54

Write each fraction as a decimal.

14. $\frac{8}{10}$ 15. $\frac{56}{100}$ 16. $\frac{7}{10}$ 17. $\frac{13}{100}$
   0.8   **0.56**   **0.7**   **0.13**

18. $\frac{85}{100}$ 19. $\frac{77}{100}$ 20. $\frac{6}{100}$ 21. $3\frac{5}{10}$
   0.85   **0.77**   **0.06**   **3.5**

Write each decimal as a fraction or mixed number.

22. 0.3   23. 0.63   24. 6.9   25. 0.17
   $\frac{3}{10}$ $\frac{63}{100}$ $6\frac{9}{10}$ $\frac{17}{100}$

26. 4.23   27. 0.01   28. 0.33   29. 1.1
   $4\frac{23}{100}$ $\frac{1}{100}$ $\frac{33}{100}$ $1\frac{1}{10}$

Katie bought 100 plants for her garden. She bought 37 tomato plants, 8 cucumber plants, 12 pumpkin plants, and the rest of her plants were onions.

30. Write a fraction and a decimal to express the part of the plants that are tomatoes. $\frac{37}{100}$; 0.37

31. **Reasoning** Write a fraction and a decimal to express the part of the plants that are onions. $\frac{43}{100}$; 0.43

© Pearson Education, Inc.

144 Intervention Lesson H30

© Pearson Education, Inc.

Decimals to Fractions

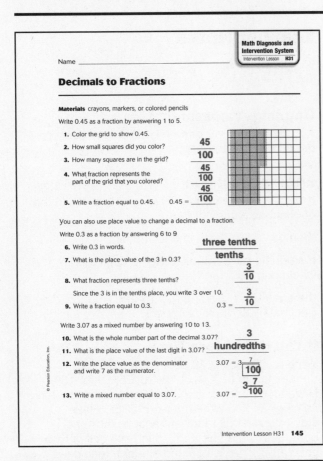

Name _____

Decimals to Fractions

Materials crayons, markers, or colored pencils

Write 0.45 as a fraction by answering 1 to 5.

1. Color the grid to show 0.45.
2. How small squares did you color? $\frac{45}{100}$
3. How many squares are in the grid? $\frac{45}{100}$
4. What fraction represents the part of the grid that you colored? $\frac{45}{100}$
5. Write a fraction equal to 0.45. $0.45 = \frac{45}{100}$

You can also use place value to change a decimal to a fraction.

Write 0.3 as a fraction by answering 6 to 9.

6. Write 0.3 in words.   **three tenths**
7. What is the place value of the 3 in 0.3?   **tenths**
8. What fraction represents three tenths? $\frac{3}{10}$
   Since the 3 is in the tenths place, you write 3 over 10. $\frac{3}{10}$
9. Write a fraction equal to 0.3. $0.3 = \frac{3}{10}$

Write 3.07 as a mixed number by answering 10 to 13.

10. What is the whole number part of the decimal 3.07?   **3**
11. What is the place value of the last digit in 3.07?   **hundredths**
12. Write the place value as the denominator and write 7 as the numerator. $3.07 = 3\frac{7}{100}$
13. Write a mixed number equal to 3.07. $3.07 = 3\frac{7}{100}$

© Pearson Education, Inc.

Name _____

Decimals to Fractions (continued)

Write each decimal as a fraction or mixed number.

14. 0.4 $\frac{4}{10}$

15. 3.7 $3\frac{7}{10}$

16. 5.27 $5\frac{27}{100}$

17. 0.8 $\frac{8}{10}$

18. 1.2 $1\frac{2}{10}$

19. 4.03 $4\frac{3}{100}$

20. 0.12 $\frac{12}{100}$

21. 10.5 $10\frac{5}{10}$

22. 0.19 $\frac{19}{100}$

23. 0.42 $\frac{42}{100}$

24. 5.75 $5\frac{75}{100}$

25. 8.6 $8\frac{6}{10}$

26. 19.09 $19\frac{9}{100}$

27. 0.01 $\frac{1}{100}$

28. 28.37 $28\frac{37}{100}$

29. Jaime put 13.9 gallons of gas in the car. What is 13.9 written as a mixed number? $13\frac{9}{10}$

30. Candice ran 2.75 miles. What is 2.75 written as a mixed number? $2\frac{75}{100}$

31. Justin's mom bought a 12.57 pound turkey. What is 12.57 written as a mixed number? $12\frac{57}{100}$

32. **Reasoning** Marco says $0.08 = \frac{8}{10}$. Is he correct? Explain why.

   No; $0.08 = \frac{8}{100}$ **not** $\frac{8}{10}$.

33. **Reasoning** $2.37 = 2\frac{37}{100}$ and $2.3 = 2\frac{3}{10}$. Explain why the 3 in 2.37 represents $\frac{3}{10}$.

   Sample answer: In 2.37 = 2 + 0.3 + 0.07, so the 3 represents $0.3 = \frac{3}{10}$.

© Pearson Education, Inc.

Teacher Notes

Ongoing Assessment

Ask: *What is 0.10 written as a fraction?* $\frac{1}{10}$

Error Intervention

If students have trouble representing decimals with grids,

then use H22: Place Value through Hundredths.

If You Have More Time

Have students work in pairs. Each student writes a decimal on a piece of notebook paper. The students exchange papers and rewrite the decimal as a fraction. Have students check their partners' work for accuracy.

Fractions to Decimals

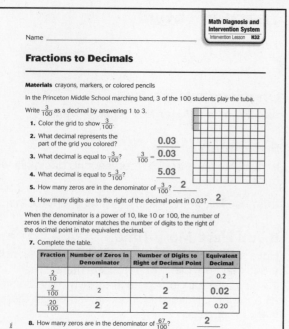

Name _____

Math Diagnosis and Intervention System
Intervention Lesson   H32

Fractions to Decimals

Materials crayons, markers, or colored pencils

In the Princeton Middle School marching band, 3 of the 100 students play the tuba.

Write $\frac{3}{100}$ as a decimal by answering 1 to 3.

1. Color the grid to show $\frac{3}{100}$.

2. What decimal represents the part of the grid you colored?   **0.03**

3. What decimal is equal to $\frac{3}{100}$? $\frac{3}{100}$ = **0.03**

4. What decimal is equal to $5\frac{3}{100}$?   **5.03**

5. How many zeros are in the denominator of $\frac{3}{100}$? **2**

6. How many digits are to the right of the decimal point in 0.03? **2**

When the denominator is a power of 10, like 10 or 100, the number of zeros in the denominator matches the number of digits to the right of the decimal point in the equivalent decimal.

7. Complete the table.

Fraction	Number of Zeros in Denominator	Number of Digits to Right of Decimal Point	Equivalent Decimal
$\frac{2}{10}$	1	1	0.2
$\frac{2}{100}$	2	2	0.02
$\frac{20}{100}$	2	2	0.20

8. How many zeros are in the denominator of $\frac{67}{100}$? **2**

So what decimal is equal to $\frac{67}{100}$? $\frac{67}{100}$ = **0.67**

You can also change a fraction to a decimal by dividing the numerator by the denominator.

9. Write $\frac{3}{20}$ as a decimal. Find the quotient of $\frac{3}{20}$ or $3 \div 20$, at the right.   **0.15** / 20)3.00

10. What decimal is equal to $\frac{3}{20}$? $\frac{3}{20}$ = **0.15**

Intervention Lesson H32   **147**

Name _____

Math Diagnosis and Intervention System
Intervention Lesson   H32

Fractions to Decimals (continued)

Write each fraction as a decimal.

11. $\frac{1}{5}$ **0.2**

12. $\frac{7}{10}$ **0.7**

13. $\frac{1}{2}$ **0.5**

14. $\frac{63}{100}$ **0.63**

15. $\frac{47}{100}$ **0.47**

16. $\frac{3}{4}$ **0.75**

17. $\frac{84}{100}$ **0.84**

18. $\frac{77}{100}$ **0.77**

19. $\frac{6}{100}$ **0.06**

20. $\frac{29}{100}$ **0.29**

21. $\frac{51}{100}$ **0.51**

22. $\frac{40}{100}$ **0.40**

The picture at the right shows the books Jason read in September. Use the picture for Exercises 23 and 24.

23. Write a fraction and a decimal to describe the part of the books that Jason read that were fiction.   **$\frac{7}{10}$, 0.7**

24. Write a fraction and a decimal to describe the part of the books that Jason read that were nonfiction.   **$\frac{3}{10}$, 0.3**

Katie bought 100 plants for her garden. She bought 37 tomato plants, 8 cucumber plants, 12 pumpkin plants, and the rest of her plants were onions. Use this information for Exercises 25 to 27.

25. Write a fraction and a decimal to express the part of the plants that are tomatoes.   **$\frac{37}{100}$, 0.37**

26. What part of her plants are cucumbers and pumpkins? Express your answer as a decimal.   **0.20**

27. **Reasoning** Explain the difference between the decimal equivalents of $\frac{9}{10}$ and $\frac{9}{100}$.

The decimal equivalent of $\frac{9}{10}$ has one place to the right of the decimal point and the decimal equivalent of $\frac{9}{100}$ has two places. So, $\frac{9}{10}$ = 0.9 and $\frac{9}{100}$ = 0.09.

148   Intervention Lesson H32

Teacher Notes

Ongoing Assessment

Ask: **How can you use division to change $\frac{1}{4}$ to a decimal?** $1 \div 4$

Error Intervention

If students have trouble dividing with zeros in the quotient as place holders,

then use G56: Zeros in the Quotient.

If students have trouble dividing decimals by a whole number,

then use G57: Dividing Money and H65: Dividing a Decimal by a Whole Number.

If You Have More Time

Write on the board 20 different fractions with denominators of 2, 4, 5, 10, 20, 25, 50, or 100. Have students create a 3 by 3 grid. In the center cell they should write the word FREE. Have students select 8 random fractions from the board and write one fraction in each cell of their grids. You, or a designated student, then calls out decimals. If the student has a fraction that is equivalent to the decimal, then the student covers that cell with a marker. The first student to correctly cover 3 cells horizontally, vertically, or diagonally wins that round.

© Pearson Education, Inc.

Relating Fractions and Decimals to Thousandths

Name _____

Math Diagnosis and Intervention System
Intervention Lesson **H33**

Relating Fractions and Decimals to Thousandths

Wyatt lost a swim race by 0.065 second. Answer 1 to 4 to learn how to write this value as a fraction.

1. In the decimal 0.065, 0 is in the tenths place, 6 is in the hundreths place and 5 is in the __**thousandths**__ place.

2. Write the value of 0.065 in words. __**sixty-five thousandths**__

3. To write sixty-five thousandths as a fraction, what value goes in the numerator? **65**

   What value goes in the denominator? **1000**

4. Write a fraction equal to 0.065 second. $0.065 = \dfrac{65}{1000}$ second

To write a fraction as a decimal, first look at the denominator of the fraction.

When the denominator is a power of 10, like 10, 100, or 1,000, the number of zeros in the denominator matches the number of digits to the right of the decimal point in the equivalent decimal.

5. Complete the table.

Fraction	Number of Zeros in Denominator	Number of Digits to Right of Decimal Point	Decimal
$\frac{4}{10}$	1	1	0.4
$\frac{45}{100}$	2	2	0.45
$\frac{455}{1000}$	3	3	0.455
$\frac{485}{1000}$	3	3	0.485

6. How many zeros are in the denominator of $\frac{285}{1000}$? **3**

   So, what decimal is equal to $\frac{285}{1000}$? $\dfrac{285}{1000} = 0.285$

7. **Reasoning** Janet beat her opponent by one hundred and sixteen thousandths second. Write this value as a fraction and a decimal. $\dfrac{116}{1000}; 0.116$

Intervention Lesson H33   **149**

Name _____

Math Diagnosis and Intervention System
Intervention Lesson **H33**

Relating Fractions and Decimals to Thousandths (continued)

Write each decimal as a fraction.

8. 0.345 $\dfrac{345}{1000}$

9. 0.043 $\dfrac{43}{1000}$

10. 0.002 $\dfrac{2}{1000}$

11. 0.507 $\dfrac{507}{1000}$

12. 0.201 $\dfrac{201}{1000}$

13. 0.011 $\dfrac{11}{1000}$

14. 0.999 $\dfrac{999}{1000}$

15. 0.058 $\dfrac{58}{1000}$

16. A major league baseball player has a batting average of 0.385. What is his batting average written as a fraction? $\dfrac{385}{1000}$

Write each fraction as a decimal.

17. $\frac{4}{1000}$ **0.004**

18. $\frac{56}{1000}$ **0.056**

19. $\frac{702}{1000}$ **0.702**

20. $\frac{23}{1000}$ **0.023**

21. $\frac{545}{1000}$ **0.545**

22. $\frac{757}{1000}$ **0.757**

23. $\frac{67}{1000}$ **0.067**

24. $\frac{1}{1000}$ **0.001**

A local ballet theater can seat 1,000 patrons. There are 64 seats in the private balcony sections, 225 seats in the orchestra section, 300 seats in the lower level, and the rest of the seats are located in the upper level. Use this information for Exercises 25 and 26.

25. Write a fraction and a decimal to represent the part of the seats that are balcony seats. $\dfrac{64}{1000}; 0.064$

26. **Reasoning** Write a fraction and a decimal to represent the part of the seats that are in the upper level. $\dfrac{411}{1000}; 0.411$

150 Intervention Lesson H33

© Pearson Education, Inc.

Teacher Notes

Ongoing Assessment

Ask: *What is the place value of the 5 in the decimal 0.325?* Thousandths *What is 0.325 as a fraction?* $\dfrac{325}{1000}$

Error Intervention

If students have trouble with place value to tenths, hundredths, and thousandths,

then use H24: Place Value through Thousandths.

If You Have More Time

Have students design a math poster explaining in their own words how to rewrite a fraction as a decimal and vice versa.

Using Models to Compare Fractions and Decimals

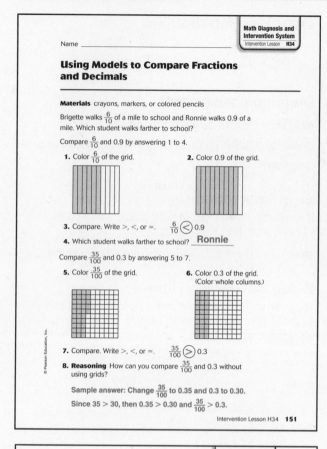

Name _____

Using Models to Compare Fractions and Decimals

Materials crayons, markers, or colored pencils

Brigette walks $\frac{6}{10}$ of a mile to school and Ronnie walks 0.9 of a mile. Which student walks farther to school?

Compare $\frac{6}{10}$ and 0.9 by answering 1 to 4.

1. Color $\frac{6}{10}$ of the grid.　　**2.** Color 0.9 of the grid.

3. Compare. Write >, <, or =.　$\frac{6}{10}$ $<$ 0.9

4. Which student walks farther to school? __Ronnie__

Compare $\frac{35}{100}$ and 0.3 by answering 5 to 7.

5. Color $\frac{35}{100}$ of the grid.　　**6.** Color 0.3 of the grid. (Color whole columns.)

7. Compare. Write >, <, or =.　$\frac{35}{100}$ $>$ 0.3

8. Reasoning How can you compare $\frac{35}{100}$ and 0.3 without using grids?

Sample answer: Change $\frac{35}{100}$ to 0.35 and 0.3 to 0.30.

Since 35 > 30, then 0.35 > 0.30 and $\frac{35}{100}$ > 0.3.

Intervention Lesson H34　**151**

Name _____

Using Models to Compare Fractions and Decimals (continued)

Color the grids to compare. Write >, <, or =. **Check student's coloring.**

9. 0.5 $>$ $\frac{3}{10}$

10. $\frac{44}{100}$ $<$ 0.8

11. 0.2 $>$ $\frac{12}{100}$

12. $\frac{8}{100}$ $=$ 0.08

13. 0.53 $<$ $\frac{57}{100}$

14. $\frac{45}{100}$ $<$ 0.54

15. Maria has 100 flowers in a garden. If 0.43 of the flowers are roses and $\frac{9}{100}$ of the flowers are daisies, does Maria have more roses or daisies? __roses__

16. Reasoning Without coloring a grid, how can you tell that 0.7 and $\frac{70}{100}$ are equal?

Sample answer: 0.7 and $\frac{70}{100}$ are equal because $\frac{70}{100} = \frac{7}{10}$ and $\frac{7}{10}$ written as a decimal is 0.7.

152　Intervention Lesson H34

Teacher Notes

Ongoing Assessment

Ask: **Why is it important to color the whole column for $\frac{2}{10}$ instead of just 2 blocks when using a grid of 100 squares?** $\frac{2}{10}$ is the same as $\frac{20}{100}$ and if you colored just 2 squares then you would be coloring $\frac{2}{100}$ and not $\frac{2}{10}$.

Error Intervention

If students have trouble comparing and ordering numbers,

then use H6: Using Models to Compare Fractions, F9: Comparing and Ordering Numbers through Hundredths, H19: Comparing and Ordering Fractions, or H28: Comparing and Ordering Decimals through Hundredths.

If You Have More Time

Give the students blank 100 grids. Have them color the grids and write the decimal or fraction of the colored part of the grid. Then have the students compare their grids with other students in the class. The goal is to find a grid that has more colored squares and a grid with less colored squares. Have the students write the inequalities on paper and share their results.

© Pearson Education, Inc.

Fractions, Decimals, and the Number Line

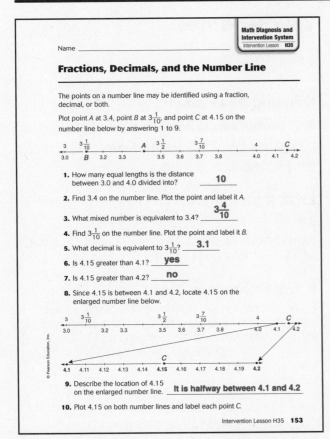

Name _____

Fractions, Decimals, and the Number Line

The points on a number line may be identified using a fraction, decimal, or both.

Plot point A at 3.4, point B at $3\frac{1}{10}$, and point C at 4.15 on the number line below by answering 1 to 9.

1. How many equal lengths is the distance between 3.0 and 4.0 divided into? **10**

2. Find 3.4 on the number line. Plot the point and label it A.

3. What mixed number is equivalent to 3.4? $3\frac{4}{10}$

4. Find $3\frac{1}{10}$ on the number line. Plot the point and label it B.

5. What decimal is equivalent to $3\frac{1}{10}$? **3.1**

6. Is 4.15 greater than 4.1? **yes**

7. Is 4.15 greater than 4.2? **no**

8. Since 4.15 is between 4.1 and 4.2, locate 4.15 on the enlarged number line below.

9. Describe the location of 4.15 on the enlarged number line. **It is halfway between 4.1 and 4.2**

10. Plot 4.15 on both number lines and label each point C.

Intervention Lesson H35 **153**

Name _____

Fractions, Decimals, and the Number Line (continued)

For Exercises 11 to 14, name the decimal and mixed number that should be written at each point on the number line below.

11. R   **1.2** $1\frac{2}{10}$

12. S   **2.1** $2\frac{1}{10}$

13. T   **1.9** $1\frac{9}{10}$

14. U   **1.7** $1\frac{7}{10}$

For Exercises 15 to 18, name the point on the number line below that represents each decimal or mixed number.

15. 9.6   **A**

16. $9\frac{3}{10}$ **B**

17. $9\frac{9}{10}$ **D**

18. 9.1   **C**

For Exercises 19 to 22, name the decimal and mixed number that should be written at each point on the number line below.

19. J   **3.78** $3\frac{78}{100}$

20. K   **3.75** $3\frac{75}{100}$

21. L   **3.72** $3\frac{72}{100}$

22. M   **3.74** $3\frac{74}{100}$

23. Reasoning Numbers on a number line are in order from the least on the left to the greatest on the right. Use the number line above to write 3.78, $3\frac{3}{4}$, $3\frac{72}{100}$, and 3.74 in order from least to greatest.

$3\frac{72}{100}$, 3.74, $3\frac{3}{4}$, 3.78

© Pearson Education, Inc.

Teacher Notes

Ongoing Assessment

Ask: *Between which two tenths is 5.17 on a number line?* 5.1 and 5.2

Error Intervention

If students have trouble locating fractions and mixed numbers on a number line,

then use H5: Fractions on the Number Line and H21: Fractions and Mixed Numbers on the Number Line.

If students have trouble locating decimals on a number line,

then use H23: Decimals on the Number Line.

If You Have More Time

Assign each student a letter. Draw a number line on the board. Have the student with letter A go to the board and tape the letter to a number, like 4.06. Then, have the student with letter B go to the board and tape the letter to a number, like $4\frac{1}{10}$. Continue until each student has had a turn. Start another number line if the first gets too crowded.

Adding Fractions with Like Denominators

Adding Fractions with Like Denominators

Materials crayons or markers

Nur wove $\frac{2}{5}$ of a rug in February and $\frac{1}{5}$ of it in March.
Find what part of the rug she has finished in all by
answering 1 to 4.

1. Color $\frac{2}{5}$ of the rectangle on the right.

2. Color $\frac{1}{5}$ more of the rectangle on the right.

3. How much of the rectangle $\boxed{\dfrac{3}{5}}$
   did you color in all?

   This is the sum of $\frac{2}{5}$ and $\frac{1}{5}$. So, $\frac{2}{5} + \frac{1}{5} = \frac{3}{5}$.

4. What part of her rug has Nur finished in all? $\underline{\frac{3}{5}}$

Jamal wove $\frac{2}{6}$ of a rug in February and $\frac{2}{6}$ in March.
Find what part of the rug he has finished in all by
answering 5 to 11.

5. Color $\frac{2}{6}$ of the rectangle on the right.

6. Color $\frac{2}{6}$ more of the rectangle on the right.

7. How much of the rectangle $\boxed{\dfrac{4}{6}}$
   did you color in all?

8. What is $\frac{2}{6} + \frac{2}{6}$? $\underline{\frac{4}{6}}$

9. What is a fraction equivalent to $\frac{4}{6}$,
   but with smaller numbers? Color $\frac{4}{6} = \boxed{\dfrac{2}{3}}$
   the second rectangle to find out.

10. So, $\frac{2}{6} + \frac{2}{6} = \frac{4}{6} = \boxed{\dfrac{2}{3}}$.

11. What part of his rug has Jamal finished in all? $\underline{\frac{2}{3}}$

Intervention Lesson H36   **155**

Adding Fractions with Like Denominators (continued)

12. **Reasoning** Explain how to add $\frac{1}{9} + \frac{4}{9}$.

    Add the 1 and the 4 to get 5. Then, put 5
    over the denominator. So, $\frac{1}{9} + \frac{4}{9} = \frac{5}{9}$.

Add.

13. $\frac{1}{3} + \frac{1}{3} = \underline{\frac{2}{3}}$

14. $\frac{1}{5} + \frac{3}{5} = \underline{\frac{4}{5}}$

15. $\frac{1}{4} + \frac{2}{4} = \underline{\frac{3}{4}}$

16. $\frac{2}{6} + \frac{3}{6} = \underline{\frac{5}{6}}$

17. $\frac{2}{8} + \frac{5}{8} = \underline{\frac{7}{8}}$

18. $\frac{3}{10} + \frac{2}{10} = \underline{\frac{5}{10}} = \underline{\frac{1}{2}}$

19. Calvin bought a gallon of yogurt. He ate $\frac{1}{6}$ gallon
    the first day, and $\frac{2}{6}$ gallon the second day.
    What fraction of the yogurt did he eat? $\underline{\frac{3}{6}}$

20. Three-fifths of Mr. James' class are wearing blue jeans
    and white shirts. One-fifth of the class are wearing blue
    jeans and red shirts. One-fifth of the class are wearing
    brown pants and white shirts. What fraction of Mr. James' $\underline{\frac{4}{5}}$
    class are wearing white shirts?

21. **Reasoning** What fraction would you add to $\frac{1}{3}$ to get $\frac{3}{3}$? $\underline{\frac{2}{3}}$

156 Intervention Lesson H36

Teacher Notes

Ongoing Assessment

Say: **Explain how to add $\frac{1}{6} + \frac{4}{6}$.** Add the
numerators $1 + 4 = 5$. Put the 5 over the
denominator 6.

Error Intervention

If students have trouble showing fractions,

then use H2: Parts of a Region, H3: Parts of a Set,
or H4: Fractions and Length.

If You Have More Time

Have students make up stories involving adding
fractions, draw a picture to match the story, and
write a number sentence to match both.

© Pearson Education, Inc.

Subtracting Fractions with Like Denominators

Name _____

Subtracting Fractions with Like Denominators

Materials crayons or markers

Tammy loves tuna bake. When she came home from school, she found $\frac{6}{8}$ of a tuna bake on the stove. She ate $\frac{1}{8}$ of it. Find how much of the tuna bake was left by answering 1 to 3.

1. Color $\frac{6}{8}$ of the rectangle on the right.

2. Cross out $\frac{1}{8}$ of the part you colored.

3. How much of the rectangle you colored is not crossed out? $\boxed{\frac{5}{8}}$

4. What is $\frac{6}{8} - \frac{1}{8}$? $\boxed{\frac{5}{8}}$

5. How much of the tuna bake was left after Tammy ate? $\frac{5}{8}$

Brad found $\frac{3}{4}$ of a submarine sandwich when he came home from school. He ate $\frac{1}{4}$ of the sandwich. Find how much of the sandwich was left by answering 6 to 12.

6. Color $\frac{3}{4}$ of the rectangle on the right.

7. Cross out $\frac{1}{4}$ of the part you colored.

8. How much of the rectangle you colored is not crossed out? $\boxed{\frac{2}{4}}$

9. What is $\frac{3}{4} - \frac{1}{4}$? $\boxed{\frac{2}{4}}$

10. What is a fraction equivalent to $\frac{2}{4}$, but with smaller numbers? Color the second rectangle to find out. $\frac{2}{4} = \boxed{\frac{1}{2}}$

11. So, $\frac{3}{4} - \frac{1}{4} = \frac{2}{4} = \boxed{\frac{1}{2}}$.

12. How much of the sandwich was left after Brad ate? $\frac{1}{2}$

© Pearson Education, Inc.

Intervention Lesson H37   **157**

Name _____

Subtracting Fractions with Like Denominators (continued)

13. **Reasoning** Explain how to subtract $\frac{5}{10} - \frac{2}{10}$.

    Subtract 5 − 2 to get 3. Then, put 3 over the denominator 10. So, $\frac{5}{10} - \frac{2}{10} = \frac{3}{10}$.

Subtract.

14. $\frac{5}{6} - \frac{3}{6} = \frac{2}{6}$

15. $\frac{3}{5} - \frac{1}{5} = \frac{2}{5}$

16. $\frac{3}{4} - \frac{1}{4} = \frac{2}{4}$

17. $\frac{4}{5} - \frac{2}{5} = \frac{2}{5}$

18. $\frac{4}{7} - \frac{3}{7} = \frac{1}{7}$

19. $\frac{5}{9} - \frac{4}{9} = \frac{1}{9}$

20. $\frac{7}{8} - \frac{1}{8} = \frac{6}{8} = \frac{3}{4}$

21. $\frac{4}{6} - \frac{1}{6} = \frac{3}{6} = \frac{1}{2}$

The table shows the distances run by members of a track team. Use the table for Exercises 22 and 23.

22. How much farther did Rosie run than Tricia? $\frac{3}{8}$ mile

23. How much farther did Caro run than Tricia? $\frac{2}{8}$ or $\frac{1}{4}$ mile

24. **Reasoning** Why would it be more difficult to subtract $\frac{2}{3} - \frac{1}{6}$ than $\frac{2}{3} - \frac{1}{3}$?

    $\frac{2}{3}$ and $\frac{1}{3}$ have the same denominator, and $\frac{2}{3}$ and $\frac{1}{6}$ have different denominators.

Runner	Distance in miles
Rosie	$\frac{7}{8}$
Tricia	$\frac{4}{8}$
Amy	$\frac{5}{8}$
Caro	$\frac{6}{8}$

© Pearson Education, Inc.

158   Intervention Lesson H37

© Pearson Education, Inc.

Teacher Notes

Ongoing Assessment

Make sure students do not try to subtract the denominators.

Error Intervention

If students have trouble showing fractions,

then use H2: Parts of a Region, H3: Parts of a Set, or H4: Fractions and Length.

If You Have More Time

Have students work in pairs. Have one student make up a story about subtracting fractions. Have the partner write a number sentence and solve. Then, have students change roles and repeat.

Adding and Subtracting Fractions with Like Denominators

Name _____

Math Diagnosis and
Intervention System
Intervention Lesson **H38**

Adding and Subtracting Fractions with Like Denominators

Carlos spent $\frac{3}{4}$ hour writing email and another $\frac{3}{4}$ hour surfing the internet. How much time did he spend on his computer in all?

Find $\frac{3}{4} + \frac{3}{4}$ by answering 1 to 4.

1. Show $\frac{3}{4} + \frac{3}{4}$ with fraction strips.

2. What is $\frac{3}{4} + \frac{3}{4}$? $\underline{\frac{6}{4}}$

3. Use the fraction strips to find $\frac{6}{4}$ as a mixed number in simplest form.

$\frac{3}{4} + \frac{3}{4} = \frac{6}{4} = 1\frac{\boxed{2}}{4} = 1\frac{1}{2}$

4. How much time did Carlos spend on his computer in all? $1\frac{1}{2}$ hours

5. **Reasoning** Explain how to find $\frac{7}{10} + \frac{9}{10}$.
Add the 7 and the 9 to get 16. Then, put 16 over the denominator to get $\frac{16}{10}$. Simplify $\frac{16}{10}$ to $1\frac{6}{10}$ and then $1\frac{3}{5}$. So, $\frac{7}{10} + \frac{9}{10} = 1\frac{3}{5}$.

Connie had $\frac{5}{6}$ hour to surf the internet. She finished with one site in $\frac{1}{6}$ hour. How much time did she have left?

Find $\frac{5}{6} - \frac{1}{6}$ by answering 6 to 11.

6. Show $\frac{5}{6}$ with fraction strips.

7. Take away $\frac{1}{6}$.

8. What is $\frac{5}{6} - \frac{1}{6}$? $\underline{\frac{4}{6}}$

9. Write the difference in simplest form. $\frac{4}{6} = \underline{\frac{2}{3}}$

10. So, $\frac{5}{6} - \frac{1}{6} = \frac{4}{6} = \underline{\frac{2}{3}}$.

11. How much time did Connie have left to surf the internet? $\frac{2}{3}$ hour

Intervention Lesson H38 **159**

Name _____

Math Diagnosis and
Intervention System
Intervention Lesson **H38**

Adding and Subtracting Fractions with Like Denominators (continued)

12. **Reasoning** Explain how to find $\frac{7}{8} - \frac{1}{8}$.
Subtract 7 − 1 to get 6. Put 6 over the denominator to get $\frac{6}{8}$. Then simplify $\frac{6}{8}$ to $\frac{3}{4}$. So, $\frac{7}{8} - \frac{1}{8} = \frac{3}{4}$.

Add. Write the sum in simplest form.

13. $\frac{5}{12} + \frac{1}{12}$ $\frac{1}{2}$

14. $\frac{5}{9} + \frac{1}{9}$ $\frac{2}{3}$

15. $\frac{4}{15} + \frac{8}{15}$ $\frac{4}{5}$

16. $\frac{3}{5} + \frac{4}{5}$ $1\frac{2}{5}$

17. $\frac{6}{7} + \frac{4}{7}$ $1\frac{3}{7}$

18. $\frac{2}{3} + \frac{2}{3}$ $1\frac{1}{3}$

19. $\frac{7}{10} + \frac{9}{10}$ $1\frac{3}{5}$

20. $\frac{7}{8} + \frac{5}{8}$ $1\frac{1}{2}$

21. $\frac{11}{12} + \frac{5}{12}$ $1\frac{1}{3}$

Subtract. Write the difference in simplest form.

22. $\frac{2}{3} - \frac{1}{3}$ $\frac{1}{3}$

23. $\frac{11}{12} - \frac{1}{12}$ $\frac{5}{6}$

24. $\frac{7}{9} - \frac{1}{9}$ $\frac{2}{3}$

25. $\frac{7}{8} - \frac{1}{8}$ $\frac{3}{4}$

26. $\frac{9}{10} - \frac{3}{10}$ $\frac{3}{5}$

27. $\frac{3}{4} - \frac{1}{4}$ $\frac{1}{2}$

28. Each class is making a friendship chain the length of the school gym, for the end of year party. The fifth grade class has $\frac{7}{10}$ of their chain finished. The sixth grade class has $\frac{9}{10}$ of theirs finished. How much more of the sixth grade chain is finished than the fifth grade chain? $\frac{1}{5}$

29. **Reasoning** Richard gathered $\frac{7}{12}$ of a dozen eggs and Karina gathered $\frac{5}{12}$ of a dozen. What part of a dozen did they gather in all? Explain.
They gathered a whole dozen eggs. $\frac{7}{12} + \frac{5}{12} = \frac{12}{12} = 1$

160 Intervention Lesson H38

Teacher Notes

Ongoing Assessment

Ask: *In order to add or subtract fractions, what needs to be true about the denominators of each fraction?* They need to be the same.

Error Intervention

If students do not know how to write fractions in simplest form,

then use H17: Simplest Form.

If You Have More Time

Have students show how to add and subtract fractions with part of a set, using counters.

© Pearson Education, Inc.

Adding and Subtracting Fractions on a Number Line

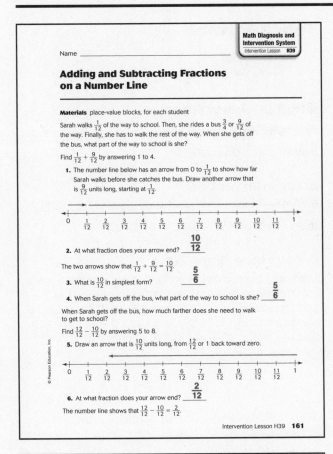

Name _____

Math Diagnosis and Intervention System
Intervention Lesson **H39**

Adding and Subtracting Fractions on a Number Line

Materials place-value blocks, for each student

Sarah walks $\frac{1}{12}$ of the way to school. Then, she rides a bus $\frac{3}{4}$ or $\frac{9}{12}$ of the way. Finally, she has to walk the rest of the way. When she gets off the bus, what part of the way to school is she?

Find $\frac{1}{12} + \frac{9}{12}$ by answering 1 to 4.

1. The number line below has an arrow from 0 to $\frac{1}{12}$ to show how far Sarah walks before she catches the bus. Draw another arrow that is $\frac{9}{12}$ units long, starting at $\frac{1}{12}$.

2. At what fraction does your arrow end? $\frac{10}{12}$

The two arrows show that $\frac{1}{12} + \frac{9}{12} = \frac{10}{12}$.

3. What is $\frac{10}{12}$ in simplest form? $\frac{5}{6}$

4. When Sarah gets off the bus, what part of the way to school is she? $\frac{5}{6}$

When Sarah gets off the bus, how much farther does she need to walk to get to school?

Find $\frac{12}{12} - \frac{10}{12}$ by answering 5 to 8.

5. Draw an arrow that is $\frac{10}{12}$ units long, from $\frac{12}{12}$ or 1 back toward zero.

6. At what fraction does your arrow end? $\frac{2}{12}$

The number line shows that $\frac{12}{12} - \frac{10}{12} = \frac{2}{12}$.

Intervention Lesson H39 **161**

Name _____

Math Diagnosis and Intervention System
Intervention Lesson **H39**

Adding and Subtracting Fractions on a Number Line (continued)

7. What is $\frac{2}{12}$ in simplest form? $\frac{1}{6}$

8. When Sarah gets off the bus, how much farther does she need to walk to get to school? $\frac{1}{6}$ of the way

Use the number line to add or subtract. Write answers in simplest form.

9. $\frac{3}{10} + \frac{4}{10} = \frac{7}{10}$ **10.** $\frac{7}{10} + \frac{1}{10} = \frac{8}{10} = \frac{4}{5}$

11. $\frac{9}{10} - \frac{3}{10} = \frac{6}{10} = \frac{3}{5}$ **12.** $\frac{8}{10} - \frac{3}{10} = \frac{5}{10} = \frac{1}{2}$

13. $\frac{1}{8} + \frac{4}{8} = \frac{5}{8}$ **14.** $\frac{3}{8} + \frac{1}{8} = \frac{4}{8} = \frac{1}{2}$

15. $\frac{7}{8} - \frac{1}{8} = \frac{6}{8} = \frac{3}{4}$ **16.** $\frac{5}{8} - \frac{3}{8} = \frac{2}{8} = \frac{1}{4}$

17. Rodney mixed $\frac{2}{9}$ of a bottle of apple juice with $\frac{4}{9}$ of a bottle of cranberry juice. How much juice was in the mixture? $\frac{2}{3}$ **of a bottle**

18. Reasoning What is $\frac{4}{9} + \frac{2}{9} - \frac{1}{9}$? $\frac{5}{9}$

162 Intervention Lesson H39

Teacher Notes

Ongoing Assessment

Make sure students count spaces on the number line, not tick marks.

Error Intervention

If students have trouble locating fractions on the number line,

then use H21: Fractions and Mixed Numbers on the Number Line.

If You Have More Time

Have students create a giant number line on the board or on a long sheet of paper, and step off the sum or difference of different fractions.

© Pearson Education, Inc.

Adding Fractions with Unlike Denominators

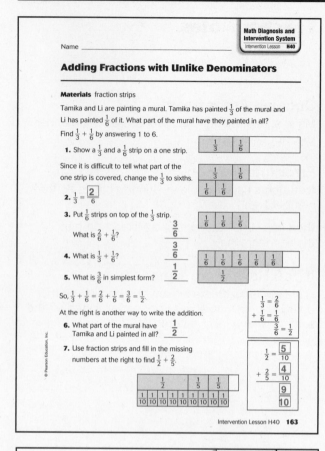

Name _____

Math Diagnosis and Intervention System
Intervention Lesson **H40**

Adding Fractions with Unlike Denominators

Materials fraction strips

Tamika and Li are painting a mural. Tamika has painted $\frac{1}{3}$ of the mural and Li has painted $\frac{1}{6}$ of it. What part of the mural have they painted in all?

Find $\frac{1}{3} + \frac{1}{6}$ by answering 1 to 6.

1. Show a $\frac{1}{3}$ and a $\frac{1}{6}$ strip on a one strip.

Since it is difficult to tell what part of the one strip is covered, change the $\frac{1}{3}$ to sixths.

2. $\frac{1}{3} = \frac{\boxed{2}}{6}$

3. Put $\frac{1}{6}$ strips on top of the $\frac{1}{3}$ strip.

What is $\frac{2}{6} + \frac{1}{6}$? $\frac{3}{6}$

4. What is $\frac{1}{3} + \frac{1}{6}$? $\frac{3}{6}$

5. What is $\frac{3}{6}$ in simplest form? $\frac{1}{2}$

So, $\frac{1}{3} + \frac{1}{6} = \frac{2}{6} + \frac{1}{6} = \frac{3}{6} = \frac{1}{2}$.

At the right is another way to write the addition.

6. What part of the mural have Tamika and Li painted in all? $\frac{1}{2}$

$$\frac{1}{3} = \frac{2}{6}$$
$$+ \frac{1}{6} = \frac{1}{6}$$
$$\frac{3}{6} = \frac{1}{2}$$

7. Use fraction strips and fill in the missing numbers at the right to find $\frac{1}{2} + \frac{2}{5}$.

$$\frac{1}{2} = \frac{\boxed{5}}{10}$$
$$+ \frac{2}{5} = \frac{\boxed{4}}{10}$$
$$\frac{\boxed{9}}{\boxed{10}}$$

© Pearson Education, Inc.

Intervention Lesson H40   **163**

Teacher Notes

Ongoing Assessment

Ask: **Why did you use sixths to add $\frac{1}{3}$ and $\frac{1}{6}$?**
Both 3 and 6 divide evenly into 6.

Error Intervention

If students have trouble finding equivalent fractions,

then use H14: Equivalent Fractions.

If You Have More Time

Have students work in pairs to create a mural with crayons or markers. Have them describe what section each partner has completed when they are partly finished. Have students add the fractions to find the part of the whole that is finished.

Name _____

Math Diagnosis and Intervention System
Intervention Lesson **H40**

Adding Fractions with Unlike Denominators (continued)

Find each sum. Use fraction strips, if you like.

8.
$$\frac{4}{8} = \frac{4}{8}$$
$$+ \frac{1}{4} = \frac{\boxed{2}}{8}$$
$$\frac{6}{8} \text{ or } \frac{3}{4}$$

9.
$$\frac{1}{2} = \frac{\boxed{3}}{6}$$
$$+ \frac{1}{3} = \frac{\boxed{2}}{6}$$
$$\frac{5}{6}$$

10. $\frac{2}{3} + \frac{1}{6} = \frac{5}{6}$ **11.** $\frac{1}{5} + \frac{3}{10} = \frac{5}{10}$ **12.** $\frac{3}{8} + \frac{2}{4} = \frac{7}{8}$

13. $\frac{3}{4} + \frac{2}{8} = \frac{8}{8} \text{ or } 1$ **14.** $\frac{1}{6} + \frac{5}{12} = \frac{7}{12}$ **15.** $\frac{1}{8} + \frac{1}{2} = \frac{5}{8}$

16. $\frac{2}{6} + \frac{1}{3} = \frac{4}{6} \text{ or } \frac{2}{3}$ **17.** $\frac{2}{4} + \frac{1}{8} = \frac{5}{8}$ **18.** $\frac{3}{8} + \frac{1}{2} = \frac{7}{8}$

19. A jar is filled with red, blue, and green marbles. Half of the marbles are red. One-third of the marbles are blue. One-sixth of the marbles are green. What fraction of the marbles are either red or blue? $\frac{5}{6}$

20. Reasoning Could you change both fractions to a denominator of 9 to add $\frac{1}{3}$ and $\frac{1}{4}$? Explain.

No; You could change $\frac{1}{3}$ to $\frac{3}{9}$, but 4 does not divide into 9 evenly.

© Pearson Education, Inc.

164 Intervention Lesson H40

© Pearson Education, Inc.

Subtracting Fractions with Unlike Denominators

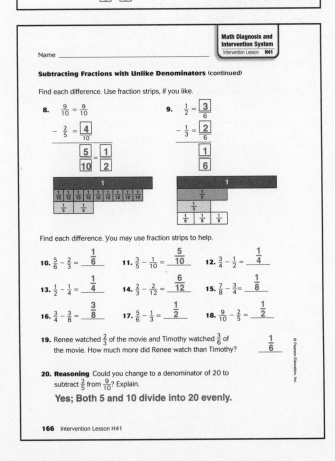

Name _____

Subtracting Fractions with Unlike Denominators

Materials fraction strips

Marion climbed $\frac{3}{4}$ of the way to the top of the climbing wall in the gym. Rober climbed $\frac{2}{3}$ of the way. Answer 1 to 6 to find what fraction farther Marion climbed than Rober.

Find $\frac{3}{4} - \frac{2}{3}$.

1. Show a one strip, three $\frac{1}{4}$ strips, and two $\frac{1}{3}$ strips.

Since it is difficult to tell how much longer $\frac{3}{4}$ is than $\frac{2}{3}$, change both fractions to twelfths.

2. $\frac{3}{4} = \frac{\boxed{9}}{12}$

3. $\frac{2}{3} = \frac{\boxed{8}}{12}$

4. What is $\frac{9}{12} - \frac{8}{12}$? $\frac{\boxed{1}}{12}$

5. So, $\frac{3}{4} - \frac{2}{3} = \frac{9}{12} - \frac{8}{12} = \frac{\boxed{1}}{\boxed{12}}$

$$\begin{array}{r} \frac{3}{4} = \frac{9}{12} \\ -\frac{2}{3} = \frac{8}{12} \\ \hline \frac{1}{12} \end{array}$$

At the right is another way to write the subtraction.

6. What fraction farther did Marion climb than Rober? $\frac{1}{12}$

7. Use fraction strips and fill in the missing numbers below to find $\frac{1}{2} - \frac{1}{6}$.

$$\begin{array}{r} \frac{1}{2} = \frac{\boxed{3}}{6} \\ -\frac{1}{6} = \frac{\boxed{1}}{6} \\ \hline \frac{\boxed{2}}{6} = \frac{\boxed{1}}{3} \end{array}$$

Intervention Lesson H41 **165**

© Pearson Education, Inc.

Teacher Notes

Ongoing Assessment

Ask: *Why did you change $\frac{3}{4}$ and $\frac{2}{3}$ to twelfths to subtract?* Sample answer: With the same denominator, you can subtract the numerators and keep that denominator. Without the same denominator, it is difficult to tell what the difference is, even with fraction strips.

Error Intervention

If students have trouble finding the least common denominator,

then have them list multiples of each denominator until they find a number that is a multiple of both.

If You Have More Time

Have students tell stories involving subtracting fractions with unlike denominators. Then, have the rest of the class or a partner solve.

Name _____

Subtracting Fractions with Unlike Denominators (continued)

Find each difference. Use fraction strips, if you like.

8. $\frac{9}{10} = \frac{9}{10}$
$-\frac{2}{5} = \frac{\boxed{4}}{10}$
$\frac{\boxed{5}}{\boxed{10}} = \frac{\boxed{1}}{\boxed{2}}$

9. $\frac{1}{2} = \frac{\boxed{3}}{6}$
$-\frac{1}{3} = \frac{\boxed{2}}{6}$
$\frac{\boxed{1}}{\boxed{6}}$

Find each difference. You may use fraction strips to help.

10. $\frac{5}{6} - \frac{2}{3} = \frac{1}{6}$
11. $\frac{3}{5} - \frac{1}{10} = \frac{5}{10}$
12. $\frac{3}{4} - \frac{1}{2} = \frac{1}{4}$

13. $\frac{1}{2} - \frac{1}{4} = \frac{1}{4}$
14. $\frac{2}{3} - \frac{2}{12} = \frac{6}{12}$
15. $\frac{7}{8} - \frac{3}{4} = \frac{1}{8}$

16. $\frac{3}{4} - \frac{3}{8} = \frac{3}{8}$
17. $\frac{5}{6} - \frac{1}{3} = \frac{1}{2}$
18. $\frac{9}{10} - \frac{2}{5} = \frac{1}{2}$

19. Renee watched $\frac{2}{3}$ of the movie and Timothy watched $\frac{3}{6}$ of the movie. How much more did Renee watch than Timothy? $\frac{1}{6}$

20. Reasoning Could you change to a denominator of 20 to subtract $\frac{2}{5}$ from $\frac{9}{10}$? Explain.
Yes; Both 5 and 10 divide into 20 evenly.

166 Intervention Lesson H41

© Pearson Education, Inc.

Estimating Sums and Differences of Mixed Numbers

Worksheet (page 167)

Estimating Sums and Differences of Mixed Numbers

Last week, Dwayne spent $4\frac{1}{3}$ hours playing basketball and $1\frac{2}{3}$ hours playing soccer. Answer 1 to 9 to estimate how much time Dwayne spent in all playing these two sports.

Estimate $4\frac{1}{3} + 1\frac{2}{3}$.

1. What two whole numbers is $4\frac{1}{3}$ between? __4__ and __5__

2. Use the number line.
   Is $4\frac{1}{3}$ closer to 4 or 5? __4__

   $4 \quad 4\frac{1}{6} \quad 4\frac{2}{6} \quad 4\frac{3}{6} \quad 4\frac{4}{6} \quad 4\frac{5}{6} \quad 5$

3. What is the number halfway between 4 and 5? __$4\frac{1}{2}$__

4. Compare. Write >, <, or =. $\frac{1}{3}$ < $\frac{1}{2}$

   By comparing $\frac{1}{3}$ and $\frac{1}{2}$, you can tell that $4\frac{1}{3}$ is closer to 4 than 5, without using a number line. So, $4\frac{1}{3}$ rounded to the nearest whole number is 4.

5. What two whole numbers is $1\frac{2}{3}$ between? __1__ and __2__

6. Compare. Write >, <, or =. $\frac{2}{3}$ > $\frac{1}{2}$

7. What is $1\frac{2}{3}$ rounded to the nearest whole number? __2__

8. Use the rounded numbers to estimate $4\frac{1}{3} + 1\frac{2}{3}$.

   $\begin{array}{r} 4\frac{1}{3} \rightarrow 4 \\ + 1\frac{2}{3} \rightarrow + 2 \end{array}$

9. About how much time did Dwayne spend playing basketball and soccer? __6 hours__ $\boxed{6}$

About how much more time did Dwayne spend playing basketball than soccer?

10. Estimate $4\frac{1}{3} - 1\frac{2}{3}$ at the right.

    $\begin{array}{r} 4\frac{1}{3} \rightarrow 4 \\ - 1\frac{2}{3} \rightarrow - 2 \end{array}$

11. About how much more time did Dwayne spend playing basketball than soccer? __2 hours__ $\boxed{2}$

Intervention Lesson H42 **167**

Worksheet (page 168)

Estimating Sums and Differences of Mixed Numbers (continued)

Estimate each sum or difference.

12. $\begin{array}{r} 2\frac{2}{3} \\ - 1\frac{1}{3} \end{array}$ $3 - 1 = 2$

13. $\begin{array}{r} 2\frac{9}{10} \\ - 1\frac{5}{10} \end{array}$ $3 - 2 = 1$

14. $\begin{array}{r} 5 \\ + 4\frac{2}{4} \end{array}$ $5 + 5 = 10$

15. $\begin{array}{r} 6\frac{4}{6} \\ + 1\frac{5}{6} \end{array}$ $7 + 2 = 9$

16. $\begin{array}{r} 6\frac{7}{8} \\ - 5\frac{3}{8} \end{array}$ $7 - 5 = 2$

17. $\begin{array}{r} 6 \\ - 3\frac{3}{9} \end{array}$ $6 - 3 = 3$

18. $\begin{array}{r} 4\frac{9}{14} \\ + 2\frac{11}{14} \end{array}$ $5 + 3 = 8$

19. $\begin{array}{r} 6 \\ + 4\frac{2}{16} \end{array}$ $6 + 4 = 10$

20. $2\frac{3}{4} - 1$ $3 - 1 = 2$

21. $7\frac{2}{6} + 6\frac{5}{6}$ $7 + 7 = 14$

22. $3\frac{2}{5} + 1\frac{2}{5}$ $3 + 1 = 4$

23. $6\frac{1}{8} - 1\frac{5}{8}$ $6 - 2 = 4$

24. $7 - 2\frac{3}{7}$ $7 - 2 = 5$

25. $3\frac{4}{8} + 1\frac{7}{8}$ $4 + 2 = 6$

26. Yolanda walked $2\frac{3}{5}$ miles on Monday, $1\frac{1}{5}$ miles on Tuesday, and $3\frac{4}{5}$ miles on Wednesday. Estimate her total distance walked. __8 miles__

27. Chris was going to add $2\frac{1}{4}$ cups of a chemical to the swimming pool until he found out that Richard already added $1\frac{1}{8}$ cups of the chemical. Estimate how much more Chris should add so that the total is his original amount. __1 cup__

28. **Reasoning** Is $3\frac{1}{2}$ closer to 3 or 4? Explain.

    $3\frac{1}{2}$ is halfway between 3 and 4, so it isn't closer to either.

168 Intervention Lesson H42

Teacher Notes

Ongoing Assessment

Ask: **How does knowing that $\frac{2}{3}$ is greater than $\frac{1}{2}$ help you to know that $1\frac{2}{3}$ is closer to 2 on a number line than to 1?** Sample answer: On a number line, $1\frac{1}{2}$ is the halfway point between 1 and 2. Since $\frac{2}{3} > \frac{1}{2}$, $1\frac{2}{3} > 1\frac{1}{2}$ and $1\frac{2}{3}$ is between $1\frac{1}{2}$ and 2 on the number line. Thus, $1\frac{2}{3}$ is closer to 2 than to 1.

Error Intervention

If students have trouble understanding the location of mixed numbers on the number line,

then use H5: Fractions on the Number Line or H21: Fractions and Mixed Numbers on the Number Line.

If You Have More Time

Have students work in pairs. Ask students to create a list of activities they participate in after school. Next to each activity, have students write the time spent on each activity, as a mixed number. Have students trade lists with their partners. Then have the partners estimate how much time was spent on two of the activities together and how much more time was spent on one activity than another.

© Pearson Education, Inc.

Adding Mixed Numbers

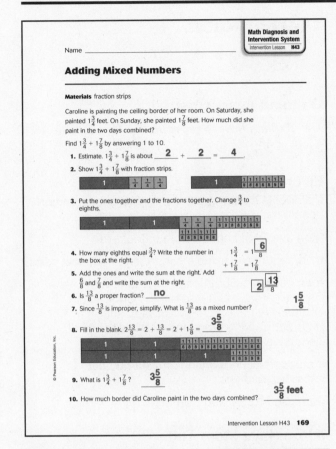

Name _____

Math Diagnosis and
Intervention System
Intervention Lesson   H43

Adding Mixed Numbers

Materials fraction strips

Caroline is painting the ceiling border of her room. On Saturday, she painted $1\frac{3}{4}$ feet. On Sunday, she painted $1\frac{7}{8}$ feet. How much did she paint in the two days combined?

Find $1\frac{3}{4} + 1\frac{7}{8}$ by answering 1 to 10.

1. Estimate. $1\frac{3}{4} + 1\frac{7}{8}$ is about __2__ + __2__ = __4__

2. Show $1\frac{3}{4} + 1\frac{7}{8}$ with fraction strips.

3. Put the ones together and the fractions together. Change $\frac{3}{4}$ to eighths.

4. How many eighths equal $3\frac{3}{4}$? Write the number in the box at the right. $1\frac{3}{4} = \boxed{6}\frac{}{8}$

5. Add the ones and write the sum at the right. Add $\frac{6}{8}$ and $\frac{7}{8}$ and write the sum at the right. $+ 1\frac{7}{8} = 1\frac{7}{8}$ $2\frac{13}{8}$

6. Is $\frac{13}{8}$ a proper fraction? __no__

7. Since $\frac{13}{8}$ is improper, simplify. What is $\frac{13}{8}$ as a mixed number? $1\frac{5}{8}$

8. Fill in the blank. $2\frac{13}{8} = 2 + \frac{13}{8} = 2 + 1\frac{5}{8} =$ __$3\frac{5}{8}$__

9. What is $1\frac{3}{4} + 1\frac{7}{8}$? $3\frac{5}{8}$

10. How much border did Caroline paint in the two days combined? $3\frac{5}{8}$ feet

Intervention Lesson H43   169

Name _____

Math Diagnosis and
Intervention System
Intervention Lesson   H43

Adding Mixed Numbers (continued)

11. Is the answer $3\frac{5}{8}$ close to the estimate of 4? __yes__

Since $3\frac{5}{8}$ is close to the estimate of 4, $3\frac{5}{8}$ is a reasonable answer.

Add. Write the sum as a simplified fraction. Estimate to check.

12. $2\frac{1}{2}$
$+ 1\frac{1}{3}$
$3\frac{5}{6}$; 4

13. $1\frac{1}{5}$
$+ 3\frac{3}{10}$
$4\frac{1}{2}$; 4

14. $1\frac{3}{4}$
$+ \frac{2}{5}$
$2\frac{3}{20}$; 2

15. $2\frac{5}{6}$
$+ 3\frac{5}{6}$
$6\frac{1}{4}$; 6

16. $6\frac{5}{6}$
$+ 5\frac{3}{8}$
$12\frac{5}{24}$; 12

17. $6\frac{1}{9}$
$+ 3\frac{3}{8}$
$9\frac{7}{9}$; 10

18. $4\frac{3}{4}$
$+ 7\frac{5}{6}$
$12\frac{7}{12}$; 13

19. $6\frac{1}{16}$
$+ 4\frac{3}{8}$
$10\frac{7}{16}$; 10

20. $6\frac{7}{8} + 1\frac{5}{6}$
$8\frac{17}{24}$; 9

21. $7\frac{1}{2} + 2\frac{3}{7}$
$9\frac{13}{14}$; 10

22. $3\frac{1}{10} + 1\frac{5}{8}$
$4\frac{29}{40}$; 5

23. Ramona bought $1\frac{2}{6}$ pounds of strawberries, $2\frac{1}{4}$ pounds of apples, and $2\frac{1}{2}$ pounds of oranges at the store. What was the total weight of Ramona's purchase? $6\frac{5}{12}$ pounds

24. Reasoning Rhonda needs 4 gallons of green paint to decorate her room. If she mixes $2\frac{1}{3}$ gallons of blue paint with $1\frac{1}{2}$ gallons of yellow paint, will she have enough? Explain.

No; $2\frac{1}{3} + 1\frac{1}{2} = 3\frac{5}{6}$ gallons. Rhonda needs 4 gallons and $3\frac{5}{6} < 4$.

170   Intervention Lesson H43

Teacher Notes

Ongoing Assessment

Ask: *Explain how to rewrite $4\frac{3}{2}$.* $4\frac{3}{2} = 4 + 1\frac{1}{2} = 5\frac{1}{2}$

Error Intervention

If students have trouble finding the least common denominator,

then use G65: Least Common Multiple.

If students have trouble adding fractional parts,

then use H36: Adding Fractions with Like Denominators, H38: Adding and Subtracting Fractions with Like Denominators, and H40: Adding Fractions with Unlike Denominators.

If students have difficulty changing improper fractions to mixed numbers,

then use H18: Mixed Numbers.

If You Have More Time

Write two mixed numbers, such as $1\frac{3}{5}$ and $3\frac{1}{10}$, on the board. Have students find what needs to be added to the first mixed number to get the second mixed number, by using Guess and Check. Encourage students to use number sense. Since $1\frac{3}{5} + 1 = 2\frac{3}{5}$ and $2\frac{3}{5} < 3\frac{1}{10}$, the number must be greater than 1. Similarly, since $1\frac{3}{5} + 2 = 3\frac{3}{5}$ and $3\frac{3}{5} > 3\frac{1}{10}$, the number must be less than 2. If students guess a number like $1\frac{3}{10}$, show that $1\frac{3}{5} + 1\frac{3}{10}$ equals $2\frac{9}{10}$. Help students see that $1\frac{3}{10}$ is too low because $2\frac{9}{10} < 3\frac{1}{10}$. The number is $1\frac{1}{2}$, $1\frac{3}{5} + 1\frac{1}{2} = 3\frac{1}{10}$.

© Pearson Education, Inc.

Subtracting Mixed Numbers

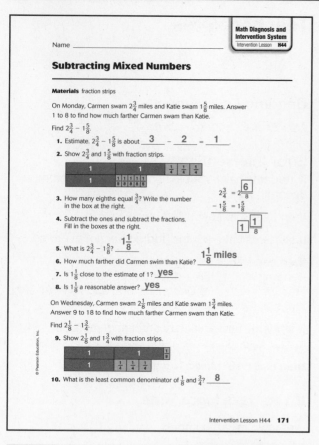

Name _____

Subtracting Mixed Numbers

Materials fraction strips

On Monday, Carmen swam $2\frac{3}{4}$ miles and Katie swam $1\frac{5}{8}$ miles. Answer 1 to 8 to find how much farther Carmen swam than Katie.

Find $2\frac{3}{4} - 1\frac{5}{8}$.

1. Estimate. $2\frac{3}{4} - 1\frac{5}{8}$ is about ___3___ – ___2___ = ___1___

2. Show $2\frac{3}{4}$ and $1\frac{5}{8}$ with fraction strips.

3. How many eighths equal $3\frac{3}{4}$? Write the number in the box at the right.

$2\frac{3}{4} = 2\frac{\boxed{6}}{8}$

4. Subtract the ones and subtract the fractions. Fill in the boxes at the right.

$-1\frac{5}{8} = 1\frac{5}{8}$

$\boxed{1}\frac{\boxed{1}}{8}$

5. What is $2\frac{3}{4} - 1\frac{5}{8}$? $1\frac{1}{8}$

6. How much farther did Carmen swim than Katie? $1\frac{1}{8}$ miles

7. Is $1\frac{1}{8}$ close to the estimate of 1? yes

8. Is $1\frac{1}{8}$ a reasonable answer? yes

On Wednesday, Carmen swam $2\frac{1}{8}$ miles and Katie swam $1\frac{3}{4}$ miles. Answer 9 to 18 to find how much farther Carmen swam than Katie.

Find $2\frac{1}{8} - 1\frac{3}{4}$.

9. Show $2\frac{1}{8}$ and $1\frac{3}{4}$ with fraction strips.

10. What is the least common denominator of $\frac{1}{8}$ and $\frac{3}{4}$? ___8___

Name _____

Subtracting Mixed Numbers (continued)

11. How many eighths equal $\frac{3}{4}$? Write the number in the box at the right.

$2\frac{1}{8} = 2\frac{1}{8}$

12. Compare. Write >, <, or =. $\frac{1}{8}$ ⊘ $\frac{6}{8}$

Since $\frac{1}{8}$ is less than $\frac{6}{8}$, you need to regroup.

$-1\frac{3}{4} = 1\frac{\boxed{6}}{8}$

13. What is $1\frac{1}{8}$ as an improper fraction? $\frac{9}{8}$

14. What is the missing number?

$2\frac{1}{8} = 1 + 1\frac{1}{8} = 1 + \frac{\boxed{9}}{8}$

Write this number at the right.

$2\frac{1}{8} = 2\frac{1}{8} = 1\frac{\boxed{9}}{8}$

15. Subtract the ones. What is 1 – 1? ___0___

$-1\frac{3}{4} = 1\frac{6}{8} = 1\frac{6}{8}$

16. Subtract the fractions. What is $\frac{9}{8} - \frac{6}{8}$? $\frac{3}{8}$
Write 3 at the right.

$\frac{\boxed{3}}{8}$

17. What is $2\frac{1}{8} - 1\frac{3}{4}$? $\frac{3}{8}$

18. How much farther did Carmen swim than Katie on Wednesday? $\frac{3}{8}$ miles

Subtract. Simplify, if possible. Estimate to check.

19. $2\frac{2}{3}$
$-1\frac{1}{6}$
$1\frac{1}{2}$; 2

20. $2\frac{4}{10}$
$-1\frac{3}{5}$
$\frac{4}{5}$; 1

21. $5\frac{1}{4}$
$-\frac{2}{5}$
$4\frac{17}{20}$; 5

22. $6\frac{7}{8}$
$-1\frac{5}{6}$
$5\frac{1}{24}$; 5

23. To make a dress, $1\frac{1}{6}$ yards of blue material is needed and $\frac{3}{4}$ yard of red material is needed. How much more blue material is needed than red material? $\frac{5}{12}$ yd

24. Reasoning If you have $7\frac{3}{16}$ and you subtract $\frac{3}{16}$, how much do you have? ___7___

Teacher Notes

Ongoing Assessment

Ask: **Explain how to regroup $3\frac{1}{4}$.** $3\frac{1}{4} = 2 + 1\frac{1}{4} = 2 + \frac{5}{4} = 2\frac{5}{4}$

Error Intervention

If students have trouble finding the least common denominator,

then use G65: Least Common Multiple.

If students have trouble subtracting fractional parts,

then use H37: Subtracting Fractions with Like Denominators, H38: Adding and Subtracting Fractions with Like Denominators, and H41: Subtracting Fractions with Unlike Denominators.

If students cannot change mixed numbers to improper fractions,

then use H18: Mixed Numbers.

If You Have More Time

Have students make up stories involving adding and subtracting mixed numbers for a partner to solve.

© Pearson Education, Inc.

Multiplying Fractions by Whole Numbers

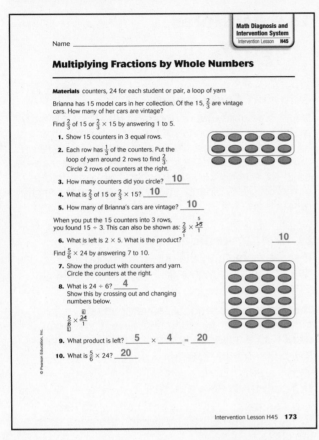

Math Diagnosis and Intervention System
Intervention Lesson **H45**

Name _____

Multiplying Fractions by Whole Numbers

Materials counters, 24 for each student or pair, a loop of yarn

Brianna has 15 model cars in her collection. Of the 15, $\frac{2}{3}$ are vintage cars. How many of her cars are vintage?

Find $\frac{2}{3}$ of 15 or $\frac{2}{3} \times 15$ by answering 1 to 5.

1. Show 15 counters in 3 equal rows.

2. Each row has $\frac{1}{3}$ of the counters. Put the loop of yarn around 2 rows to find $\frac{2}{3}$. Circle 2 rows of counters at the right.

3. How many counters did you circle? __10__

4. What is $\frac{2}{3}$ of 15 or $\frac{2}{3} \times 15$? __10__

5. How many of Brianna's cars are vintage? __10__

When you put the 15 counters into 3 rows, you found $15 \div 3$. This can also be shown as: $\frac{2}{3} \times \frac{\overset{5}{\cancel{15}}}{1}$

6. What is left is 2×5. What is the product? ____ __10__

Find $\frac{5}{6} \times 24$ by answering 7 to 10.

7. Show the product with counters and yarn. Circle the counters at the right.

8. What is $24 \div 6$? __4__
Show this by crossing out and changing numbers below.

$\frac{5}{\square} \times \frac{\overset{24}{\cancel{24}}}{1}$

9. What product is left? __5__ × __4__ = __20__

10. What is $\frac{5}{6} \times 24$? __20__

Intervention Lesson H45   **173**

Teacher Notes

Ongoing Assessment

Make sure students understand that 2 out of 3 rows of counters equal $\frac{2}{3}$ of the counters.

Error Intervention

If students have trouble dividing the whole number by the denominator of the fraction,

then use some of the intervention lessons on basic division facts, G38 to G40.

If You Have More Time

Have a group of 12 students come to the front of the class. Assign a student to organize the group into rows to find $\frac{2}{3}$. Assign another student to organize the group to find $\frac{3}{4}$ and then another to find $\frac{5}{6}$. Repeat with other group sizes of students and appropriate fractions.

Math Diagnosis and Intervention System
Intervention Lesson **H45**

Name _____

Multiplying Fractions by Whole Numbers (continued)

Find each product.

11. $\frac{8}{9} \times 45$ ____ **40**

12. $42 \times \frac{3}{7}$ ____ **18**

13. $\frac{7}{12}$ of 96 ____ **56**

14. $\frac{2}{11} \times 77$ ____ **14**

15. $\frac{3}{8} \times 64$ ____ **24**

16. $\frac{1}{6}$ of 102 ____ **17**

17. $\frac{2}{9} \times 72$ ____ **16**

18. $\frac{3}{4} \times 168$ ____ **126**

19. $\frac{2}{5}$ of 25 ____ **10**

20. $\frac{7}{9} \times 81$ ____ **63**

21. $\frac{1}{2} \times 52$ ____ **26**

22. $\frac{2}{3}$ of 66 ____ **44**

Use the information in the table for Exercises 23 and 24.

Zoo Animals	Population	Zoo Animals	Population
Wild Dogs	10	Elephants	3
Monkeys	21	Tigers	8
Bears	18	Giraffes	5

23. If $\frac{2}{7}$ of the monkey population are spider monkeys, how many spider monkeys are at the zoo? ____ **6**

24. If $\frac{3}{5}$ of the animals listed are female, how many females are in the list? ____ **39**

25. You earned $141 babysitting last month. You told your parents that you will saved $\frac{2}{3}$ of your earnings. How much did you save last month? ____ **$94**

26. Emperor penguins are approximately 45 inches tall, while rockhopper penguins are about $\frac{5}{9}$ of that height. How tall is a typical rockhopper penguin? ____ **25 inches**

27. **Reasoning** If you know that $\frac{3}{4}$ of a number is 18, what is $\frac{1}{4}$ of the same number? ____ **6**

174 Intervention Lesson H45

© Pearson Education, Inc.

Multiplying Two Fractions

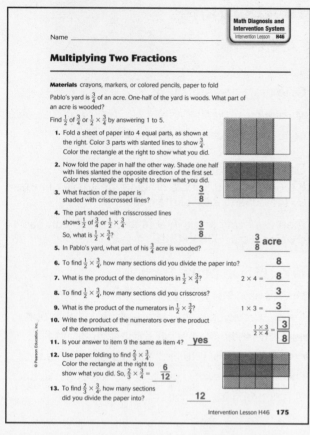

Name _____

Multiplying Two Fractions

Materials crayons, markers, or colored pencils, paper to fold

Pablo's yard is $\frac{3}{4}$ of an acre. One-half of the yard is woods. What part of an acre is wooded?

Find $\frac{1}{2}$ of $\frac{3}{4}$ or $\frac{1}{2} \times \frac{3}{4}$ by answering 1 to 5.

1. Fold a sheet of paper into 4 equal parts, as shown at the right. Color 3 parts with slanted lines to show $\frac{3}{4}$. Color the rectangle at the right to show what you did.

2. Now fold the paper in half the other way. Shade one half with lines slanted the opposite direction of the first set. Color the rectangle at the right to show what you did.

3. What fraction of the paper is shaded with crisscrossed lines? $\frac{3}{8}$

4. The part shaded with crisscrossed lines shows $\frac{1}{2}$ of $\frac{3}{4}$ or $\frac{1}{2} \times \frac{3}{4}$.
So, what is $\frac{1}{2} \times \frac{3}{4}$? $\frac{3}{8}$

5. In Pablo's yard, what part of his $\frac{3}{4}$ acre is wooded? $\frac{3}{8}$ acre

6. To find $\frac{1}{2} \times \frac{3}{4}$, how many sections did you divide the paper into?   8

7. What is the product of the denominators in $\frac{1}{2} \times \frac{3}{4}$? $2 \times 4 =$ 8

8. To find $\frac{1}{2} \times \frac{3}{4}$, how many sections did you crisscross?   3

9. What is the product of the numerators in $\frac{1}{2} \times \frac{3}{4}$? $1 \times 3 =$ 3

10. Write the product of the numerators over the product of the denominators. $\frac{1 \times 3}{2 \times 4}$ $\boxed{\frac{3}{8}}$

11. Is your answer to item 9 the same as item 4?   **yes**

12. Use paper folding to find $\frac{2}{3} \times \frac{3}{4}$. Color the rectangle at the right to show what you did. So, $\frac{2}{3} \times \frac{3}{4} =$ $\frac{6}{12}$

13. To find $\frac{2}{3} \times \frac{3}{4}$, how many sections did you divide the paper into?   12

Intervention Lesson H46   **175**

Name _____

Multiplying Two Fractions (continued)

14. What is the product of the denominators in $\frac{2}{3} \times \frac{3}{4}$? $3 \times 4 =$ 12

15. To find $\frac{2}{3} \times \frac{3}{4}$, how many sections did you crisscross?   6

16. What is the product of the numerators in $\frac{2}{3} \times \frac{3}{4}$? $2 \times 3 =$ 6

17. Complete: $\frac{2}{3} \times \frac{3}{4} = \frac{2 \times 3}{3 \times 4} = \frac{\boxed{6}}{\boxed{12}}$

To multiply two fractions, you can multiply the numerators and then the denominators. Then simplify, if possible.

$\frac{2}{3} \times \frac{3}{4} = \frac{2 \times 3}{3 \times 4} = \frac{6}{12} = \frac{1}{2}$

18. **Reasoning** Shari found $\frac{3}{10} \times \frac{5}{9}$ as shown at the right. Why does Shari's method work?
She simplified before multiplying, instead of after.

$\frac{3}{10} \times \frac{5}{9} = \frac{\overset{1}{\cancel{3}} \times \overset{1}{\cancel{5}}}{\underset{2}{\cancel{10}} \times \underset{3}{\cancel{9}}} = \frac{1}{6}$

Multiply. Simplify, if possible.

19. $\frac{1}{8} \times \frac{2}{3} =$ $\frac{1}{12}$ 20. $\frac{5}{6} \times \frac{1}{2} =$ $\frac{5}{12}$ 21. $\frac{1}{4} \times \frac{3}{5} =$ $\frac{3}{20}$

22. $\frac{6}{7} \times \frac{1}{3} =$ $\frac{2}{7}$ 23. $\frac{3}{4} \times \frac{3}{8} =$ $\frac{9}{32}$ 24. $\frac{1}{5} \times \frac{4}{5} =$ $\frac{4}{25}$

25. $\frac{2}{3} \times \frac{4}{7} =$ $\frac{8}{21}$ 26. $\frac{3}{7} \times \frac{3}{10} =$ $\frac{9}{70}$ 27. $\frac{4}{9} \times \frac{3}{4} =$ $\frac{1}{3}$

28. $\frac{5}{8} \times \frac{4}{5} =$ $\frac{1}{2}$ 29. $\frac{7}{9} \times \frac{3}{5} =$ $\frac{7}{15}$ 30. $\frac{1}{10} \times \frac{5}{7} =$ $\frac{1}{14}$

31. $\frac{7}{8} \times \frac{5}{14} =$ $\frac{5}{16}$ 32. $\frac{3}{11} \times \frac{1}{9} =$ $\frac{1}{33}$ 33. $\frac{1}{12} \times \frac{4}{5} =$ $\frac{1}{15}$

34. There are 45 tents at the summer camp. Girls will use $\frac{2}{3}$ of the tents. How many tents will the girls use?   **30 tents**

176 Intervention Lesson H46

Teacher Notes

Ongoing Assessment

Make sure students understand that they need to multiply both the numerators and denominators to multiply fractions. Make sure students are not getting this procedure confused with the procedure used for adding and subtracting fractions: find a common denominator and add or subtract only the numerators.

Error Intervention

If students multiply the numerators and denominators together and then make mistakes simplifying,

then encourage students to remove common factors before they multiply. This way, they can work with smaller numbers and are less likely to make computation errors.

If You Have More Time

Have students find more products using paper folding and show their product to a partner or to the class.

© Pearson Education, Inc.

Understanding Division with Fractions

Understanding Division with Fractions

Materials crayons, markers, or colored pencils

Donna has 3 kilograms of clay. She uses $\frac{1}{2}$ kilogram for each vase.
Answer 1 to 3 to find the number of vases she can make.

Find $3 \div \frac{1}{2}$.

1. Color each half of a rectangle at the right a
   different color. How many $\frac{1}{2}$'s are in 3? __6__

   Check that students color
   each half differently.

2. What is $3 \div \frac{1}{2}$? __6__

3. How many vases can Donna make? __6 vases__

You could also find $3 \div \frac{1}{2}$ by multiplying $3 \times \frac{2}{1}$.

The numbers $\frac{1}{2}$ and $\frac{2}{1}$ or 2 have a special relationship because $\frac{1}{2} \times 2 = 1$. The
numbers $\frac{1}{2}$ and 2 are reciprocals. Similarly, $\frac{3}{4}$ and $\frac{4}{3}$ are reciprocals. Note that $\frac{3}{4} \times \frac{4}{3} = 1$.

4. What is the reciprocal of $\frac{1}{3}$? __3 or $\frac{3}{1}$__

5. What is the reciprocal of $\frac{5}{7}$? __$\frac{7}{5}$__

So, $3 \div \frac{1}{2}$ can be written as 3×2, because 2 is the reciprocal of $\frac{1}{2}$.

Thomas has $\frac{9}{10}$ kilogram of clay. He uses $\frac{3}{10}$ kilogram for each small
bowl. Answer 6 to 8 to find how many small bowls Thomas can make.

Find $\frac{9}{10} \div \frac{3}{10}$ using a model.

6. Color each $\frac{3}{10}$ of the rectangle at the right a
   different color. How many $\frac{3}{10}$'s are in $\frac{9}{10}$? __3__

   Check that students use
   3 different colors to color
   3 sections each time.

7. What is $\frac{9}{10} \div \frac{3}{10}$? __3__

8. How many small bowls can Thomas make? __3 small bowls__

Find $\frac{9}{10} \div \frac{3}{10}$ by using the reciprocal.

9. What is the reciprocal of $\frac{3}{10}$? __$\frac{10}{3}$__

Understanding Division with Fractions (continued)

10. To find $\frac{9}{10} \div \frac{3}{10}$, can you multiply $\frac{9}{10}$ by the reciprocal of $\frac{3}{10}$? __yes__

11. Complete: $\frac{9}{10} \times \frac{10}{3} = \frac{9 \times 10}{10 \times \boxed{3}} = \frac{90}{\boxed{30}} = \boxed{3}$

12. Is the answer to item 11 the same as item 8? __yes__

Find the reciprocal of each number.

13. $\frac{3}{4}$ __$\frac{4}{3}$__   14. $\frac{1}{15}$ __$\frac{15}{1}$__   15. $\frac{7}{9}$ __$\frac{9}{7}$__   16. $1\frac{3}{7}$ __$\frac{7}{10}$__

Find each quotient.

17. How many $\frac{1}{4}$ are in 2? __8__   18. How many $\frac{1}{2}$ are in 3? __6__

19. How many $\frac{1}{4}$ are in 4? __16__   20. How many $\frac{3}{4}$ are in 3? __4__

21. How many $\frac{1}{8}$ are in 2? __16__   22. How many $\frac{2}{8}$ are in 1? __4__

23. How many $\frac{3}{8}$ are in 3? __8__   24. How many $\frac{6}{8}$ are in 3? __4__

25. $3 \div \frac{1}{6}$ __18__   26. $9 \div \frac{3}{5}$ __15__   27. $4 \div \frac{1}{4}$ __16__

28. $10 \div \frac{5}{6}$ __12__   29. $9 \div \frac{3}{4}$ __12__   30. $6 \div \frac{1}{3}$ __18__

31. $2 \div \frac{1}{7}$ __14__   32. $6 \div \frac{3}{5}$ __10__   33. $10 \div \frac{1}{10}$ __100__

34. Bonnie is cutting 7 apples. Each apple is cut into eighths.
    How many slices of apple will she have? __56__

35. **Reasoning** Explain how to find $\frac{3}{4} \div \frac{3}{8}$ by using the reciprocal of $\frac{3}{8}$.

    $\frac{3}{4} \div \frac{3}{8} = \frac{3}{4} \times \frac{8}{3} = 2.$

© Pearson Education, Inc.

Teacher Notes

Ongoing Assessment

Ask: **How do you divide two fractions?** Multiply
the first fraction by the reciprocal of the second
one.

Error Intervention

If students have trouble finding reciprocals,

then tell them they can just interchange or swap
the numerator and denominator.

If You Have More Time

Have students draw a picture to show why
$4 \div \frac{2}{3} = 4 \times \frac{3}{2}$.

Dividing Fractions

Name _____

Dividing Fractions

A serving of juice is $\frac{1}{16}$ of a gallon. Answer 1 to 6 to find how many servings are in $\frac{7}{8}$ of a gallon.

Find $\frac{7}{8} \div \frac{1}{16}$.

1. What is the reciprocal of $\frac{1}{16}$?   __16__

2. Write $\frac{7}{8} \div \frac{1}{16}$ as $\frac{7}{8}$ times the reciprocal of $\frac{1}{16}$. $\frac{7}{8} \div \frac{1}{16} = \frac{7}{8} \times$ __16__

3. Does $16 = \frac{16}{1}$?   __yes__

4. Multiply. Remove common factors first. $\frac{7}{8} \times \frac{16}{1} = \frac{7 \times \overset{2}{\cancel{16}}}{\cancel{8} \times 1} = \boxed{14}{1}$

5. What is $\frac{7}{8} \div \frac{1}{16}$? $\frac{7}{8} \div \frac{1}{16} = \frac{7}{8} \times 16 =$ __14__

6. How many $\frac{1}{16}$ gallon servings are in $\frac{7}{8}$ gallon of juice?   __14 servings__

Answer 7 to 11 to find how many $\frac{3}{8}$ gallon servings are in $\frac{1}{2}$ gallon of water.

Find $\frac{1}{2} \div \frac{3}{8}$.

7. What is the reciprocal of $\frac{3}{8}$? $\frac{8}{3}$

8. Write $\frac{1}{2} \div \frac{3}{8}$ as $\frac{1}{2}$ times the reciprocal of $\frac{3}{8}$. $\frac{1}{2} \div \frac{3}{8} = \frac{1}{2} \times \frac{8}{3}$

9. Multiply. Remove common factors first. $\frac{1}{2} \times \frac{8}{3} = \frac{1 \times \overset{4}{\cancel{8}}}{\underset{1}{\cancel{2}} \times 3} = \boxed{\frac{4}{3}}$

10. Write the answer in simplest form. So, $\frac{1}{2} \div \frac{3}{8} = \frac{1}{2} \times \frac{8}{3} = \frac{4}{3} = 1\frac{1}{3}$

11. How many $\frac{3}{8}$ gallon servings are in $\frac{1}{2}$ gallon of water? $1\frac{1}{3}$ servings

12. Fill in the missing numbers to divide. Remove common factors before multiplying.

$\frac{2}{3} \div \frac{5}{12} = \frac{2}{3} \times \frac{12}{5} = \frac{8}{5} = 1\frac{3}{5}$

Intervention Lesson H48   **179**

© Pearson Education, Inc.

Teacher Notes

Ongoing Assessment

Ask: **Why does $16 = \frac{16}{1}$?** Sample answer: 16 is equal to 16 whole rectangles.

Error Intervention

If students do not know what a reciprocal is,

then use H47: Understanding Division of Fractions.

If students do not know how to multiply fractions,

then use H46: Multiplying Two Fractions.

If You Have More Time

Have students make up word problems involving division of fractions and give them to a partner to solve.

Name _____

Dividing Fractions (continued)

Divide. Simplify, if possible.

13. $\frac{1}{8} \div \frac{2}{3} = \frac{3}{16}$

14. $\frac{5}{6} \div \frac{1}{2} = 1\frac{2}{3}$

15. $\frac{1}{4} \div \frac{3}{5} = \frac{5}{12}$

16. $\frac{6}{7} \div \frac{3}{4} = 1\frac{1}{7}$

17. $\frac{3}{4} \div \frac{3}{8} = 2$

18. $\frac{1}{5} \div \frac{4}{5} = \frac{1}{4}$

19. $\frac{2}{3} \div \frac{4}{7} = 1\frac{1}{6}$

20. $\frac{3}{7} \div \frac{3}{10} = 1\frac{3}{7}$

21. $\frac{4}{9} \div \frac{3}{4} = \frac{16}{27}$

22. $\frac{5}{8} \div \frac{4}{5} = \frac{25}{32}$

23. $\frac{7}{9} \div \frac{3}{5} = 1\frac{8}{27}$

24. $\frac{1}{10} \div \frac{5}{7} = \frac{7}{50}$

25. $\frac{7}{8} \div \frac{5}{14} = 2\frac{9}{20}$

26. $\frac{3}{11} \div \frac{1}{9} = 2\frac{5}{11}$

27. $\frac{1}{12} \div \frac{4}{5} = \frac{5}{48}$

28. $\frac{2}{5} \div \frac{5}{7} = \frac{14}{25}$

29. $\frac{1}{3} \div \frac{3}{8} = \frac{8}{9}$

30. $\frac{1}{4} \div \frac{1}{4} = 1$

31. $\frac{5}{12} \div \frac{3}{5} = \frac{25}{36}$

32. $\frac{9}{10} \div \frac{5}{7} = 1\frac{13}{50}$

33. $\frac{4}{5} \div \frac{5}{9} = 1\frac{11}{25}$

34. **Reasoning** For the school cafeteria, 15 pounds of vegetables were ordered by the chef. If each student usually gets $\frac{3}{8}$ of a pound of vegetables each day for lunch, how many students could be fed with the vegetables in one day?   __40 students__

35. Draw a picture to show $\frac{7}{8} \div \frac{1}{16} = 14$.

Answers will vary. Drawings should show $\frac{7}{8}$ divided into sixteenths and that there are 14 sixteenths in $\frac{7}{8}$.

180   Intervention Lesson H48

© Pearson Education, Inc.

© Pearson Education, Inc.

Estimating Products and Quotients of Mixed Numbers

Teacher Notes

Ongoing Assessment

Ask: ***What are some compatible numbers you could use to estimate $9\frac{1}{2} \div 2\frac{1}{2}$?*** Answers may vary. Sample answers are $10 \div 2$ and $9 \div 3$.

Error Intervention

If students have trouble comparing fractions to $\frac{1}{2}$,

then use H6: Using Models to Compare Fractions, H9: Comparing Fractions, and H19: Comparing and Ordering Fractions.

If You Have More Time

Have students measure their desks to the nearest $\frac{1}{4}$ inch. Then have them estimate how long 5 desks in a row would be. Finally, have them estimate how long $3\frac{1}{2}$ desks in a row would be.

Name _____

Estimating Products and Quotients of Mixed Numbers

Karina's recipe for tacos uses $1\frac{3}{4}$ pounds of beef. She needs to make $3\frac{1}{3}$ times the recipe for a party. About how many pounds of beef does she need?

Estimate $3\frac{1}{3} \times 1\frac{3}{4}$ by answering 1 to 9.

1. What two whole numbers is $3\frac{1}{3}$ between? __3__ and __4__

2. Use the number line below. Is $3\frac{1}{3}$ closer to 3 or 4? __3__

number line: 3, $3\frac{1}{6}$, $3\frac{2}{6}$ (marked $3\frac{1}{3}$ with dot), $3\frac{3}{6}$, $3\frac{4}{6}$, $3\frac{5}{6}$, 4

3. What number is halfway between 3 and 4? $3\frac{1}{2}$

4. Compare. Write >, <, or =. $\frac{1}{3}$ $<$ $\frac{1}{2}$

By comparing $\frac{1}{3}$ and $\frac{1}{2}$, you can tell that $3\frac{1}{3}$ is closer to 3 than 4, without using a number line.

$3\frac{1}{3}$ rounded to the nearest whole number is 3.

5. What two whole numbers is $1\frac{3}{4}$ between? __1__ and __2__

6. Compare. Write >, <, or =. $\frac{3}{4}$ $>$ $\frac{1}{2}$

7. What is $1\frac{3}{4}$ rounded to the nearest whole number? __2__

8. Use the rounded numbers to estimate.

$3\frac{1}{3} \times 1\frac{3}{4}$ is about __3__ × __2__ = __6__

9. About how many pounds of beef does Karina need? About __6 pounds__

Marco is making $12\frac{2}{3}$ pounds of lasagna. Each pan can hold $2\frac{3}{4}$ pounds. About how many pans does he need?

Estimate $12\frac{2}{3} \div 2\frac{3}{4}$ by answering 10 to 13.

10. What is $12\frac{2}{3}$ rounded to the nearest whole number? __13__

Estimating Products and Quotients of Mixed Numbers (continued)

Name _____

11. What is $2\frac{3}{4}$ rounded to the nearest whole number? __3__

12. Since $13 \div 3$ is not easy to divide, use compatible numbers. What numbers are close to $12\frac{2}{3} \div 2\frac{3}{4}$ and easy to divide?

$12\frac{2}{3} \div 2\frac{3}{4}$ is about __12__ ÷ __3__ = __4__ .

13. About how many pans does Marco need? About __4 pans__

Estimate.

14. $2\frac{7}{8} \times 7\frac{3}{5}$
$3 \times 8 = 24$

15. $6\frac{1}{5} \times 8\frac{3}{4}$
$6 \times 9 = 54$

16. $5\frac{7}{12} \div 1\frac{1}{5}$
$6 \div 1 = 6$

17. $5\frac{2}{7} \times 9\frac{4}{5}$
$5 \times 10 = 50$

18. $8\frac{5}{7} \div 2\frac{2}{3}$
$9 \div 3 = 3$

19. $7\frac{5}{7} \div 1\frac{9}{10}$
$8 \div 2 = 4$

20. $3\frac{5}{12} \times 1\frac{3}{5}$
$3 \times 2 = 6$

21. $1\frac{5}{9} \times 7\frac{1}{2}$
$2 \times 8 = 16$

22. $1\frac{1}{3} \times 5\frac{2}{9}$
$1 \times 5 = 5$

23. $4\frac{3}{12} \times 7$
$4 \times 7 = 28$

24. $25 \div 4\frac{7}{9}$
$25 \div 5 = 5$

25. $9\frac{1}{10} \div 3\frac{1}{12}$
$9 \div 3 = 3$

26. The Hummingbird Trail at Camp Redlands is $1\frac{7}{8}$ miles long. Surinder, a camp counselor, hikes the train $2\frac{1}{4}$ times a day. About how far does he hike each day? About __4 miles__

27. Tammy needs to hike $15\frac{1}{4}$ miles to win an award. About how many times does she need to hike a trail that is $2\frac{7}{8}$ miles long? About __5 times__

28. **Reasoning** Explain how to use compatible numbers to find $17\frac{2}{3} \div 5\frac{9}{10}$.

Answers may vary. Sample answer: $17\frac{2}{3} \div 5\frac{9}{10}$ is about $18 \div 6$, or 3.

© Pearson Education, Inc.

Multiplying Mixed Numbers

Math Diagnosis and Intervention System
Intervention Lesson H50

Name ______________________

Math Diagnosis and Intervention System
Intervention Lesson H50

Multiplying Mixed Numbers

Materials crayons, markers, or colored pencils

George made a rectangular quilt that is $2\frac{1}{2}$ yards long and $1\frac{2}{3}$ yards wide. Answer 1 to 6 to find the area of the quilt.

Find $1\frac{2}{3} \times 2\frac{1}{2}$.

1. The rectangular quilt at the right is $2\frac{1}{2}$ units by $1\frac{2}{3}$ units. The shaded area represents one whole yard. Shade another region that is equal to one whole yard.

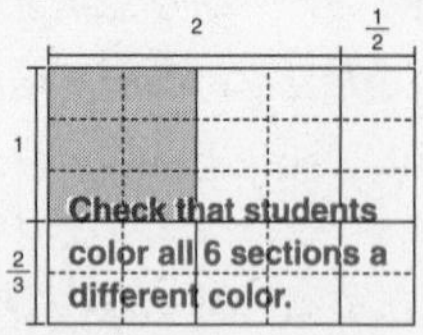

2. The quilt is divided into equal parts. Six equal parts equal one whole yard. Each part is what fraction of one whole yard? $\frac{1}{6}$

3. Color another whole yard with a different color. Then another, as many times as you can. How many total whole yards are there in the quilt? 4

4. What part of a whole yard is left over? $\frac{1}{6}$

5. So, what is $1\frac{2}{3} \times 2\frac{1}{2}$? $4\frac{1}{6}$

6. What is the area of George's quilt? $4\frac{1}{6}$ square yards

Find $1\frac{2}{3} \times 2\frac{1}{2}$ another way by answering 7 to 9.

7. Write $1\frac{2}{3}$ as an improper fraction. $\frac{5}{3}$

8. Write $2\frac{1}{2}$ as an improper fraction. $\frac{5}{2}$

9. Now find $\frac{5}{3} \times \frac{5}{2}$. $\frac{25}{6} = 4\frac{1}{6}$

Notice that the product of the numerators, $5 \times 5 = 25$, is the number of equal parts in the rectangle. Also, the products of the denominators, $3 \times 2 = 6$, is the number of equal parts in each whole.

© Pearson Education, Inc.

Name ______________________

Math Diagnosis and Intervention System
Intervention Lesson H50

Multiplying Mixed Numbers (continued)

Fill in the blanks to find each product. Change mixed numbers to improper fractions. Write whole numbers over 1. Remove common factors before multiplying to make the computations easier.

10. $\frac{2}{3} \times 1\frac{3}{8} = \frac{2}{3} \times \frac{11}{8} = \frac{\not{2}^{1} \times 11}{3 \times \not{8}_{4}} = \frac{11}{12}$

11. $5 \times 1\frac{3}{10} = \frac{5}{1} \times \frac{13}{10} = \frac{\not{5}^{1} \times 13}{1 \times \not{10}_{2}} = \frac{13}{2} = 6\frac{1}{2}$

Multiply. Simplify, if possible.

12. $2\frac{6}{7} \times 1\frac{3}{4} =$ 5

13. $\frac{3}{4} \times 3\frac{1}{5} =$ $2\frac{2}{5}$

14. $3\frac{2}{5} \times \frac{5}{7} =$ $2\frac{3}{7}$

15. $5\frac{5}{8} \times 3\frac{4}{5} =$ $21\frac{3}{8}$

16. $2\frac{2}{7} \times 5\frac{3}{5} =$ $12\frac{4}{5}$

17. $2\frac{1}{10} \times 2\frac{1}{7} =$ $4\frac{1}{2}$

18. $4\frac{1}{12} \times \frac{4}{5} =$ $3\frac{4}{15}$

19. $2\frac{1}{10} \times 6\frac{5}{7} =$ $14\frac{1}{10}$

20. $3\frac{4}{5} \times 5 =$ 19

21. Pam is making a cake. The recipe calls for $2\frac{1}{8}$ cups of flour. How much flour is needed for 4 cakes? $8\frac{1}{2}$ cups

22. Reasoning Find each product and compare it to $2\frac{1}{2}$. What is true when multiplying by numbers less than 1 and when multiplying by numbers greater than 1?

$\frac{1}{3} \times 2\frac{1}{2} = \frac{5}{6}$ $1\frac{1}{3} \times 2\frac{1}{2} = 3\frac{1}{3}$ $\frac{2}{3} \times 2\frac{1}{2} = 1\frac{2}{3}$ $1\frac{2}{3} \times 2\frac{1}{2} = 4\frac{1}{6}$

Sample answer: When $2\frac{1}{2}$ is multiplied by a number less than 1, the product is less than $2\frac{1}{2}$. When $2\frac{1}{2}$ is multiplied by a number greater than 1, the product is greater than $2\frac{1}{2}$.

© Pearson Education, Inc.

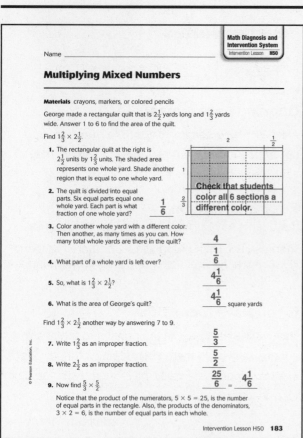

Teacher Notes

Ongoing Assessment

Ask: ***Why does $4\frac{1}{3} \times 1\frac{3}{5} = \frac{13}{3} \times \frac{8}{5}$?*** The products are equal because $4\frac{1}{3} = \frac{13}{3}$ and $1\frac{3}{5} = \frac{8}{5}$.

Error Intervention

If students do not know how to change mixed numbers to improper fractions or vice versa,

then use H18: Mixed Numbers.

If students do not know how to multiply fractions,

then use H46: Multiplying Two Fractions.

If You Have More Time

Have students check their answers for reasonableness.

© Pearson Education, Inc.

Dividing Mixed Numbers

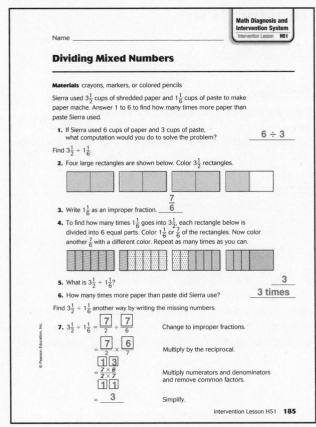

Name _____

Dividing Mixed Numbers

Materials crayons, markers, or colored pencils

Sierra used $3\frac{1}{2}$ cups of shredded paper and $1\frac{1}{6}$ cups of paste to make paper mache. Answer 1 to 6 to find how many times more paper than paste Sierra used.

1. If Sierra used 6 cups of paper and 3 cups of paste, what computation would you do to solve the problem? $6 \div 3$

Find $3\frac{1}{2} \div 1\frac{1}{6}$.

2. Four large rectangles are shown below. Color $3\frac{1}{2}$ rectangles.

3. Write $1\frac{1}{6}$ as an improper fraction. $\frac{7}{6}$

4. To find how many times $1\frac{1}{6}$ goes into $3\frac{1}{2}$, each rectangle below is divided into 6 equal parts. Color $1\frac{1}{6}$ or $\frac{7}{6}$ of the rectangles. Now color another $\frac{7}{6}$ with a different color. Repeat as many times as you can.

5. What is $3\frac{1}{2} \div 1\frac{1}{6}$? 3

6. How many times more paper than paste did Sierra use?   3 times

Find $3\frac{1}{2} \div 1\frac{1}{6}$ another way by writing the missing numbers.

7. $3\frac{1}{2} \div 1\frac{1}{6} = \frac{7}{2} \div \frac{7}{6}$ Change to improper fractions.

$= \frac{7}{2} \times \frac{6}{7}$ Multiply by the reciprocal.

$= \frac{\overset{1}{7} \times \overset{3}{6}}{\underset{1}{2} \times \underset{1}{7}}$ Multiply numerators and denominators and remove common factors.

$= 3$ Simplify.

Intervention Lesson H51   **185**

© Pearson Education, Inc.

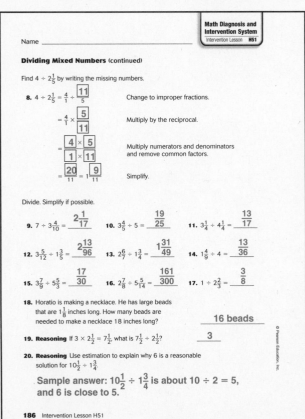

Name _____

Dividing Mixed Numbers (continued)

Find $4 \div 2\frac{1}{5}$ by writing the missing numbers.

8. $4 \div 2\frac{1}{5} = \frac{4}{1} \div \frac{11}{5}$ Change to improper fractions.

$= \frac{4}{1} \times \frac{5}{11}$ Multiply by the reciprocal.

$= \frac{4 \times 5}{1 \times 11}$ Multiply numerators and denominators and remove common factors.

$= \frac{20}{11} = 1\frac{9}{11}$ Simplify.

Divide. Simplify if possible.

9. $7 \div 3\frac{4}{10} = \underline{2\frac{1}{17}}$ 10. $3\frac{4}{5} \div 5 = \underline{\frac{19}{25}}$ 11. $3\frac{1}{4} \div 4\frac{1}{4} = \underline{\frac{13}{17}}$

12. $3\frac{5}{12} \div 1\frac{3}{5} = \underline{2\frac{13}{96}}$ 13. $2\frac{6}{7} \div 1\frac{3}{4} = \underline{1\frac{31}{49}}$ 14. $1\frac{4}{9} \div 4 = \underline{\frac{13}{36}}$

15. $3\frac{7}{9} \div 5\frac{5}{3} = \underline{\frac{17}{30}}$ 16. $2\frac{7}{8} \div 5\frac{5}{14} = \underline{\frac{161}{300}}$ 17. $1 \div 2\frac{2}{3} = \underline{\frac{3}{8}}$

18. Horatio is making a necklace. He has large beads that are $1\frac{1}{8}$ inches long. How many beads are needed to make a necklace 18 inches long?   16 beads

19. **Reasoning** If $3 \times 2\frac{1}{2} = 7\frac{1}{2}$, what is $7\frac{1}{2} \div 2\frac{1}{2}$? 3

20. **Reasoning** Use estimation to explain why 6 is a reasonable solution for $10\frac{1}{2} \div 1\frac{3}{4}$.

Sample answer: $10\frac{1}{2} \div 1\frac{3}{4}$ is about $10 \div 2 = 5$, and 6 is close to 5.

186   Intervention Lesson H51

© Pearson Education, Inc.

Teacher Notes

Ongoing Assessment

Ask: *What do you multiply to find $1\frac{1}{4} \div 6$?*
$\frac{5}{4} \times \frac{1}{6}$

Error Intervention

If students do not know how to change mixed numbers to improper fractions or vice versa,

then use H18: Mixed Numbers.

If students do not know what a reciprocal is,

then use H47: Understanding Division with Fractions.

If You Have More Time

Tell students that a bag of flour holds $18\frac{1}{4}$ cups and a batch of pancakes takes $2\frac{1}{2}$ cups of flour. Have students work in pairs to figure out how many batches of pancakes could be made from a bag of flour. Since $18\frac{1}{4} \div 2\frac{1}{2} = 7\frac{3}{10}$, 7 batches can be made.

Using Models to Add and Subtract Decimals

Name _____

Using Models to Add and Subtract Decimals

Materials crayons, markers, or colored pencils

Mr. Mantini bought 0.45 pound of apples and 0.37 pound of oranges. Answer 1 to 7 to find the total weight of the fruit.

Find 0.45 + 0.37.

  1. How many squares are in the grid shown below?   __100__

  2. If the entire grid represents one unit, how many squares represent 0.45? __45__ Color in 4 columns and 5 squares.

  3. How many squares represent 0.37? __37__ Color in 3 columns and 7 squares a different color.

  4. How many squares are colored all together? __82__

  5. What part of the grid did you color in all? __0.82__

  6. What is 0.45 + 0.37? __0.82__

  7. What is the total weight of the fruit? __0.82__ pound

Answer 8 to 12 to find how much more the apples weigh than the oranges.

Find 0.45 − 0.37.

  8. Color 0.45 of the grid.

  9. Cross out 37 of the squares that are colored. This represents 0.37, the weight of the oranges.

  10. How many squares are colored in but not crossed out? __8__

  11. What is 0.45 − 0.37? __0.08__

  12. How much more do the apples weigh than the oranges? __0.08__ pound

Intervention Lesson H52 **187**

© Pearson Education, Inc.

Teacher Notes

Ongoing Assessment

Ask: *What does it mean if more than 100 squares are colored in when using a 100-grid to add two numbers?* It means that the answer is more than 1.

Error Intervention

If students have trouble understanding how to represent decimals on a grid,

then use H22: Place Value through Hundredths.

If You Have More Time

Have students work in pairs. One student can color in hundreds grids to represent any addition or subtraction of decimals. The other student finds the addition or subtraction problem that is represented.

Name _____

Using Models to Add and Subtract Decimals (continued)

  13. Reasoning How can the sum 45 + 37 = 82 be used to find that 0.45 + 0.37 = 0.82?

  The sum 45 + 37 = 82 tells how many small squares are colored. Since there are 100 small squares in all, 0.82 of the grid is colored and so 0.45 + 0.37 = 0.82.

Use the grids to find the sum or difference.

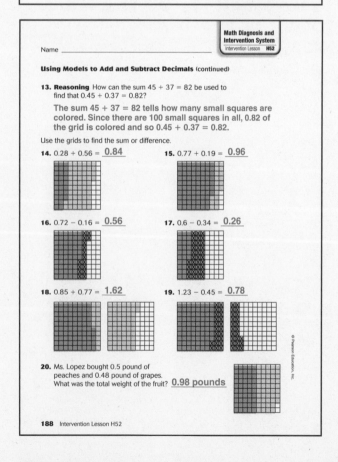

  14. 0.28 + 0.56 = __0.84__

  15. 0.77 + 0.19 = __0.96__

  16. 0.72 − 0.16 = __0.56__

  17. 0.6 − 0.34 = __0.26__

  18. 0.85 + 0.77 = __1.62__

  19. 1.23 − 0.45 = __0.78__

  20. Ms. Lopez bought 0.5 pound of peaches and 0.48 pound of grapes. What was the total weight of the fruit? __0.98 pounds__

© Pearson Education, Inc.

© Pearson Education, Inc.

Estimating Decimal Sums and Differences

Math Diagnosis and Intervention System
Intervention Lesson **H53**

Name _____

Estimating Decimal Sums and Differences

A recipe calls for 20.8 ounces of pineapple and 16.2 ounces of mandarin oranges. Answer 1 to 6 to find how many ounces of fruit the recipe calls for.

1. What word in the question indicates that an estimate is enough? **About**

Estimate 20.8 + 16.2.

2. What is 20.8 rounded to the nearest whole number? **21**

3. What is 16.2 rounded to the nearest whole number? **16**

4. Find the sum of the two rounded whole numbers. 21 + 16 = **37**

5. So, what is a good estimate for 20.8 + 16.2? **37**

6. About how many ounces of fruit does the recipe call for? About **37** ounces

In a fishing derby, Starla caught a 5.7 pound fish and Roberto caught a 2.43 pound fish. Answer 7 to 11 to find about how many more pounds Starla's fish weighed than Roberto's.

Estimate 5.7 − 2.43.

7. What is 5.7 rounded to the nearest whole number? **6**

8. What is 2.43 rounded to the nearest whole number? **2**

9. Find the difference of the two rounded whole numbers. 6 − 2 = **4**

10. So, what is a good estimate for 5.7 − 2.43? **4**

11. About how many more pounds did Starla's fish weigh than Roberto's? About **4** pounds

Intervention Lesson H53 **189**

Math Diagnosis and Intervention System
Intervention Lesson **H53**

Name _____

Estimating Decimal Sums and Differences (continued)

Estimate each sum or difference. **Sample answers are given.**

12. 4.6 + 5.2   **13.** 99.6 − 21.7   **14.** 89.7 − 42.4   **15.** 9.1 + 5.8

  10   **78**   **50**   **15**

16. 0.61 + 0.91   **17.** 5.21 − 0.7   **18.** 14.23 + 1.82   **19.** 31.6 − 10.5

  2   **4**   **16**   **20**

20. 7.06 + 3.72   **21.** 5.39 − 1.74   **22.** 33.7 − 10.08   **23.** 16.18 + 10.02

  11   **3**   **24**   **26**

24. 10.7 + 2.38   **25.** 57.09 + 12.62   **26.** 47 − 12.43   **27.** 6.1 − 0.85

  13   **70**   **35**   **5**

Use the table at the right for Exercises 28 to 30.

28. About how much taller is Derek than Peppe? **11 inches**

29. What is the approximate combined measure of Amy and Barnaby? **105 inches**

30. Who is about 10 inches taller than Peppe? **Barnaby**

Heights of Students	
Jozie	46.5 in.
Derek	52.25 in.
Peppe	41.4 in.
Amy	53.75 in.
Barnaby	50.5 in.

31. Reasoning Explain how to estimate 3.85 + 5.27.

Round 3.85 to 4 and 5.27 to 5. Then add 4 + 5 to get an estimate of 9.

190 Intervention Lesson H53

Teacher Notes

Ongoing Assessment

Ask: *How do word problems indicate that an estimate is enough?* When the question uses the terms about, approximately, or estimate, an estimate is enough. Also, estimates can be used to determine whether or not an exact answer is reasonable.

Error Intervention

If students have trouble rounding decimals,

then use H26: Rounding Decimals Through Hundredths.

If You Have More Time

Have each student create cards with decimals written on them. Student pairs can play a game where they each turn over one of their cards and find an estimate of the sum or difference of the two numbers.

© Pearson Education, Inc.

Adding Decimals to Hundredths

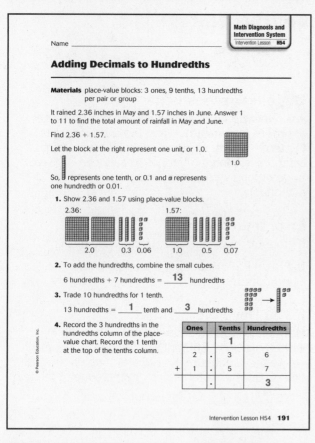

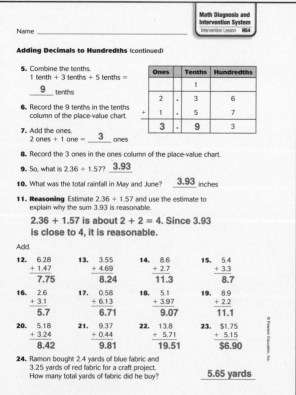

Teacher Notes

Ongoing Assessment

Ask: *When adding two decimals, if there are a total of 12 hundredths in the hundredths place, how should that be recorded?* A 2 is recorded in the hundredths place and one tenth is recorded at the top of the tenths column.

Error Intervention

If students have trouble understanding the use of place-value blocks with decimals,

then use pennies, dimes, and dollars to represent hundredths, tenths, and ones.

If You Have More Time

Draw a large place-value chart on the board with columns for tens, ones, tenths, and hundredths. Choose a group of 4 students and have each stand in front of a column that is assigned to them. Give the group an addition or subtraction problem. Let them work together to write the numbers in the correct columns with each student responsible for only their assigned column. The student who is assigned the hundredths column starts the addition or subtraction and once they have regrouped, then the student who is assigned the tenths column continues until each column is completed.

© Pearson Education, Inc.

Subtracting Decimals to Hundredths

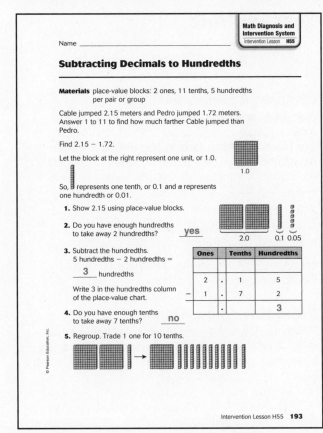

Name _____

Subtracting Decimals to Hundredths

Materials place-value blocks: 2 ones, 11 tenths, 5 hundredths per pair or group

Cable jumped 2.15 meters and Pedro jumped 1.72 meters. Answer 1 to 11 to find how much farther Cable jumped than Pedro.

Find 2.15 − 1.72.

Let the block at the right represent one unit, or 1.0.

1.0

So, ▌ represents one tenth, or 0.1 and ▪ represents one hundredth or 0.01.

1. Show 2.15 using place-value blocks.

2. Do you have enough hundredths to take away 2 hundredths?   **yes**

2.0   0.1 0.05

3. Subtract the hundredths.
   5 hundredths − 2 hundredths =
   3 hundredths

   Write 3 in the hundredths column of the place-value chart.

Ones	Tenths	Hundredths
2 .	1	5
− 1 .	7	2
.		3

4. Do you have enough tenths to take away 7 tenths?   **no**

5. Regroup. Trade 1 one for 10 tenths.

Intervention Lesson H55   **193**

Name _____

Subtracting Decimals to Hundredths (continued)

6. How many ones do you have left?   **1**
   Record this value in the chart. Cross out the 2 ones and write 1 above it.

7. How many tenths do you have now?   **11**
   Record this value in the chart. Cross out the 1 tenth and write 11 above it.

Ones	Tenths	Hundredths
1	11	
2̸ . 1̸		5
− 1 .	7	2
0 .	4	3

8. Subtract the tenths. 11 tenths − 7 tenths = **4** tenths
   Write 4 in the tenths column of the chart.

9. Subtract the ones. 1 one − 1 one = **0** ones
   Write 0 in the ones column of the chart.

10. So, what is 2.15 − 1.72?   **0.43**

11. How much farther did Cable jump than Pedro?   **0.43** meters

Subtract.

12. 7.34
    − 2.18
    5.16

13. 5.27
    − 4.58
    0.69

14. 6.7
    − 1.5
    5.2

15. 9.2
    − 2.7
    6.5

16. 7.4
    − 3.8
    3.6

17. 3.68
    − 1.93
    1.75

18. 3.4
    − 2.2
    1.2

19. 5.69
    − 4.35
    1.34

20. Paulie caught two fish. One weighed 1.43 pounds and the other weighed 5.7 pounds. Janice caught one 7.09 pound fish. Who caught more pounds of fish?   **Paulie;**

    How much more?   **0.04 lb more**

21. **Reasoning** What regrouping do you need to do to subtract 8 − 5.43?

    Trade 1 one for 10 tenths and then trade one of those tenths for 10 hundredths.

194 Intervention Lesson H55

Teacher Notes

Ongoing Assessment

Ask: *If three hundredths need to be subtracted and there are none, what can be done?* One of the tenths can be exchanged for 10 hundredths.

Error Intervention

If students have trouble understanding the use of place-value blocks with decimals,

then relate the flat block used as a one to a hundreds grid and use H22: Place Value Through Hundredths.

If You Have More Time

Have students see how far they can jump. Student pairs can use meter sticks to measure the distance to the hundredth place (centimeters). Students can then find the difference between their jumps.

© Pearson Education, Inc.

More Estimation of Decimal Sums and Differences

Name _____

Math Diagnosis and
Intervention System
Intervention Lesson H56

**More Estimation of Decimal Sums and
Differences**

Ryan used 12.56 liters of saline solution (salt water) for a chemistry
experiment and 7.815 liters of saline solution for another experiment.
What is the approximate amount of saline solution he used all together?

1. What word in the question indicates
that an estimate is enough?　　　　　　　　　**approximate**

Estimate 12.56 + 7.815 by answering 2 to 6.

2. What is 12.56 rounded to the nearest whole number?　　　**13**

3. What is 7.815 rounded to the nearest whole number?　　　**8**

4. Find the sum of the two rounded numbers.　13 + 8 = **21**

5. So, what is a good estimate for 12.56 + 7.815?　　　**21**

6. What is the approximate amount of saline
solution Ryan used all together?　　　About **21** liters

Estimate 12.56 + 7.815 using compatible numbers, by answering
7 to 9.

7. What are two compatible numbers, numbers that
are easy to add, close to 12.56 and 7.815?　　**12** and **8**

8. What is the sum of the compatible numbers you chose?　**20**

9. What is another good estimate for 12.56 + 7.815?　　**20**

About how much more saline was used in the first experiment than in
the second experiment?

Estimate 12.56 − 7.815 by answering 10 to 12. Use the rounded
numbers 13 and 8 found above.

10. What is the difference of the rounded numbers?　13 − 8 = **5**

11. What is a good estimate for 12.56 − 7.815?　　　**5**

12. About how much more saline solution was used in
the first experiment than in the second experiment?　About **5** liters

Intervention Lesson H56　**195**

Teacher Notes

Ongoing Assessment

Ask: *Why are estimates of 3.145 + 4.85 and
3.05 + 5.2 the same when the estimates
are found by rounding to the nearest whole
number?* Both 3.145 and 3.03 round to 3. Both
4.85 and 5.2 round to 5. So, the estimate for both
is 3 + 5 = 8.

Error Intervention

If students have trouble rounding decimals,

then use H27: Rounding Decimals Through
Thousandths.

If You Have More Time

Have student write word problems that involve
estimating the sum or difference of decimals. Then
have them trade problems with a partner to solve.

Name _____

Math Diagnosis and
Intervention System
Intervention Lesson H56

More Estimation of Decimal Sums and Differences (continued)

Estimate each sum or difference.

13. 5.68 + 28.5
35

14. 67.415 − 8.62
58

15. 32.912 + 47.622
81

16. 16.225 − 0.92
15

17. 0.89 + 2.4
3

18. 77.561 − 1.944
76

19. 45.61 + 36.2
82

20. 85.3 + 4.937
90

21. 17.5 − 11.289
7

22. 15.8 + 35.9
52

23. 14.822 − 8.1
7

24. 5.96 + 7.25
13

25. 16.1 − 3.81
12

26. 5.83 + 0.83
7

27. 16.854 − 2.1
15

28. 42.83
− 19.116
24

29. 81.674
− 2.52
79

30. 22
+ 10.3
32

31. 51.3
+ 22.68
74

32. 33.8
+ 8.223
42

33. 12.54
+ 86.142
99

34. 6.882
− 0.52
6

35. 37.65
− 22.9
15

36. Jean is 2.4 inches taller than Stefano. If Stefano
is 48.125 inches tall, about how tall is Jean?　**about 50 inches tall**

37. Reasoning Are the estimates always the same when you use
rounding to the nearest whole number and compatible numbers?

**No; Compatible numbers are not necessarily the
same as the nearest whole number. If you round to
the nearest whole number to find an estimate you
might get a different answer than if you rounded to
compatible numbers.**

196 Intervention Lesson H56

© Pearson Education, Inc.

Adding and Subtracting Decimals to Thousandths

Math Diagnosis and Intervention System
Intervention Lesson   H57

Name _____

Adding and Subtracting Decimals to Thousandths

At a gymnastics competition Claudia earned a score of 7.75 on the uneven parallel bars. She scored 1.465 points higher on the beam. Answer 1 to 9 to find how many points she earned on the beam.

Find 7.75 + 1.465.

Ones		Tenths	Hundredths	Thousandths
1		1		
7	.	7	5	
+ 1	.	4	6	5
9	.	2	1	5

1. How many thousandths are in 7.75?
   0

2. Add 0 thousandths and 5 thousandths and record the value in the place-value chart.

3. Add the hundredths.   5 hundredths + 6 hundredths = **11** hundredths

4. Regroup the hundredths. 11 hundredths = **1** tenth and **1** hundredth
   Record the 1 hundredth at the bottom of the hundredths column and the 1 tenth at the top of the tenths column.

5. Add the tenths.   1 tenth + 7 tenths + 4 tenths = **12** tenths

6. Regroup the tenths.   12 tenths = **1** one and **2** tenths
   Record the 2 tenths at the bottom of the tenths column and the 1 one at the top of the ones column.

7. Add the ones and record.   1 one + 7 ones + 1 one = **9** ones

8. So, what is 7.75 + 1.465?   **9.215**

9. How many points did Claudia earn on the beam?   **9.215** points

Claudia also earned a score of 6.825 on her floor routine. How many more points did she earn on the uneven parallel bars than the floor routine?

Find 7.75 − 6.825 by answering 10 to 18.

10. Since 7.75 has 0 thousandths, write a zero in the place-value chart on the next page, to change 7.75 to 7.750.

Intervention Lesson H57   **197**

© Pearson Education, Inc.

Math Diagnosis and Intervention System
Intervention Lesson   H57

Name _____

Adding and Subtracting Decimals to Thousandths (continued)

11. Regroup. Trade 1 hundredth for 10 thousandths. In the chart, cross out the 5 hundredths and write 4 above it. Cross out the 0 thousandths and write 10 above it.

Ones		Tenths	Hundredths	Thousandths
6		17	4	10
7̶	.	7̶	5̶	0̶
− 6	.	8	2	5
0	.	9	2	5

12. Subtract the thousandths. 10 thousandths − 5 thousandths = **5** thousandths
    Record the 5 in the thousandths column.

13. Subtract the hundredths. 4 hundredths − 2 hundredths = **2** hundredths
    Record the 2 in the hundredths column.

14. Regroup. Trade 1 one for 10 tenths. Cross out the 7 ones and write 6 above it. Cross out the 7 tenths and write 17 above it.

15. Subtract the tenths.   17 tenths − 8 tenths = **9** tenths
    Record the 9 in the tenths column.

16. Subtract the ones and record the value in the ones column.

17. So, what is 7.75 − 6.825?   **0.925**

18. How many more points did Claudia earn on the uneven parallel bars than the floor routine?   **0.925** point

Find each sum or difference.

19.	43.72 − 18.68 **25.04**	20.	25.83 + 14.76 **40.59**	21.	75.77 − 64.89 **10.88**	22.	865.80 + 74.95 **940.75**

23.	0.951 − 0.678 **0.273**	24.	0.810 + 0.125 **0.935**	25.	7.618 − 4.909 **2.709**	26.	6.234 + 5.195 **11.429**

27. Bart is 1.486 meters tall and Sergio is 1.817 meters tall. What is the difference in their heights?   **0.331 meter**

198   Intervention Lesson H57

© Pearson Education, Inc.

© Pearson Education, Inc.

Teacher Notes

Ongoing Assessment

Ask: **How is adding and subtracting decimals different from adding and subtracting whole numbers? How is it the same?** When you add and subtract decimals, you have to line up the decimal points. When you add and subtract whole numbers, the numbers are always lined up to the right. In both cases, the place values are lined up underneath each other.

Error Intervention

If students have trouble understanding place value of decimal numbers,

then use H24: Place Value Through Thousandths.

If You Have More Time

Have students look up stock prices and find the difference between the prices of different stocks.

Multiplying with Decimals and Whole Numbers

Name _____

Math Diagnosis and Intervention System
Intervention Lesson   **H58**

Multiplying with Decimals and Whole Numbers

Materials place-value blocks: 1 one, 15 tenths, 12 hundredths per pair or group

A small jar of spice weighs 0.54 ounce. What is the weight of three jars?

Find 3 × 0.54 by answering 1 to 10.

Let the block at the right represent one unit, or 1.0.

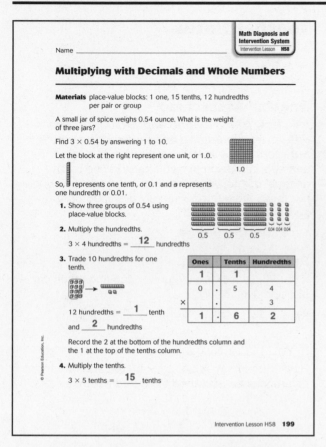

1.0

So, ▮ represents one tenth, or 0.1 and ▫ represents one hundredth or 0.01.

1. Show three groups of 0.54 using place-value blocks.

0.5   0.5   0.5   0.04 0.04 0.04

2. Multiply the hundredths.

3 × 4 hundredths = __12__ hundredths

3. Trade 10 hundredths for one tenth.

12 hundredths = __1__ tenth
and __2__ hundredths

Ones	Tenths	Hundredths
1	1	
0 .	5	4
× .		3
1 .	6	2

Record the 2 at the bottom of the hundredths column and the 1 at the top of the tenths column.

4. Multiply the tenths.

3 × 5 tenths = __15__ tenths

© Pearson Education, Inc.

Intervention Lesson H58   **199**

Teacher Notes

Ongoing Assessment

Ask: ***When multiplying 2.4 by 5, the product of 5 × 4 tenths is 20 tenths. How should that be recorded?*** A zero is recorded in the tenths place and two ones are recorded at the top of the ones place.

Error Intervention

If students have trouble recording multiplication using the traditional algorithm,

then use G49: Multiplying Two-Digit Numbers, G50: Multiplying Three-Digit Numbers, and G70: Multiplying by Two-Digit Numbers.

If You Have More Time

Have students look up the nutritional content of various types of food. Choose items that include saturated fat since it is usually measured to a decimal place. Have them calculate the amount of the nutritional item in several servings of the food.

Name _____

Multiplying with Decimals and Whole Numbers (continued)

5. Add the regrouped tenth.   15 tenths + 1 tenth = __16__ tenths

6. Trade 10 tenths for 1 one.   16 tenths = __1__ one and __6__ tenths

Record the 6 at the bottom of the tenths column and the 1 at the top of the ones column.

7. Multiply the ones.   3 × 0 ones = __0__ ones

8. Add the regrouped one.   0 one + 1 one = __1__ one

Record the 1 at the bottom of the ones column.

9. What is 3 × 0.54?   __1.62__

10. What is the weight of three jars?   __1.62 ounces__

11. How many decimal places are there in 0.54?   __2__

12. How many decimal places are there in 3?   __0__

13. How many decimal places are there in both factors combined?   __2__

14. How many decimal places are in the product of 0.54 × 3 = 1.62?   __2__

The total number of decimal places in the factors always equals the number of decimal places in the product.

15. Reasoning If 5 × 83 = 415, what is 5 × 0.83? Explain.

__4.15; 5 × 0.83 has two decimal places.__

Find each product.

16. 8.6	**17.** 42.5	**18.** 40	**19.** $9.12
× 4	× 6	× 1.3	× 3
34.4	**255.0**	**52.0**	**$27.36**

20. Louis bought 5 pens that cost $0.79 each. How much did he pay for them?   __$3.95__

21. A small bottle of perfume holds 0.25 ounce. How many ounces would 5 of these bottles hold?   __1.25 ounces__

© Pearson Education, Inc.

© Pearson Education, Inc.

Multiplying Decimals by 10, 100, or 1,000

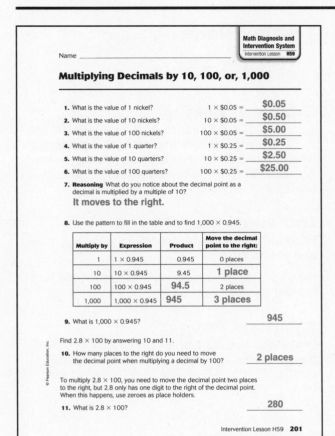

Name _____

Multiplying Decimals by 10, 100, or 1,000

1. What is the value of 1 nickel? $1 \times \$0.05 =$ __$0.05__
2. What is the value of 10 nickels? $10 \times \$0.05 =$ __$0.50__
3. What is the value of 100 nickels? $100 \times \$0.05 =$ __$5.00__
4. What is the value of 1 quarter? $1 \times \$0.25 =$ __$0.25__
5. What is the value of 10 quarters? $10 \times \$0.25 =$ __$2.50__
6. What is the value of 100 quarters? $100 \times \$0.25 =$ __$25.00__

7. **Reasoning** What do you notice about the decimal point as a decimal is multiplied by a multiple of 10?
   It moves to the right.

8. Use the pattern to fill in the table and to find $1,000 \times 0.945$.

Multiply by	Expression	Product	Move the decimal point to the right:
1	1×0.945	0.945	0 places
10	10×0.945	9.45	**1 place**
100	100×0.945	**94.5**	2 places
1,000	$1,000 \times 0.945$	**945**	**3 places**

9. What is $1,000 \times 0.945$?   **945**

Find 2.8×100 by answering 10 and 11.

10. How many places to the right do you need to move the decimal point when multiplying a decimal by 100?   **2 places**

To multiply 2.8×100, you need to move the decimal point two places to the right, but 2.8 only has one digit to the right of the decimal point. When this happens, use zeroes as place holders.

11. What is 2.8×100?   **280**

Intervention Lesson H59   **201**

© Pearson Education, Inc.

Name _____

Multiplying Decimals by 10, 100, or 1,000 (continued)

Use mental math to find each product.

12. $6.74 \times 1 =$ __6.74__
    $6.74 \times 10 =$ __67.4__
    $6.74 \times 100 =$ __674__
    $6.74 \times 1,000 =$ __6,740__

13. $42.19 \times 1 =$ __42.19__
    $42.19 \times 10 =$ __421.9__
    $42.19 \times 100 =$ __4,219__
    $42.19 \times 1,000 =$ __42,190__

14. $0.0125 \times 1 =$ __0.0125__
    $0.0125 \times 10 =$ __0.125__
    $0.0125 \times 100 =$ __1.25__
    $0.0125 \times 1,000 =$ __12.5__

15. $295.81 \times 1 =$ __295.81__
    $295.81 \times 10 =$ __2,958.1__
    $295.81 \times 100 =$ __29,581__
    $295.81 \times 1,000 =$ __295,810__

16. $0.0007 \times 1 =$ __0.0007__
    $0.0007 \times 10 =$ __0.007__
    $0.0007 \times 100 =$ __0.07__
    $0.0007 \times 1,000 =$ __0.7__

17. $1,400 \times 1 =$ __1,400__
    $1,400 \times 10 =$ __14,000__
    $1,400 \times 100 =$ __140,000__
    $1,400 \times 1,000 =$ __1,400,000__

18. One box weighs 3.25 pounds. What is the weight of 10 boxes?   **32.5 pounds**

19. **Reasoning** How is multiplying a decimal by 100 the same as multiplying a whole number by 100? How is it different?
    In both cases, the decimal moves two places to the right. When a whole number is multiplied by 100, two zeros are always added. When a decimal is multiplied, the number of decimal places determines how many zeros to add, if any.

© Pearson Education, Inc.

202 Intervention Lesson H59

Math Diagnosis and Intervention System

Teacher Notes

Ongoing Assessment

Ask: *How does the number of places that the decimal moves relate to the number of zeros in the factor by which you are multiplying?* The number of zeros is the same as the number of places that the decimal moves.

Error Intervention

If students have trouble understanding the examples using money,

then use place-value blocks to show the results when multiplying by a multiple of ten.

If You Have More Time

Have students make two decks of cards. One deck includes cards with numbers with up to three decimal places and the other deck includes cards with 10, 100, or 1,000. Students take turns drawing a card from each deck and recording the product of the two cards. The first student to reach a predetermined number of points wins.

© Pearson Education, Inc.

Estimating the Product of a Whole Number and a Decimal

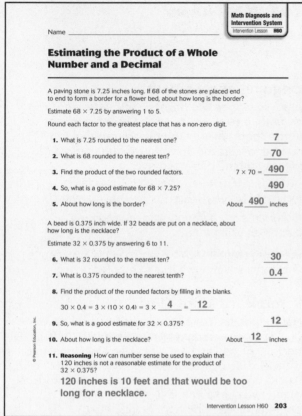

Name _____

Math Diagnosis and Intervention System
Intervention Lesson **H60**

Estimating the Product of a Whole Number and a Decimal

A paving stone is 7.25 inches long. If 68 of the stones are placed end to end to form a border for a flower bed, about how long is the border?

Estimate 68 × 7.25 by answering 1 to 5.

Round each factor to the greatest place that has a non-zero digit.

1. What is 7.25 rounded to the nearest one?   **7**

2. What is 68 rounded to the nearest ten?   **70**

3. Find the product of the two rounded factors.   7 × 70 = **490**

4. So, what is a good estimate for 68 × 7.25?   **490**

5. About how long is the border?   About **490** inches

A bead is 0.375 inch wide. If 32 beads are put on a necklace, about how long is the necklace?

Estimate 32 × 0.375 by answering 6 to 11.

6. What is 32 rounded to the nearest ten?   **30**

7. What is 0.375 rounded to the nearest tenth?   **0.4**

8. Find the product of the rounded factors by filling in the blanks.

     30 × 0.4 = 3 × (10 × 0.4) = 3 × **4** = **12**

9. So, what is a good estimate for 32 × 0.375?   **12**

10. About how long is the necklace?   About **12** inches

11. **Reasoning** How can number sense be used to explain that 120 inches is not a reasonable estimate for the product of 32 × 0.375?

   120 inches is 10 feet and that would be too long for a necklace.

Intervention Lesson H60   **203**

Teacher Notes

Ongoing Assessment

Ask: **What is the advantage of estimating 0.375 to the nearest tenth rather than to the nearest whole number?** If it was estimated to the nearest whole number, the number would round to zero and the product would not be very accurate.

Error Intervention

If students have trouble multiplying whole numbers and decimals,

then use H58: Multiplying with Decimals and Whole Numbers.

If You Have More Time

Give students a number and have them find two numbers whose estimated product is the given number. Students can work in pairs for this activity.

Name _____

Math Diagnosis and Intervention System
Intervention Lesson **H60**

Estimating the Product of a Whole Number and a Decimal (continued)

Estimate each product.

12. 2.6 × 4 **12**	**13.** 7.8 × 5 **40**	**14.** 0.34 × 9 **2.7**	**15.** 0.051 × 6 **0.3**
16. 18 × 1.07 **20**	**17.** 23 × 5.69 **120**	**18.** 4 × 0.081 **0.32**	**19.** 56 × 0.19 **12**
20. 6.21 × 5 **30**	**21.** 8.05 × 7 **56**	**22.** 1.7 × 6 **12**	**23.** 0.82 × 4 **3.2**
24. 0.074 × 3 **0.21**	**25.** 26 × 2.51 **90**	**26.** 32 × 8.9 **270**	**27.** 45 × 0.036 **2**
28. 26 × 0.89 **3**	**29.** 13 × 1.25 **10**	**30.** 74 × 3.3 **210**	**31.** 0.046 × 159 **10**
32. 89 × 0.25 **27**	**33.** 14 × 3.47 **30**	**34.** 5.39 × 24 **100**	**35.** 6.54 × 76 **560**

36. A bobcat weighs about 17.5 pounds. About how much would 2 bobcats weigh?   **40 pounds**

37. Erik needs 12 pieces of posterboard to make signs for a car wash. Each posterboard costs $0.36. About how much money will it cost him?   **$4.00**

38. A golf ball weighs about 1.62 ounces. If a package of 6 golf balls is purchased for $5.59, about how much does the package weigh?   **12 ounces**

39. **Reasoning** When estimating by rounding, if both numbers to be multiplied are rounded up, will the actual answer be greater than or less than the estimate?   **Less than**

204   Intervention Lesson H60

© Pearson Education, Inc.

Multiplying Decimals Using Grids

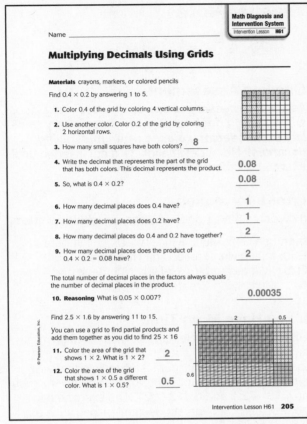

Name _____

Math Diagnosis and Intervention System
Intervention Lesson **H61**

Multiplying Decimals Using Grids

Materials crayons, markers, or colored pencils

Find 0.4 × 0.2 by answering 1 to 5.

1. Color 0.4 of the grid by coloring 4 vertical columns.

2. Use another color. Color 0.2 of the grid by coloring 2 horizontal rows.

3. How many small squares have both colors? __8__

4. Write the decimal that represents the part of the grid that has both colors. This decimal represents the product. __0.08__

5. So, what is 0.4 × 0.2? __0.08__

6. How many decimal places does 0.4 have? __1__

7. How many decimal places does 0.2 have? __1__

8. How many decimal places do 0.4 and 0.2 have together? __2__

9. How many decimal places does the product of 0.4 × 0.2 = 0.08 have? __2__

The total number of decimal places in the factors always equals the number of decimal places in the product.

10. **Reasoning** What is 0.05 × 0.007? __0.00035__

Find 2.5 × 1.6 by answering 11 to 15.

You can use a grid to find partial products and add them together as you did to find 25 × 16

11. Color the area of the grid that shows 1 × 2. What is 1 × 2? __2__

12. Color the area of the grid that shows 1 × 0.5 a different color. What is 1 × 0.5? __0.5__

Intervention Lesson H61 **205**

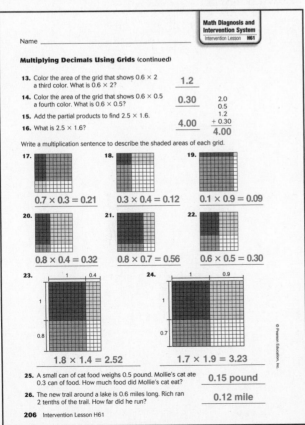

Name _____

Math Diagnosis and Intervention System
Intervention Lesson **H61**

Multiplying Decimals Using Grids (continued)

13. Color the area of the grid that shows 0.6 × 2 a third color. What is 0.6 × 2? __1.2__

14. Color the area of the grid that shows 0.6 × 0.5 a fourth color. What is 0.6 × 0.5? __0.30__

15. Add the partial products to find 2.5 × 1.6.

16. What is 2.5 × 1.6? __4.00__

```
 2.0
 0.5
 1.2
+0.30
─────
 4.00
```

Write a multiplication sentence to describe the shaded areas of each grid.

17. 0.7 × 0.3 = 0.21

18. 0.3 × 0.4 = 0.12

19. 0.1 × 0.9 = 0.09

20. 0.8 × 0.4 = 0.32

21. 0.8 × 0.7 = 0.56

22. 0.6 × 0.5 = 0.30

23. 1.8 × 1.4 = 2.52

24. 1.7 × 1.9 = 3.23

25. A small can of cat food weighs 0.5 pound. Mollie's cat ate 0.3 can of food. How much food did Mollie's cat eat? __0.15 pound__

26. The new trail around a lake is 0.6 miles long. Rich ran 2 tenths of the trail. How far did he run? __0.12 mile__

206 Intervention Lesson H61

Math Diagnosis and Intervention System

Intervention Lesson **H61**

Teacher Notes

Ongoing Assessment

Ask: **When multiplying 0.6 by 0.2, is the answer larger or smaller than 0.2?** Smaller **Why is that the case?** Because 0.6 of a number is only part of the number which makes it smaller.

Error Intervention

If students have trouble representing decimals on a grid,

then use H22: Place Value Through Hundredths.

If students have trouble with arrays and partial products,

then use G68: Using Arrays to Multiply Two-Digit Factors.

If You Have More Time

Have students color in 24 squares on a hundred grid and write a multiplication sentence with a product of 0.24. Then, have them write two more number sentences, similarly, with the same product.

© Pearson Education, Inc.

Multiplying Decimals by Decimals

Multiplying Decimals by Decimals

Hans lives 2.35 miles from school. Jamal lives 1.2 times as far. How far
from school does Jamal live?

Find 1.2 × 2.35 by answering 1 to 7.

1. Multiply 1.2 × 2.35 as you would with
   whole numbers. What is 12 × 235? __2,820__

$$\begin{array}{r} 235 \\ \times\ \ 12 \\ \hline 2,820 \end{array}$$

2. How many decimal places are in 1.2? __1__

3. How many decimal places are in 2.35? __2__

4. How many decimal places are in both factors together? __3__

The number of decimal places in the product equals the total number
of decimal places in the factors.

5. How many decimal places should be in the product 1.2 × 2.35? __3__

6. So, what is 1.2 × 2.35? __2.820__

7. How far from the school does Jamal live? __2.82__ miles

8. **Reasoning** Why are there only 2 decimal places in the correct
   answer of 2.82 when 1.2 and 2.35 have 3 decimal places
   altogether?

   **Because the last decimal place was a zero
   and zeros on the end of decimals don't
   have to be written in the answer.**

Rico lives 0.03 as far from the school as Hans. How far from the school
does Rico live?

Find 0.03 × 2.35 by answering 9 to 13.

9. What is 3 × 235? __705__

$$\begin{array}{r} 235 \\ \times\ \ \ 3 \\ \hline 705 \end{array}$$

10. How many decimal places are in
    both factors, 0.03 and 2.35, together? __4__

11. How many decimal places should be in the product? __4__

© Pearson Education, Inc.

Multiplying Decimals by Decimals (continued)

If necessary, zeros may need to be added at the beginning of the
number to place the decimal point correctly.

12. So, what is 0.03 × 2.35? __0.0705__

13. How far from the school does Rico live? __0.0705__ miles

Find each product.

14. 0.8 × 0.01   15. 1.5 × 0.02   16. 6.7 × 0.005   17. 0.2 × 0.03
    __0.008__   __0.03__   __0.0335__   __0.006__

18. 0.5 × 0.05   19. 1.2 × 0.03   20. 0.9 × 0.08   21. 0.3 × 0.3
    __0.025__   __0.036__   __0.072__   __0.09__

22. 0.06 × 0.3   23. 1.2 × 0.07   24. 0.04 × 0.09   25. 0.7 × 0.09
    __0.018__   __0.084__   __0.0036__   __0.063__

26. 9.8   27. 5.6   28. 0.4   29. 0.85   30. 1.95
   × 1.2   × 3.7   × 0.6   × 0.2   × 0.4
   11.76   **20.72**   **0.24**   **0.17**   **0.78**

31. 17.6   32. 4.05   33. 6.10   34. 2.09   35. 0.49
   × 0.23   × 8.1   × 5.2   × 0.7   × 0.3
   4.048   **32.805**   **31.720**   **1.463**   **0.147**

36. An inch is 2.54 centimeters. How many
    centimeters are in 6.5 inches?   __16.51 centimeters__

37. A cell phone company offers telephone calls
    for $0.05 for one minute. How much should it cost
    to make a cell phone call for 0.5 minute?   __$0.025__

38. **Reasoning** Is the product 1.01 × 1.01 less than or greater
    than 1? Explain.

    Greater than 1, since 1.01 is greater than 1.

© Pearson Education, Inc.

Teacher Notes

Ongoing Assessment

Ask: *Is it necessary to line up the decimal places
when adding decimals?* Yes *Is it necessary to
line up the decimal places when multiplying
decimals?* No; A decimal place is not inserted until
after the numbers are multiplied.

Error Intervention

If students have trouble multiplying whole numbers,

then use G49: Multiplying Two-Digit Numbers,
G50: Multiplying Three-Digit Numbers,
G70: Multiplying by Two-Digit Numbers, and
G71: Multiplying Greater Numbers.

If You Have More Time

Give students a whole number multiplication
equation such as 413 × 21 = 8,673. Ask them
to find as many factor pairs as possible that will
equal 8.673 based upon the expression given, such
as 4.13 × 2.1 and 0.413 × 21. The exercise can
be repeated with varying decimal places such as
0.8673 or 867.3.

© Pearson Education, Inc.

Dividing with Decimals and Whole Numbers

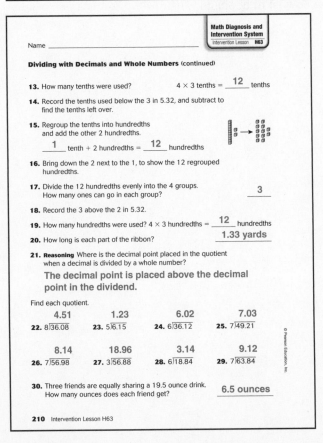

Name _____

Dividing with Decimals and Whole Numbers

Materials place-value blocks: 5 ones, 13 tenths and 12 hundredths for each pair or group

Danica has 5.32 yards of ribbon to use on a craft project. If she divides the ribbon into 4 equal parts, how long is each part?

Find 5.32 ÷ 4 by answering 1 to 20 and completing the division problem below.

1. Use place-value blocks to show 5.32.

2. Divide the 5 ones evenly into 4 equal groups.

3. How many ones can go into each group? ___1___

4. Record the 1 above the 5 in 5.32, at the right.

5. How many ones were used?

   4 × 1 one = ___4___ ones

6. Record the ones used below the 5 in 5.32, at the right.

7. How many ones are leftover? 5 − 4 = ___1___ ones

8. Record the ones left below the 4 and the line.

9. Regroup the one into tenths and add the other 3 tenths.

   ___1___ one + 3 tenths = ___13___ tenths

10. Bring down the 3 next to the 1, to show the 13 regrouped tenths.

11. Divide the 13 tenths evenly into the 4 groups. How many tenths can go in each group? ___3___

12. Record the 3 above the 3 in 5.32.

Intervention Lesson H63   **209**

Name _____

Dividing with Decimals and Whole Numbers (continued)

13. How many tenths were used?   4 × 3 tenths = ___12___ tenths

14. Record the tenths used below the 3 in 5.32, and subtract to find the tenths left over.

15. Regroup the tenths into hundredths and add the other 2 hundredths.

    ___1___ tenth + 2 hundredths = ___12___ hundredths

16. Bring down the 2 next to the 1, to show the 12 regrouped hundredths.

17. Divide the 12 hundredths evenly into the 4 groups. How many ones can go in each group? ___3___

18. Record the 3 above the 2 in 5.32.

19. How many hundredths were used? 4 × 3 hundredths = ___12___ hundredths

20. How long is each part of the ribbon?   **1.33 yards**

21. **Reasoning** Where is the decimal point placed in the quotient when a decimal is divided by a whole number?

    The decimal point is placed above the decimal point in the dividend.

Find each quotient.

22. 8)36.08   **4.51**
23. 5)6.15   **1.23**
24. 6)36.12   **6.02**
25. 7)49.21   **7.03**

26. 7)56.98   **8.14**
27. 3)56.88   **18.96**
28. 6)18.84   **3.14**
29. 7)63.84   **9.12**

30. Three friends are equally sharing a 19.5 ounce drink. How many ounces does each friend get?   **6.5 ounces**

210   Intervention Lesson H63

Teacher Notes

Ongoing Assessment

Ask: ***What happened to the fifth flat block when you divided the ones of 5.32 into four groups?*** It was regrouped into tenths and combined with the other 3 tenths.

Error Intervention

If students have trouble recording division using the traditional algorithm,

then use some of the lessons on dividing whole numbers and money, G54 to G58.

If You Have More Time

Have students look up the average speed of an animal, such as a snail or turtle, to at least a tenth of a unit. Give the students a distance compatible with the rate. For example, if the speed is feet per minute, give a distance in feet. Have students find the amount of time it takes the animal to travel that distance by dividing the distance by the speed.

© Pearson Education, Inc.

Dividing Decimals by 10, 100, or 1,000

Math Diagnosis and Intervention System
Intervention Lesson   **H64**

Name _____

Dividing Decimals by 10, 100, or 1,000

1. If $250 is divided evenly by 10 people, how much does each person get?   **$25**

2. If $250 is divided evenly by 100 people, how much does each person get?   **$2.50**

3. If $250 is divided evenly by 1,000 people, how much does each person get?   **$0.25**

4. What do you notice about the decimal point as a decimal is divided by multiples of 10?   **It moves to the left.**

5. Use the pattern to fill in the table and to find 873.2 ÷ 1,000.

Divide by	Expression	Answer	Move the decimal point to the left
1	873.2 ÷ 1	873.2	0 places
10	873.2 ÷ 10	87.32	**1 place**
100	873.2 ÷ 100	**8.732**	2 places
1,000	873.2 ÷ 1,000	**0.8732**	**3 places**

6. What is 873.2 ÷ 1,000?   **0.8732**

Find 3.6 ÷ 100 by answering 7 to 9.

7. How many places to the left does the decimal point move when dividing by 100?   **2 places**

To divide 3.6 ÷ 100, you need to move the decimal point two places to the left, but 3.6 only has one digit to the left of the decimal point. When this happens, use zeroes as place holders.

8. What is 3.6 ÷ 100?   **0.036**

9. **Reasoning** How can you check your answer?
Multiply 0.036 by 100 and see if it equals 3.6.

Intervention Lesson H64   **211**

Math Diagnosis and Intervention System
Intervention Lesson   **H64**

Name _____

Dividing Decimals by 10, 100, or 1,000 (continued)

Use mental math to find each quotient.

10. 18.4 ÷ 1 = **18.4**
18.4 ÷ 10 = **1.84**
18.4 ÷ 100 = **0.184**
18.4 ÷ 1,000 = **0.0184**

11. 73 ÷ 1 = **73**
73 ÷ 10 = **7.3**
73 ÷ 100 = **0.73**
73 ÷ 1,000 = **0.073**

12. 106.2 ÷ 1 = **106.2**
106.2 ÷ 10 = **10.62**
106.2 ÷ 100 = **1.062**
106.2 ÷ 1,000 = **0.1062**

13. 9 ÷ 1 = **9**
9 ÷ 10 = **0.9**
9 ÷ 100 = **0.09**
9 ÷ 1,000 = **0.009**

14. 45.3 ÷ 1 = **45.3**
45.3 ÷ 10 = **4.53**
45.3 ÷ 100 = **0.453**
45.3 ÷ 1,000 = **0.0453**

15. 575 ÷ 1 = **575**
575 ÷ 10 = **57.5**
575 ÷ 100 = **5.75**
575 ÷ 1,000 = **0.575**

16. 6.2 ÷ 10
0.62

17. 83.9 ÷ 100
0.839

18. 27.5 ÷ 1,000
0.0275

19. 375 ÷ 1,000
0.375

20. 93.3 ÷ 100
0.933

21. 12.4 ÷ 10
1.24

22. 214 ÷ 1,000
0.214

23. 5.04 ÷ 100
0.0504

24. 37 ÷ 10
3.7

25. 564 ÷ 10
56.4

26. 72.9 ÷ 1,000
0.0729

27. 4.1 ÷ 100
0.041

28. 97.6 ÷ 100
0.976

29. 813 ÷ 1,000
0.813

30. 3.7 ÷ 10
0.37

31. 8 ÷ 100
0.08

32. 17.65 ÷ 10
1.765

33. 3,175 ÷ 1,000
3.175

34. 0.54 ÷ 10
0.054

35. 2.06 ÷ 100
0.0206

36. A 220-foot long coil of rope is to be divided into 10 equal pieces. How long will each piece be?   **22 feet**

37. A 40-acre plot of land is to be subdivided into 100 equal size plots. How large will each plot be?   **0.40 acres**

212   Intervention Lesson H64

Teacher Notes

Ongoing Assessment

Ask: ***How does the number of places that the decimal moves relate to the number of zeros in the multiple of ten by which you are dividing?***
The number of zeros is the same as the number of places that the decimal moves to the left.

Error Intervention

If students have trouble understanding the examples using money,

then use place-value blocks to show the results when dividing by a multiple of ten.

If You Have More Time

Have students create two decks of cards. One deck includes cards with numbers with up to three decimal places and the other deck includes cards with 10, 100, or 1,000. Students take turns drawing a card from each deck and recording the quotient of the decimal number divided by the multiple of 10. At the end of 10 turns, the player with the lowest total points wins.

© Pearson Education, Inc.

Dividing a Decimal by a Whole Number

Name _____

Math Diagnosis and Intervention System
Intervention Lesson **H65**

Dividing a Decimal by a Whole Number

A plot of land that is 29.4 acres is divided into 12 equal parts. How many acres is each part?

Find 29.4 ÷ 12 by answering 1 to 11 and completing the long division problem at the right.

1. How many groups of 12 are there in 29? __2__

   Record the 2 above the 9 in 29.4 at the right.

2. Multiply and subtract.
   How many ones are leftover? 29 − 24 = __5__ ones

   Record this value below the 24 and the line.

3. How many tenths are 5 ones and 4 tenths? __54__ tenths
   Bring down the 4 next to the 5, to show the 54 tenths.

4. How many groups of 12 are there in 54? __4__

   Record the 4 above the 4 in 29.4.

5. Multiply and subtract.
   How many tenths are leftover? 54 tenths − 48 tenths = __6__ tenths

   Record this value below the 48 and the line.

6. Does 29.4 = 29.40? __yes__ Since there is a remainder, add a zero to the dividend to change 29.4 to 29.40.

7. How many hundredths are in 6 tenths and 0 hundredths? __60__ hundredths

   Bring down the 0 next to the 6, to show the 60 hundredths.

8. How many groups of 12 are there in 60? __5__

   Record the 5 above the 0 in 29.40.

9. Multiply and subtract.
   How many hundredths are leftover? 60 − 60 = __0__ hundredths

   Since there are no hundredths left, the division is finished. Notice that the decimal point in the quotient is directly above the decimal point in the dividend

10. So, what is 29.4 ÷ 12? __2.45__

11. How many acres is each piece of land? __2.45 acres__

Long division:
```
      2.45
 12)29.40
     24
     ‾‾
     54
     48
     ‾‾
     60
     60
     ‾‾
      0
```

Intervention Lesson H65 **213**

Name _____

Math Diagnosis and Intervention System
Intervention Lesson **H65**

Dividing a Decimal by a Whole Number (continued)

Find each quotient.

12. 4)12.8 = **3.2**
13. 37)55.5 = **1.5**
14. 35)2.1 = **0.06**
15. 2)37.4 = **18.7**

16. 11)97.9 = **8.9**
17. 41)129.15 = **3.15**
18. 30)13.5 = **0.45**
19. 9)45.54 = **5.06**

20. 6)72.24 = **12.04**
21. 5)43.75 = **8.75**
22. 3)7.41 = **2.47**
23. 30)188.4 = **6.28**

24. 9)67.86 = **7.54**
25. 3)39.09 = **13.03**
26. 52)72.8 = **1.4**
27. 81)32.4 = **0.4**

28. 2)621.5 = **310.75**
29. 16)75.2 = **4.7**
30. 24)151.2 = **6.3**
31. 9)132.3 = **14.7**

32. A 12-pack of canned juice costs $3.24. What is the cost of each juice can? **$0.27**

33. **Reasoning** How many zeros can be placed after the last digit in a decimal without changing the value of the number?
    There is no limit to the number of zeros that may be added.

Teacher Notes

Ongoing Assessment

Ask: *The first digit in the quotient goes in which place when dividing 6.45 by 3?* Ones

Error Intervention

If students have trouble recording division using the traditional algorithm,

then use some of the lessons on dividing whole numbers, G54 to G58 and G75 to G77.

If students have trouble understanding the division process with decimals,

then use H63: Dividing with Decimals and Whole Numbers and use place-value blocks to illustrate.

If You Have More Time

Have students work in small groups. Give each group of students a package of items, such as nuts. Have students divide the weight of the package by the number of items in the package to find the average weight of each item.

© Pearson Education, Inc.

Estimating the Quotient of a Decimal and a Whole Number

Estimating the Quotient of a Decimal and a Whole Number

A butcher has 62.75 pounds of ground beef. If he divides it into 34 packages of equal weight, about how many pounds should he put in each package?

Estimate 62.75 ÷ 34 by answering 1 to 6.

Round the dividend and the divisor to the greatest place that has a non-zero digit.

1. What is the greatest place in 62.75 that has a non-zero digit? _____ **tens**

2. What is 62.75 rounded to the nearest ten? **60**

3. What is 34 rounded to the nearest ten? **30**

4. What is 60 ÷ 30? **2**

5. So, what is a good estimate for 62.75 ÷ 34? **2**

6. About how many pounds should the butcher put in each package? About __**2**__ pounds

Compatible numbers can also be used to find an estimate. Compatible numbers are close to the actual numbers, but easy to divide.

The Delgato family drove 473.6 miles over a period of 8 hours. About how far did they drive each hour?

Estimate 473.6 ÷ 8 by answering 7 to 13.

7. What is the greatest place in 473.6 that has a non-zero digit? **hundreds**

8. What is 473.6 rounded to the nearest hundred? **500**

9. Is it easy to divide 500 by 8? **no**

10. What is a number close to 473.6 that is easy to divide by 8? **480**

11. What is 480 ÷ 8? **60**

12. So, what is a good estimate for 473.6 ÷ 8? **60**

13. About how far did the Delgato family drive each hour? About __**60**__ miles

© Pearson Education, Inc.

Estimating the Quotient of a Decimal and a Whole Number (continued)

Estimate each quotient.

14. 352.84 ÷ 10   **35**

15. 42.9 ÷ 8   **5**

16. 397.52 ÷ 42   **10**

17. 754.61 ÷ 74   **10**

18. 84.69 ÷ 5   **17**

19. 198.6 ÷ 51   **4**

20. 41.9 ÷ 7   **6**

21. 28.68 ÷ 9   **3**

22. 225.81 ÷ 69   **3**

23. 633.4 ÷ 73   **9**

24. 410.88 ÷ 18   **20**

25. 69.3 ÷ 8   **9**

26. 159.1 ÷ 19   **8**

27. 542.98 ÷ 58   **9**

28. 158.6 ÷ 4   **40**

29. Mr. Chen worked 148.6 hours last month. If he worked 22 days during the month, about how many hours did he work each day? **About 7 hours**

30. **Reasoning** About how many 26-ounce cartons can be filled from 231 ounces of juice? Find the estimate two ways and explain how you found each.
Sample answers: 225 ÷ 25 = 9 and 240 ÷ 30 = 8; About 8 or 9 cartons can be filled.

31. **Reasoning** Why is more than one answer correct when estimating quotients?
Because there are different methods of estimating and different combinations of compatible numbers that can be used. As long as the estimate is close to the actual quotient, it is considered a good estimate.

© Pearson Education, Inc.

Teacher Notes

Ongoing Assessment

Ask: *When rounding 62.75 to the greatest digit, why is it rounded to the nearest ten?* Because the greatest digit in 62.75 is the six which is in the tens place. So 62.75 rounded to the greatest digit is rounded to the nearest ten.

Error Intervention

If students have trouble finding compatible numbers,

then use G44: Mental Math: Division Patterns.

If You Have More Time

Have students measure their height to the nearest quarter inch with a yard stick. Have students estimate the quotient of their height and their age in years to find an approximate number of meters they grew each year.

© Pearson Education, Inc.

Dividing a Decimal by a Decimal

Math Diagnosis and Intervention System
Intervention Lesson **H67**

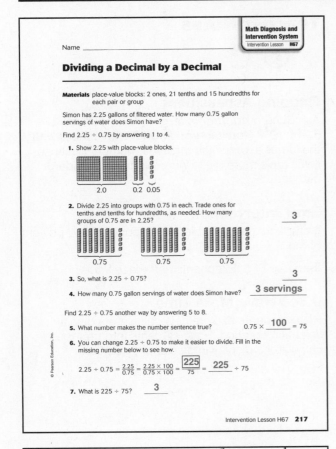

Name _____

Math Diagnosis and Intervention System
Intervention Lesson **H67**

Dividing a Decimal by a Decimal

Materials place-value blocks: 2 ones, 21 tenths and 15 hundredths for each pair or group

Simon has 2.25 gallons of filtered water. How many 0.75 gallon servings of water does Simon have?

Find 2.25 ÷ 0.75 by answering 1 to 4.

1. Show 2.25 with place-value blocks.

2.0   0.2 0.05

2. Divide 2.25 into groups with 0.75 in each. Trade ones for tenths and tenths for hundredths, as needed. How many groups of 0.75 are in 2.25?   **3**

0.75   0.75   0.75

3. So, what is 2.25 ÷ 0.75?   **3**

4. How many 0.75 gallon servings of water does Simon have?   **3 servings**

Find 2.25 ÷ 0.75 another way by answering 5 to 8.

5. What number makes the number sentence true? $0.75 \times \underline{100} = 75$

6. You can change 2.25 ÷ 0.75 to make it easier to divide. Fill in the missing number below to see how.

$2.25 \div 0.75 = \frac{2.25}{0.75} = \frac{2.25 \times 100}{0.75 \times 100} = \frac{\boxed{225}}{75} = \underline{225} \div 75$

7. What is 225 ÷ 75?   **3**

Intervention Lesson H67   **217**

Name _____

Math Diagnosis and Intervention System
Intervention Lesson **H67**

Dividing a Decimal by a Decimal (continued)

8. Since 225 ÷ 75 = 2.25 ÷ 0.75, what is 2.25 ÷ 0.75?   **3**

To divide decimals, multiply the divisor by 10 or 100 to make it a whole number. Multiply the dividend by the same amount. The quotient of the resulting amounts equals the quotient of the original numbers.

Find 2.96 ÷ 0.4 by answering 9 to 12.

9. What number makes the number sentence true? $0.4 \times \underline{10} = 4$

10. Multiply 2.96 by the same number. $2.96 \times 10 = \underline{29.6}$

11. What is 29.6 ÷ 4?   **7.4**

12. What is 2.96 ÷ 0.4?   **7.4**

Divide.

13. 12.2 ÷ 6.1	**14.** 35.7 ÷ 5.1	**15.** 0.18 ÷ 0.2	**16.** 53.4 ÷ 8.9
2	**7**	**0.9**	**6**

17. 125 ÷ 0.25	**18.** 0.48 ÷ 0.16	**19.** 26.8 ÷ 6.7	**20.** 1.008 ÷ 5.6
500	**3**	**4**	**0.18**

21. Baseball card packages cost $3.50 each. How many packages can be purchased for $17.50?   **5 packages**

22. Reasoning When dividing a number which is greater than 1 by a number less than 1, will the quotient be greater than or less than the dividend? Explain.

The quotient will be greater than the dividend.
For example, 5 ÷ 0.2 = 25.

218   Intervention Lesson H67

Teacher Notes

Ongoing Assessment

Ask: ***What whole numbers can you divide to find 4.2 ÷ 16?*** 420 ÷ 16.

Error Intervention

If students have trouble deciding which power of ten to use or have trouble with the multiplication,

then use H59: Multiplying Decimals by 10, 100 or 1,000.

If You Have More Time

Have students choose a number and divide it by 0.5. Have students compare their answer to their original number and find a pattern. The quotient will always be two times the dividend because 0.5 is equal to $\frac{1}{2}$. Point out that dividing by $\frac{1}{2}$ is the same as multiplying by 2. The activity can be repeated by dividing by 0.25. Point out that the quotient will always be four times the dividend.

© Pearson Education, Inc.

Scientific Notation

Name _____

Math Diagnosis and
Intervention System
Intervention Lesson H68

Scientific Notation

Scientific notation is a method of writing large numbers so that they are easier to write, to read, and to use, than standard form.

Find the relationship between scientific notation and standard notation by answering 1 to 3.

1. Complete the table.

Scientific Notation	Expanded Form	Standard Notation	Places Decimal Point Moved
2.1×10^2	2.1×100	210	2
2.1×10^3	$2.1 \times 1{,}000$	2,100	3
2.1×10^4	$2.1 \times 10{,}000$	21,000	4
2.1×10^5	$2.1 \times 100{,}000$	210,000	5

2. Reasoning What is the relationship between the exponent on the 10 and the number of places the decimal point moves when rewriting a number in scientific notation to standard notation?

The number of digits the decimal point moves is the same as the exponent on the 10.

3. Using the pattern from the table, write 2.1×10^{11} in standard notation. **210,000,000,000**

A mole is a measurement commonly used in chemistry. One mole of an item represents about 6.023×10^{23} molecules. Write this number in standard notation by answering 4 to 6.

4. How many places do you move the decimal point? **23**

5. How many zeros does 6.023×10^{23} have when written in standard form? **20**

6. Write one mole of an item in standard notation.
602,300,000,000,000,000,000,000

Intervention Lesson H68   **219**

Name _____

Math Diagnosis and
Intervention System
Intervention Lesson H68

Scientific Notation (continued)

The mass of the Earth is about 5,970,000,000,000,000,000,000,000 kilograms. Write this number in scientific notation by answering 7 to 9.

7. The first number in scientific notation is always between 1 and 10. What is the first number? **5**

8. How many digits are between the new position for the decimal and the end of the given number? **24**

9. $5{,}970{,}000{,}000{,}000{,}000{,}000{,}000{,}000 = 5.97 \times 10^{24}$

10. What is the mass of the Earth in scientific notation? $\underline{5.97 \times 10^{24}}$ kilograms

Write each number in standard notation.

11. 3.25×10^8 **12.** 6.887×10^{10} **13.** 1.2×10^3

325,000,000   68,870,000,000   1,200

14. 8.1×10^{12} **15.** 5.7×10^5 **16.** 6.117×10^7

8,100,000,000,000   570,000   61,170,000

Write each number in scientific notation.

17. 38,500,000,000   **18.** 577,000,000   **19.** 6,100,000,000

$3.85 \times 10^{\boxed{10}}$ $5.77 \times 10^{\boxed{8}}$ $6.1 \times 10^{\boxed{9}}$

20. 116,000,000   **21.** 3,800,000,000,000   **22.** 85,000

1.16×10^8 3.8×10^{12} 8.5×10^4

23. 599,000,000,000,000   **24.** 1,214,000   **25.** 46,000,000,000

5.99×10^{14} 1.214×10^6 4.6×10^{10}

26. A light-year is the distance that light can travel in one year. It is equal to 9,500,000,000,000 kilometers. What is one light-year written in scientific notation? 9.5×10^{12} kilometers

220 Intervention Lesson H68

Teacher Notes

Ongoing Assessment

Ask: *Which number is larger: 1.2×10^5 or 5.7×10^4? How did you know?* The number with the larger exponent is the larger number because it will have more digits when written in standard notation.

Error Intervention

If students have trouble with exponents and powers of ten,

then use F15: Exponents and Place Value.

If You Have More Time

Have students explore how calculators display scientific notation. Have students interpret the calculator's display into scientific notation.

Understanding Ratios

Math Diagnosis and Intervention System
Intervention Lesson **H69**

Name _____

Understanding Ratios

A ratio is a comparison of like or unlike quantities. A ratio of 2 items to
3 items can be expressed in three different ways: 2 to 3, $\frac{2}{3}$ or 2:3.

Answers will vary. Check that ratios match numbers.

Examine ratios in your classroom by answering 1 to 12.

1. How many boys are in the classroom? _____

How many girls are in the classroom? _____

2. What is the ratio of boys to girls in words? _____ to _____

3. What is the ratio of boys to girls as a fraction? _____

4. Write the ratio of girls to boys using a colon. _____

5. How many students are in the classroom? _____

6. What is the ratio of boys to students in words? _____

7. What is the ratio of students to girls as a fraction? _____

8. Write the ratio of girls to students using a colon. _____

9. Reasoning How does the ratio of girls to boys differ from the ratio
of boys to girls?

**The numbers will be the same but the order
of the numbers will be different.**

10. How many students in the classroom have brown hair? _____

How many students in the classroom have black hair? _____

11. What is the ratio of students with black hair
to total students as a fraction? _____

12. Write the ratio of students with brown hair
to those with black hair using a colon. _____

© Pearson Education, Inc.

Intervention Lesson H69   **221**

Math Diagnosis and Intervention System
Intervention Lesson **H69**

Name _____

Understanding Ratios (continued)

Write each ratio in three different ways.

△ ♡△ ☺ △ □ □
□ ♡ ♡ □ ☺ △ △
☺ △ □ ☺ ♡ □ △

13. hearts to triangles   5:6, 5 to 6, $\frac{5}{6}$

14. smiley faces to triangles   4:6, 4 to 6, $\frac{4}{6}$

15. squares to all figures   6:21; 6 to 21; $\frac{6}{21}$

16. triangles to squares   6:6, 6 to 6, $\frac{6}{6}$

17. all figures to smiley faces   21:4, 21 to 4, $\frac{21}{4}$

18. triangles to hearts   6:5, 6 to 5, $\frac{6}{5}$

19. hearts and triangles to all figures   11:21, 11 to 21, $\frac{11}{21}$

For Exercises 20–24, use the information in the table to write
a ratio for each comparison.

20. chickens to goats   12 to 22; 12:22; $\frac{12}{22}$

21. sheep to chickens   9 to 12; 9:12; $\frac{9}{12}$

22. pigs to cows   15 to 8; 15:8, $\frac{15}{8}$

23. chickens to all animals   12 to 66; 12:66; $\frac{12}{66}$

24. rabbits to goats   0 to 22; 0:22; $\frac{0}{22}$

Animals on a Farm	
Animals	**Number**
Chickens	12
Goats	22
Cows	8
Sheep	9
Pigs	15
Rabbits	0

© Pearson Education, Inc.

25. Reasoning Karina's stuffed animals are only teddy bears and dogs.
The ratio of teddy bears to dogs is 5:3. What is the ratio of dogs to
all stuffed animals? Explain your answer.
**3:8; She has 5 teddy bears, 3 dogs, and 8 stuffed animals
in all. So, the ratio of 3 dogs to 8 animals is 3 to 8.**

222   Intervention Lesson H69

© Pearson Education, Inc.

Teacher Notes

Ongoing Assessment

Ask: ***Does the order of the numbers in a ratio
make a difference?*** Yes, the order of the numbers
in a ratio should be the same as the order of the
items asked for in the ratio.

Error Intervention

If students have trouble deciding on the order of
the numbers in a ratio,

then have them use two highlighters of different
colors. One color can be used for the first item
and the other color for the second item. Students
can highlight the first item (such as "boys") in the
question using one color and the second item using
another color.

If You Have More Time

Have students discuss situations in the real world
where ratios are used. (Sample answers: student to
teacher ratio, miles per gallon)

Rates and Unit Rates

Name _____

Rates and Unit Rates

A rate is a special type of ratio that compares quantities with unlike units of measure, such as hits per game.

The table shows the number of hits for some members of a baseball team. Use the table for 1 to 7.

Name	Number of Hits	Number of Games
Maurice	20	10
Wade	24	8
Alfonso	30	12

1. What is Maurice's rate of hits to games?   __20__ hits in __10__ games

2. To find Maurice's unit rate, divide the number of hits by the number of games.

__20__ ÷ __10__ = __2__ hits per game

On average, Maurice gets 2 hits per game.

3. What is Wade's rate of hits to games?   __24 hits in 8 games__

4. On average, how many hits per game does Wade get?

__24__ ÷ __8__ = __3__ hits per game

5. What is Alfonso's rate of hits to games?   __30 hits in 12 games__

6. On average, how many hits per game does Alfonso get?

__30__ ÷ __12__ = __2.5__ hits per game

7. Reasoning Although Alfonso had the most hits, his unit rate was not the highest. Why not?

**Alfonso played in more games than the others, so
his number of hits was divided by a larger number.**

Intervention Lesson H70   **223**

Name _____

Rates and Unit Rates (continued)

Find the unit rate.

8. 525 points in 15 games

__35 points per game__

9. 54 teachers for 6 schools

__9 teachers/school__

10. 33 apples for 11 fruit baskets

__3 apples per basket__

11. $1.77 for 3 pounds of bananas

__$0.59/lb of bananas__

12. 312 miles every 12 gallons

__26 miles per gallon__

13. 185 feet in 37 seconds

__5 feet per second__

14. 42 tennis balls in 14 cans

__3 tennis balls per can__

15. 110 calories in 4 servings

__27.5 cal per serving__

16. $1.50 for 3 power bars

__$0.50 per power bar__

17. 1,530 miles in 6 hours

__255 miles per hour__

18. $48 in 8 hours

__$6 per hour__

19. 96 aces in 12 sets

__8 aces per set__

20. Samantha scored 6 goals playing soccer in 18 games. What units would you use to describe her rate? What is her rate?

__Goals per game; 0.33 goals per game__

21. A light bulb manufacturer claims that each bulb lasts at least 480 hours. Suppose you get 3,000 hours of use from 6 light bulbs. Write this information as a rate.

__500 hours per light bulb__

Teacher Notes

Ongoing Assessment

Ask: ***Does Alfonso's unit rate mean that he had exactly 2 hits in each ballgame that he played?*** No, the unit rate is more of an average but it doesn't mean the hits were divided up evenly between the games.

Error Intervention

If students have trouble understanding the relationship between rates and unit rates,

then use equivalent fractions to show that the rate and the unit rate are equal when written in fraction form.

If You Have More Time

Have students make paper balls out of wadded up paper and shoot the balls into a trashcan. Student pairs can time each other for 2, 3, or 4 minutes each and count the number of baskets, that is, the number of times the paper ball goes into the trashcan. They can then calculate and compare their rates of baskets per minute.

© Pearson Education, Inc.

Comparing Rates

Comparing Rates

Larry's Market sells 6 bagels for $2.28. Sal's Convenience Mart sells the same bagels, but charges $3.50 for 10. Find which store has the better buy by answering 1 to 8.

1. What is Larry's rate of cost of bagels? $\underline{2.28}$ dollars per $\underline{6}$ bagels

To compare two prices, find the unit price for each. The unit price is the same as the unit rate.

2. To find the unit price, divide the price by the number of bagels. $\underline{2.28} \div \underline{6} = \underline{0.38}$

3. What is the unit price for Larry's bagels? $\underline{0.38}$ per bagel

4. What is Sal's rate of cost to bagels? $\underline{3.50}$ dollars per $\underline{10}$ bagels

5. To find the unit price, divide the price by the number of bagels. $\underline{3.50} \div \underline{10} = \underline{0.35}$

6. What is the unit price for Sal's bagels? $\underline{0.35}$ per bagel

7. Compare. Write > or <. $0.38 \; \boxed{>} \; 0.35

8. Which market has the better buy? $\underline{\text{Sal's}}$

The Thompson family drove 5 hours and traveled a total of 275 miles. The Gonzalez family drove 8 hours and traveled a total of 400 miles. Find which family traveled at a faster rate by answering 9 to 14.

To find the unit rate, divide the miles by the number of hours.

9. Divide total miles by hours to find the Thompson family's unit rate of speed. $\underline{275} \div \underline{5} = \underline{55}$

10. What was the Thompson family's unit rate of speed? $\underline{55}$ miles per hour

11. Divide to find the Gonzalez family's unit rate of speed. $\underline{400} \div \underline{8} = \underline{50}$

© Pearson Education, Inc.

Comparing Rates (continued)

12. What was the Gonzalez family's unit rate of speed? $\underline{50}$ miles per hour

13. Compare. Write > or <. 55 miles per hour $\boxed{>}$ 50 miles per hour

14. Which family traveled at a faster rate?   **Thompsons**

Find each unit price. Determine the better buy.

15. $3 for 4 baseballs or $4 for 5 baseballs
$0.75; $0.80; $3 for 4 baseballs

16. 6 wristbands for $1.68 or 9 wristbands for $2.43
$0.28; $0.27; 9 wristbands for $2.43

17. $65 for 2 wallets or $93 for 3 wallets
$32.50; $31; $93 for 3 wallets

Find each unit rate and determine which rate is greater.

18. 12 runs in 4 games or 20 runs in 5 games
**3 runs per game; 4 runs per game;
20 runs in 5 games is greater**

19. 8 feet in 4 seconds or 15 feet in 5 seconds
**2 feet per second; 3 feet per second;
15 feet in 5 seconds is greater**

20. 6 fish in 8 hours or 7 fish in 10 hours
**0.75 fish per hour; 0.7 fish per hour;
6 fish in 8 hours is greater**

21. Your pulse rate is the number of times your heart beats per minute. Betty counted 130 beats in 2 minutes and Sarah counted 204 beats in 3 minutes. Who had the higher pulse rate?   **Sarah**

22. Reasoning Suppose Store A has 28 pencils for $7.50, and Store B has 29 pencils for $7.25. Explain without doing any calculations why Store B has the better buy.
Store B has more pencils for less money.

© Pearson Education, Inc.

Teacher Notes

Ongoing Assessment

Ask: ***When comparing two choices of varying quantities, if both prices are the same, how can you quickly find the better buy?*** The choice with more items is the better buy. ***If both quanities are the same, how can you quickly find the better buy?*** The choice with the lower price is the better buy.

Error Intervention

If students have trouble dividing money and decimals,

then use G57: Dividing Money, H63: Dividing with Decimals and Whole Numbers, and H65: Dividing a Decimal by a Whole Number.

If You Have More Time

Have students use advertisements from two different grocery stores and compare items to find the better buys.

Distance, Rate, and Time

Teacher Notes

Ongoing Assessment

Ask: *If you only know the value for one of the three variables in d = r × t, can you find a solution for one of the two missing variables?* No, you have to know two of the values to find a solution for a missing value.

Error Intervention

If students have trouble solving the equations,

then use F48: Solving Multiplication and Division Equations.

If You Have More Time

Have students use maps to find the distance between cities and then find the time to travel between the chosen cities using different rates.

Name _____

Math Diagnosis and Intervention System
Intervention Lesson H72

Distance, Rate, and Time

The formula $d = r \times t$ relates distance, d, rate, r and time, t. Rate in this formula means average speed.

The table shows the results of practice races run by some members of a track team. Rates written as 6 meters/second are read 6 meters per second.

Complete the table by answering 1 to 13.

Name	Distance	Rate	Time
Hannah	600 meters	6 meters/second	100 seconds
Mya	800 meters	5 meters/second	160 seconds
Adrienne	600 meters	5 meters/second	120 seconds

1. What is the formula that relates distance, rate and time? $d = r \times t$

2. For Hannah, what is the value of d?   600

3. For Hannah, what is the value of r?   6

4. For Hannah, which variable is unknown? t

5. Substitute Hannah's values for d and r in the formula.

$$d = r \times t$$
$$600 = 6 \times t$$

6. Solve $600 = 6t$. Show your work.

$t = \underline{100}$

7. How fast did Hannah run the race?
   Write this amount in the table.   100 seconds

8. Substitute Mya's values for d and r in the formula.

$$d = r \times t$$
$$800 = r \times 160$$

Intervention Lesson H72   **227**

Name _____

Math Diagnosis and Intervention System
Intervention Lesson H72

Distance, Rate, and Time (continued)

9. Solve the equation $800 = 160r$.

$r = \underline{5}$

10. How fast did Mya run the race?
    Write this amount in the table.   5 meters/second

11. Substitute Adrienne's values for r and t in the formula.

$$d = r \times t$$
$$d = 5 \times 120$$

12. What is the value of d?   600

13. How far did Adrienne run?
    Write this amount in the table.   600 meters

Solve the equation for the missing variable.

14. $d = 55$ miles/hour $\times 7$ hours

15. 300 feet $= 15$ feet/second $\times t$

$d = \underline{385 \text{ miles}}$ $t = \underline{20 \text{ seconds}}$

Complete the table.

	Distance	Rate	Time
16.	200 meters	2 meters/second	100 seconds
17.	10 miles	2.5 miles/hour	4 hours
18.	80 yards	8 yards/minute	10 minutes

19. **Reasoning** If two people run the same distance but one person takes less time than the other, how do their rates compare?

The person who took the shorter time will have a higher rate because they are faster.

228   Intervention Lesson H72

© Pearson Education, Inc.

Equal Ratios and Proportions

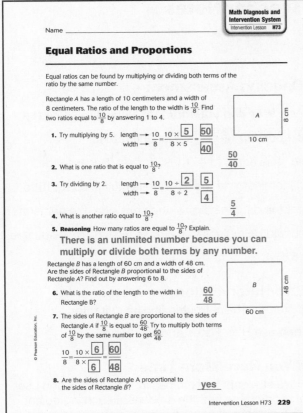

Name _____

Equal Ratios and Proportions

Equal ratios can be found by multiplying or dividing both terms of the ratio by the same number.

Rectangle A has a length of 10 centimeters and a width of 8 centimeters. The ratio of the length to the width is $\frac{10}{8}$. Find two ratios equal to $\frac{10}{8}$ by answering 1 to 4.

A   8 cm   10 cm

1. Try multiplying by 5.   length → $\frac{10}{8} = \frac{10 \times \boxed{5}}{8 \times 5} = \frac{\boxed{50}}{\boxed{40}}$ width →

2. What is one ratio that is equal to $\frac{10}{8}$? $\frac{50}{40}$

3. Try dividing by 2.   length → $\frac{10}{8} = \frac{10 \div \boxed{2}}{8 \div 2} = \frac{\boxed{5}}{\boxed{4}}$ width →

4. What is another ratio equal to $\frac{10}{8}$? $\frac{5}{4}$

5. **Reasoning** How many ratios are equal to $\frac{10}{8}$? Explain.
   There is an unlimited number because you can multiply or divide both terms by any number.

Rectangle B has a length of 60 cm and a width of 48 cm. Are the sides of Rectangle B proportional to the sides of Rectangle A? Find out by answering 6 to 8.

B   48 cm   60 cm

6. What is the ratio of the length to the width in Rectangle B? $\frac{60}{48}$

7. The sides of Rectangle B are proportional to the sides of Rectangle A if $\frac{10}{8}$ is equal to $\frac{60}{48}$. Try to multiply both terms of $\frac{10}{8}$ by the same number to get $\frac{60}{48}$.

   $\frac{10}{8} = \frac{10 \times \boxed{6}}{8 \times \boxed{6}} = \frac{\boxed{60}}{\boxed{48}}$

8. Are the sides of Rectangle A proportional to the sides of Rectangle B?   **yes**

© Pearson Education, Inc.

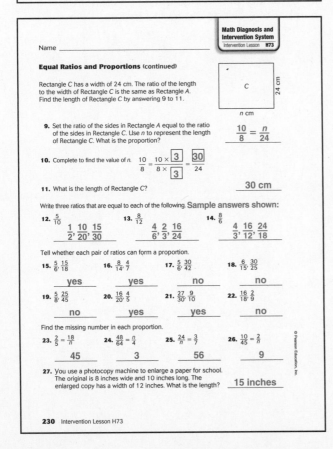

Name _____

Equal Ratios and Proportions (continued)

Rectangle C has a width of 24 cm. The ratio of the length to the width of Rectangle C is the same as Rectangle A. Find the length of Rectangle C by answering 9 to 11.

C   24 cm   n cm

9. Set the ratio of the sides in Rectangle A equal to the ratio of the sides in Rectangle C. Use n to represent the length of Rectangle C. What is the proportion? $\frac{10}{8} = \frac{n}{24}$

10. Complete to find the value of n. $\frac{10}{8} = \frac{10 \times \boxed{3}}{8 \times \boxed{3}} = \frac{\boxed{30}}{24}$

11. What is the length of Rectangle C?   **30 cm**

Write three ratios that are equal to each of the following. **Sample answers shown:**

12. $\frac{5}{10}$ $\frac{1}{2}, \frac{10}{20}, \frac{15}{30}$

13. $\frac{8}{12}$ $\frac{4}{6}, \frac{2}{3}, \frac{16}{24}$

14. $\frac{8}{6}$ $\frac{4}{3}, \frac{16}{12}, \frac{24}{18}$

Tell whether each pair of ratios can form a proportion.

15. $\frac{5}{6}, \frac{15}{18}$ **yes**

16. $\frac{8}{14}, \frac{4}{7}$ **yes**

17. $\frac{5}{6}, \frac{30}{42}$ **no**

18. $\frac{6}{15}, \frac{30}{25}$ **no**

19. $\frac{5}{8}, \frac{25}{45}$ **no**

20. $\frac{16}{20}, \frac{4}{5}$ **yes**

21. $\frac{27}{30}, \frac{9}{10}$ **yes**

22. $\frac{16}{18}, \frac{2}{9}$ **no**

Find the missing number in each proportion.

23. $\frac{2}{5} = \frac{18}{n}$ **45**

24. $\frac{48}{64} = \frac{n}{4}$ **3**

25. $\frac{24}{n} = \frac{3}{7}$ **56**

26. $\frac{10}{45} = \frac{2}{n}$ **9**

27. You use a photocopy machine to enlarge a paper for school. The original is 8 inches wide and 10 inches long. The enlarged copy has a width of 12 inches. What is the length?   **15 inches**

© Pearson Education, Inc.

Teacher Notes

Ongoing Assessment

Ask: *If two ratios are proportional, what can you say about the unit rate of each?* They will be the same.

Error Intervention

If students have trouble understanding equal ratios,

then relate equal ratios to equal fractions and use H14: Equivalent Fractions and H17: Simplest Form.

If You Have More Time

Have students look up the standard dimensions of various playing surfaces such as soccer fields, baseball fields, and basketball courts. Have students use proportions to find the dimensions of playing surfaces that are smaller but proportional to the standard fields.

Solving Proportions

Name _____

Solving Proportions

When thawing a turkey, it can take 12 hours of thawing time for every 3 pounds of turkey. How many hours should be allowed to thaw a 15 pound turkey? You can use a table or a proportion to find the answer.

1. Complete the ratio table to find the number of hours.

Hours of Thawing Time	12	24	36	48	60
Pounds of Turkey	3	6	9	12	15

2. How many hours of thawing time should be allowed for a 15 pound turkey?   **60 hours**

3. You can also use a proportion to find the number of hours. Set the ratio 12 hours to 3 pounds equal to a ratio of n hours to 15 pounds.

Write the proportion. $\dfrac{12 \text{ hours}}{3 \text{ pounds}} = \dfrac{n \text{ hours}}{15 \text{ pounds}}$

4. What is the unit rate for thawing?   **4 hours per pound**

5. Multiply 15 by the unit rate to find the number of hours.

What is 15×4?   **60**

6. How many hours of thawing time should be allowed for a 15 pound turkey?   **60 hours**

How many hours of thawing time should be allowed for a 20 pound turkey?

7. Can the answer be found in the ratio table above?   **no**

8. So, use a proportion to find the number of hours. Set the ratio 12 hours to 3 pounds equal to a ratio of n hours to 20 pounds.

Write the proportion. $\dfrac{12 \text{ hours}}{3 \text{ pounds}} = \dfrac{n \text{ hour}}{20 \text{ pounds}}$

9. What is the unit rate for thawing?   **4 hours per pound**

© Pearson Education, Inc.

Intervention Lesson H74   **231**

Name _____

Solving Proportions (continued)

10. Multiply 20 by the unit rate to find the number of hours.

What is 20×4?   **80**

11. How many hours of thawing time should be allowed for a 20 pound turkey?   **80 hours**

12. Rachel is paid $13 for 2 hours of babysitting. Complete the ratio table and use the table to answer 13 to 15.

Dollar amount	13	26	39	52	65
Hours of Babysitting	2	4	6	8	10

13. How much money does Rachel make for 4 hours of babysitting?   **$26**

14. How much money does Rachel make for 8 hours of babysitting?   **$52**

15. How long does Rachel have to baby sit to make $65?   **10 hours**

Use unit rates to solve the proportions.

16. $\dfrac{21 \text{ people}}{\text{class}} = \dfrac{x \text{ people}}{3 \text{ classes}}$ $x =$ **63**

17. $\dfrac{36 \text{ feet}}{12 \text{ sec}} = \dfrac{n \text{ feet}}{20 \text{ sec}}$ $n =$ **60**

18. $\dfrac{9 \text{ fouls}}{2 \text{ games}} = \dfrac{f \text{ fouls}}{10 \text{ games}}$ $f =$ **45**

19. $\dfrac{16 \text{ pages}}{4 \text{ hours}} = \dfrac{m \text{ pages}}{24 \text{ hours}}$ $m =$ **96**

20. $\dfrac{10 \text{ points}}{4 \text{ items}} = \dfrac{p \text{ points}}{18 \text{ items}}$ $p =$ **45**

21. $\dfrac{8 \text{ pictures}}{\text{day}} = \dfrac{a \text{ pictures}}{7 \text{ days}}$ $a =$ **56**

22. The average snow fall in a town is 22 inches per year. How much snow would be expected to fall in this town in 4 years?

88 inches

23. Reasoning Do unit rates have an advantage over ratio tables when finding an unknown in a proportion? Explain.

Yes, unit rates work for any values while ratio table only contain values that are multiples of the original ratio.

232   Intervention Lesson H74

Teacher Notes

Ongoing Assessment

Ask: **Why can you multiply 15 by 4 to solve the proportion $\dfrac{12}{3} = \dfrac{n}{15}$?** The unit rate for $\dfrac{12}{3}$ is $\dfrac{4}{1}$, so $\dfrac{12}{3}$ is equal to $\dfrac{4}{1}$. Thus, $\dfrac{4}{1} = \dfrac{n}{15}$. Because the denominator of the left side is multiplied by 15 to get the denominator of the right side, the numerator should be multiplied by 15 as well. So, n is equal to 15×4.

Error Intervention

If students have trouble finding unit rates,

then use H70: Rates and Unit Rates.

If You Have More Time

Have students find recipes in a cookbook and use proportions to find the amount of each ingredient for a number of servings that is different from the number of servings the recipe makes.

© Pearson Education, Inc.

Solving Proportions Using Cross Products

Name _____

Solving Proportions Using Cross Products

The Cougars scored 5 touchdowns during the first 4 football games of the season. At this rate, how many touchdowns should the team score in a 10-game season?

Write a proportion and solve to find the number of touchdowns, by answering 1 to 5.

1. Write a proportion.

Touchdowns scored → $\boxed{5}$ = $\dfrac{n}{}$ ← Touchdowns for season
Number of games → $\boxed{4}$ $\boxed{10}$ ← Games in season

2. Find the cross products.

$\dfrac{5}{4} \diagdown \dfrac{n}{10}$ $4 \times n = \dfrac{4n}{}$
$5 \times 10 = \dfrac{50}{}$

3. Set the cross products equal. $4n = \underline{50}$

4. Solve $4n = 50$.

$n = \underline{12.5 \text{ or } 12\frac{1}{2}}$

5. How many touchdowns should the Cougars score in a 10-game season? $\underline{12 \text{ or } 13}$ touchdowns

The Rodriguez family is taking a 385 mile trip. After 3 hours they traveled a distance of 165 miles. How many total hours will they need to travel to complete their trip? Find out by answering 6 to 11.

6. Write a proportion. Use h to represent the hours needed to complete the trip.

Distance traveled → $\boxed{165}$ = $\boxed{385}$ ← Total Distance
Hours traveled → $\boxed{3}$ h ← Total hours

7. What is one cross product? $\underline{165 \times h}$

8. What is the other cross product? $\underline{3 \times 385}$

Intervention Lesson H75   **233**

Name _____

Solving Proportions Using Cross Products (continued)

9. Write an equation using the cross products. $\underline{165h = 1{,}155}$

10. Solve $165h = 1{,}155$.

$h = \underline{7}$

11. How long will it take to complete the trip? $\underline{7 \text{ hours}}$

Write the cross products for each proportion.

12. $\dfrac{5}{10} = \dfrac{12}{n}$ **13.** $\dfrac{1}{12} = \dfrac{n}{9}$ **14.** $\dfrac{n}{15} = \dfrac{10}{6}$
$\underline{10n = 60}$ $\underline{12n = 9}$ $\underline{6n = 150}$

Find the missing number in each proportion.

15. $\dfrac{6}{8} = \dfrac{n}{20}$ **16.** $\dfrac{n}{5} = \dfrac{27}{45}$ **17.** $\dfrac{9}{8} = \dfrac{81}{n}$ **18.** $\dfrac{5}{n} = \dfrac{10}{12}$
$\underline{15}$ $\underline{3}$ $\underline{72}$ $\underline{6}$

19. $\dfrac{6}{7} = \dfrac{n}{56}$ **20.** $\dfrac{n}{12} = \dfrac{3}{36}$ **21.** $\dfrac{66}{n} = \dfrac{11}{12}$ **22.** $\dfrac{1.5}{6} = \dfrac{10}{n}$
$\underline{48}$ $\underline{1}$ $\underline{72}$ $\underline{40}$

23. $\dfrac{n}{5} = \dfrac{11}{2.2}$ **24.** $\dfrac{20}{18} = \dfrac{30}{n}$ **25.** $\dfrac{3}{2} = \dfrac{n}{6}$ **26.** $\dfrac{25}{n} = \dfrac{15}{12}$
$\underline{25}$ $\underline{27}$ $\underline{9}$ $\underline{20}$

27. Five bags of rice weigh 70 ounces. How much do four bags of rice weigh? $\underline{56 \text{ ounces}}$

28. If 15 pieces of gum cost \$0.90, how much do 12 pieces of gum cost? $\underline{\$0.72}$

29. A babysitter earns \$51 for working 8.5 hours. How much does the sitter earn for working 40 hours? $\underline{\$240}$

30. Reasoning When solving a proportion involving the lengths and widths of two rectangles, does it matter whether you put length or width in the top of the ratio?

$\underline{\text{No, as long as you put them in the same order}}$
$\underline{\text{in both ratios.}}$

234   Intervention Lesson H75

© Pearson Education, Inc.

Teacher Notes

Ongoing Assessment

Ask: **Does it matter which cross product you find first?** No, either cross product can go on the left side of the equation. Since they are equal, order does not matter.

Error Intervention

If students have trouble solving one step equations with multiplication,

then use F48: Solving Multiplication and Division Equations.

If You Have More Time

Have student work in pairs. Students should choose three numbers and write each on an index card. The numbers are then placed so that they form a proportion with a fourth blank index card, acting as an unknown. Students should then manipulate the cards to show the cross products. The resulting equation can then be solved to find a solution.

Similar Figures and Proportions

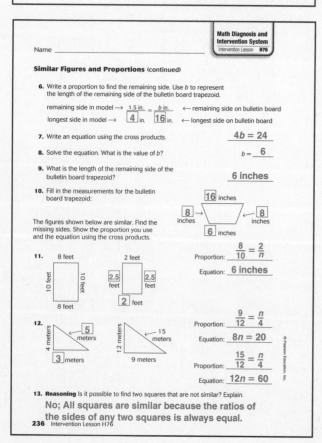

Name _____

Math Diagnosis and
Intervention System
Intervention Lesson H76

Similar Figures and Proportions

Similar figures have the same shape, but not necessarily the same size.
The lengths of the sides of similar figures are proportional.

In the trapezoids below, $\frac{12}{15} = \frac{24}{30}$.

1. Complete the proportion for the trapezoids above.

$$\frac{10}{12} = \frac{\boxed{20}}{24}$$

Mrs. King enlarged the trapezoid shown below for a bulletin board
display so the longest side is 16 inches. The enlarged shape is similar
to the shape shown. Find the lengths of the remaining sides of the
bulletin board trapezoid by answering 2 to 10.

2. Write a proportion to find the legs of the trapezoid. Use n to
represent the length of the legs of the trapezoid on the bulletin board.

legs in model → $\quad \frac{2 \text{ in.}}{\boxed{4} \text{ in.}} = \frac{n \text{ in.}}{\boxed{16} \text{ in.}}$ ← legs on bulletin board

longest side in model → $\qquad\qquad\qquad$ ← longest side on bulletin board

3. Write an equation using the cross products. $\qquad 4n = 32$

4. Solve $4n = 32$. What is the value of n? $\qquad n = \underline{8}$

5. What is the length of the legs of the bulletin board trapezoid? $\quad \underline{8 \text{ inches}}$

© Pearson Education, Inc.

Intervention Lesson H76   **235**

Name _____

Math Diagnosis and
Intervention System
Intervention Lesson H76

Similar Figures and Proportions (continued)

6. Write a proportion to find the remaining side. Use b to represent
the length of the remaining side of the bulletin board trapezoid.

remaining side in model → $\quad \frac{1.5 \text{ in.}}{\boxed{4} \text{ in.}} = \frac{b \text{ in.}}{\boxed{16} \text{ in.}}$ ← remaining side on bulletin board

longest side in model → $\qquad\qquad\qquad$ ← longest side on bulletin board

7. Write an equation using the cross products. $\qquad 4b = 24$

8. Solve the equation. What is the value of b? $\qquad b = \underline{6}$

9. What is the length of the remaining side of the
bulletin board trapezoid? $\qquad \underline{6 \text{ inches}}$

10. Fill in the measurements for the bulletin
board trapezoid:

The figures shown below are similar. Find the
missing sides. Show the proportion you use
and the equation using the cross products.

11. 8 feet 2 feet

Proportion: $\frac{8}{10} = \frac{2}{n}$

Equation: 6 inches

12.

Proportion: $\frac{9}{12} = \frac{n}{4}$

Equation: $8n = 20$

Proportion: $\frac{15}{12} = \frac{n}{4}$

Equation: $12n = 60$

13. Reasoning Is it possible to find two squares that are not similar? Explain.

No; All squares are similar because the ratios of
the sides of any two squares is always equal.

© Pearson Education, Inc.

236 Intervention Lesson H76

Teacher Notes

Ongoing Assessment

Ask: *Why is it not necessary to use two
proportions to find the length of each leg of the
trapezoid individually?* Since the lengths of the
legs in the trapezoid are equal in the model, they
will be equal in the trapezoid that is similar.

Error Intervention

If students have difficulty understanding the
concept of similar figures,

then use an overhead projector or a copy
machine to show students enlarged pictures. Take
measurements of each object and use proportions
to show they are similar.

If You Have More Time

Have students cut out a triangle or quadrilateral
from construction paper with whole number sides.
Then have them cut out a shape that is similar.

© Pearson Education, Inc.

Math Diagnosis and
Intervention System
Intervention Lesson   **H76**

Maps and Scale Drawings

Name _____

Maps and Scale Drawings

Materials centimeter ruler

In a scale drawing, the dimensions of an object are reduced or enlarged by the same scale. The dimensions of the scale drawing and the original figure are proportional and therefore, similar. A map is typically a scale drawing.

1. What is the relationship between a scale drawing and the original figure?

   They are similar or proportional.

   The scale drawing or map of the island shown has a scale of $\frac{1 \text{ centimeter}}{300 \text{ meters}}$. Answer 2 to 9 to find the actual length of the island.

   X [island drawing] ? centimeters

2. What distance on the map represents 300 meters?

   1 centimeter

3. Use a centimeter ruler to measure the length of the island.

   What is the length of the island in the drawing?

   5 centimeters

4. Write a proportion that can be used to find the actual length of the island. Let x equal the actual length.

   $\frac{1 \text{ cm}}{300 \text{ m}} = \frac{\boxed{5}}{x} \text{ cm}$ ← length in drawing
   ← actual length

5. What is one cross product in the proportion?

   $1 \times x$

6. What is the other cross product?

   5×300

7. Write an equation using the cross products.

   $1x = 1,500$

8. Solve the equation. What is the value of x?

   $1,500$

9. What is the actual length of the island?

   1,500 meters

Intervention Lesson H77 **237**

Name _____

Maps and Scale Drawings (continued)

A buried treasure is located 900 meters from the tree on the island. Answer 10 to 14 to find the scale distance between the tree and the treasure.

10. Write a proportion that can be used to find the scale distance between the tree and the treasure. Let d equal the scale distance.

    $\frac{1 \text{ cm}}{300 \text{ m}} = \frac{d}{900 \text{ m}}$

11. Write an equation using the cross products.

    $300d = 900$

12. Solve the equation. What is the value of d?

    3

13. What is the scale distance between the tree and the treasure?

    3 centimeters

14. Place an X on the drawing that could represent the location of the treasure.

If the scale is $\frac{1 \text{ inch}}{12 \text{ feet}}$, what is the actual length for each scale length?

15. $4\frac{1}{2}$ inches   16. 5 inches   17. 3 inches
    54 feet   **60 feet**   **36 feet**

If the scale is $\frac{1 \text{ inch}}{30 \text{ feet}}$, what is the scale length for each actual length?

18. 60 feet   19. 150 feet   20. 75 feet
    2 inches   **5 inches**   **2.5 inches**

21. A scale drawing of a house shows a scale of $\frac{1 \text{ inch}}{3 \text{ feet}}$.

    The drawing shows a room which is 5 inches long. How long is the actual room?

    15 feet

22. A treasure map shows a scale of $\frac{1 \text{ inch}}{40 \text{ feet}}$.

    If the map shows the treasure to be located 2 inches from a large rock, how many feet in actual distance is the treasure from the rock?

    80 feet

23. **Reasoning** How is a scale similar to a rate?

    Both are ratios that compare unlike quanities.

238 Intervention Lesson H77

Teacher Notes

Ongoing Assessment

Ask: *Is there only one way to write a proportion like $\frac{1 \text{ cm}}{300 \text{ m}} = \frac{5 \text{ cm}}{x \text{ m}}$?* No, the order of the terms can be changed as long as the two ratios are consistent in the order of the terms. Another way to write the proportions is actual length over length in the drawing: $\frac{300 \text{ m}}{1 \text{ cm}} = \frac{x \text{ m}}{5 \text{ cm}}$. Ask students if there is another way. $\frac{1 \text{ cm}}{5 \text{ cm}} = \frac{300 \text{ m}}{x \text{ m}}$

Error Intervention

If students have trouble understanding and solving proportions,

then use H73: Equal Ratios and Proportions, H74: Solving Proportions, and H75: Solving Proportions Using Cross Products.

If You Have More Time

Have students make a scale drawing of the classroom or the top of their desk, including a pencil and a book placed on top.

© Pearson Education, Inc.

Understanding Percent

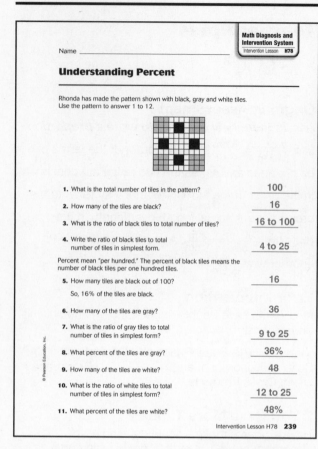

Name _____

Math Diagnosis and
Intervention System
Intervention Lesson **H78**

Understanding Percent

Rhonda has made the pattern shown with black, gray and white tiles.
Use the pattern to answer 1 to 12.

1. What is the total number of tiles in the pattern? — **100**

2. How many of the tiles are black? — **16**

3. What is the ratio of black tiles to total number of tiles? — **16 to 100**

4. Write the ratio of black tiles to total number of tiles in simplest form. — **4 to 25**

Percent mean "per hundred." The percent of black tiles means the number of black tiles per one hundred tiles.

5. How many tiles are black out of 100? — **16**

   So, 16% of the tiles are black.

6. How many of the tiles are gray? — **36**

7. What is the ratio of gray tiles to total number of tiles in simplest form? — **9 to 25**

8. What percent of the tiles are gray? — **36%**

9. How many of the tiles are white? — **48**

10. What is the ratio of white tiles to total number of tiles in simplest form? — **12 to 25**

11. What percent of the tiles are white? — **48%**

Intervention Lesson H78   **239**

Math Diagnosis and
Intervention System
Intervention Lesson **H78**

Name _____

Understanding Percent (continued)

12. **Reasoning** What percent of the tiles are either black, gray or white?

    Because all of the tiles are black, gray or white, the ratio is 100 out of 100. Therefore 100% are either black, gray or white.

Write each ratio as a percent.

13. $\frac{13}{100}$ — **13%**

14. 87 out of 100 — **87%**

15. $\frac{29}{100}$ — **29%**

Tell what percent of each grid is shaded. Then write the ratio in simplest form.

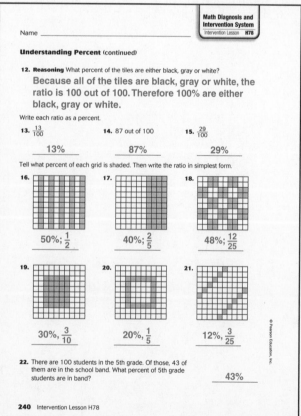

16. **50%; $\frac{1}{2}$**

17. **40%; $\frac{2}{5}$**

18. **48%; $\frac{12}{25}$**

19. **30%, $\frac{3}{10}$**

20. **20%, $\frac{1}{5}$**

21. **12%, $\frac{3}{25}$**

22. There are 100 students in the 5th grade. Of those, 43 of them are in the school band. What percent of 5th grade students are in band? — **43%**

Teacher Notes

Ongoing Assessment

Ask: *Is the pattern of the shaded tiles important when finding a percent?* No, just the number of shaded tiles is important, not the pattern.

Error Intervention

If students have trouble understanding percents,

then show students different ways to represent the same percent. For example, show a hundreds grid with 10 tiles shaded in a row, another grid with 5 tiles shaded in each of two rows and another grid with 10 tiles shaded on a diagonal. Also use grids that are different sizes and explain to students that all of them represent 10%.

If You Have More Time

Have students bring one hundred items to school and find the percent of those items that are different in a particular way. For example, if they bring 100 pennies, they might find the percent that are from a particular year.

© Pearson Education, Inc.

Relating Percents, Decimals, and Fractions

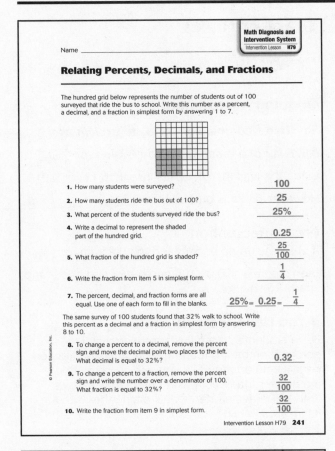

Name _____

Math Diagnosis and Intervention System
Intervention Lesson **H79**

Relating Percents, Decimals, and Fractions

The hundred grid below represents the number of students out of 100 surveyed that ride the bus to school. Write this number as a percent, a decimal, and a fraction in simplest form by answering 1 to 7.

1. How many students were surveyed? — **100**

2. How many students ride the bus out of 100? — **25**

3. What percent of the students surveyed ride the bus? — **25%**

4. Write a decimal to represent the shaded part of the hundred grid. — **0.25**

5. What fraction of the hundred grid is shaded? — $\frac{25}{100}$

6. Write the fraction from item 5 in simplest form. — $\frac{1}{4}$

7. The percent, decimal, and fraction forms are all equal. Use one of each form to fill in the blanks. — $25\% = 0.25 = \frac{1}{4}$

The same survey of 100 students found that 32% walk to school. Write this percent as a decimal and a fraction in simplest form by answering 8 to 10.

8. To change a percent to a decimal, remove the percent sign and move the decimal point two places to the left. What decimal is equal to 32%? — **0.32**

9. To change a percent to a fraction, remove the percent sign and write the number over a denominator of 100. What fraction is equal to 32%? — $\frac{32}{100}$

10. Write the fraction from item 9 in simplest form. — $\frac{32}{100}$

© Pearson Education, Inc.

Intervention Lesson H79 **241**

Teacher Notes

Ongoing Assessment

Ask: **When converting a percent to a fraction, why is it possible to simply place the number over a denominator of 100?** Because a percent is always representing the portion out of 100.

Error Intervention

If students have trouble converting between fractions and decimals,

then use H31: Decimals to Fractions and H32: Fractions to Decimals.

If You Have More Time

Have students find examples of percents used in current events and express these percents as fractions and decimals.

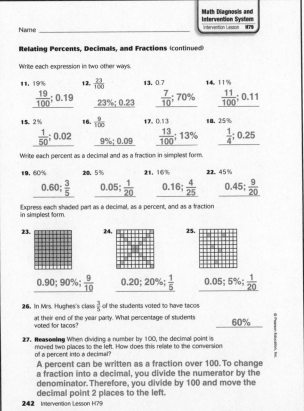

Name _____

Math Diagnosis and Intervention System
Intervention Lesson **H79**

Relating Percents, Decimals, and Fractions (continued)

Write each expression in two other ways.

11. 19% — $\frac{19}{100}$; 0.19

12. $\frac{23}{100}$ — 23%; 0.23

13. 0.7 — $\frac{7}{10}$; 70%

14. 11% — $\frac{11}{100}$; 0.11

15. 2% — $\frac{1}{50}$; 0.02

16. $\frac{9}{100}$ — 9%; 0.09

17. 0.13 — $\frac{13}{100}$; 13%

18. 25% — $\frac{1}{4}$; 0.25

Write each percent as a decimal and as a fraction in simplest form.

19. 60% — 0.60; $\frac{3}{5}$

20. 5% — 0.05; $\frac{1}{20}$

21. 16% — 0.16; $\frac{4}{25}$

22. 45% — 0.45; $\frac{9}{20}$

Express each shaded part as a decimal, as a percent, and as a fraction in simplest form.

23. 0.90; 90%; $\frac{9}{10}$

24. 0.20; 20%; $\frac{1}{5}$

25. 0.05; 5%; $\frac{1}{20}$

26. In Mrs. Hughes's class $\frac{3}{5}$ of the students voted to have tacos at their end of the year party. What percentage of students voted for tacos? — **60%**

27. **Reasoning** When dividing a number by 100, the decimal point is moved two places to the left. How does this relate to the conversion of a percent into a decimal?

A percent can be written as a fraction over 100. To change a fraction into a decimal, you divide the numerator by the denominator. Therefore, you divide by 100 and move the decimal point 2 places to the left.

© Pearson Education, Inc.

242 Intervention Lesson H79

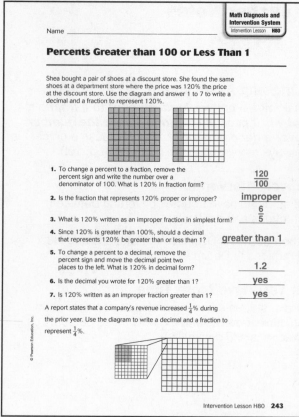

1. To change a percent to a fraction, remove the percent sign and write the number over a denominator of 100. What is 120% in fraction form? — $\frac{120}{100}$

2. Is the fraction that represents 120% proper or improper? — improper

3. What is 120% written as an improper fraction in simplest form? — $\frac{6}{5}$

4. Since 120% is greater than 100%, should a decimal that represents 120% be greater than or less than 1? — greater than 1

5. To change a percent to a decimal, remove the percent sign and move the decimal point two places to the left. What is 120% in decimal form? — 1.2

6. Is the decimal you wrote for 120% greater than 1? — yes

7. Is 120% written as an improper fraction greater than 1? — yes

A report states that a company's revenue increased $\frac{1}{4}$% during the prior year. Use the diagram to write a decimal and a fraction to represent $\frac{1}{4}$%.

Intervention Lesson H80 **243**

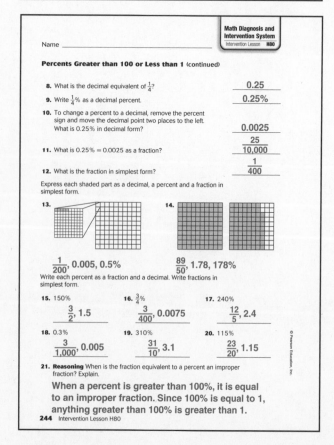

Percents Greater than 100 or Less than 1 (continued)

8. What is the decimal equivalent of $\frac{1}{4}$? — 0.25

9. Write $\frac{1}{4}$% as a decimal percent. — 0.25%

10. To change a percent to a decimal, remove the percent sign and move the decimal point two places to the left. What is 0.25% in decimal form? — 0.0025

11. What is 0.25% = 0.0025 as a fraction? — $\frac{25}{10,000}$

12. What is the fraction in simplest form? — $\frac{1}{400}$

Express each shaded part as a decimal, a percent and a fraction in simplest form.

13.

$\frac{1}{200}$, 0.005, 0.5%

14.

$\frac{89}{50}$, 1.78, 178%

Write each percent as a fraction and a decimal. Write fractions in simplest form.

15. 150%

$\frac{3}{2}$, 1.5

16. $\frac{3}{4}$%

$\frac{3}{400}$, 0.0075

17. 240%

$\frac{12}{5}$, 2.4

18. 0.3%

$\frac{3}{1,000}$, 0.005

19. 310%

$\frac{31}{10}$, 3.1

20. 115%

$\frac{23}{20}$, 1.15

21. Reasoning When is the fraction equivalent to a percent an improper fraction? Explain.

When a percent is greater than 100%, it is equal to an improper fraction. Since 100% is equal to 1, anything greater than 100% is greater than 1.

244 Intervention Lesson H80

Teacher Notes

Ongoing Assessment

Say: *Use a comparison to 1% to explain why 0.075 is not a reasonable conversion for $\frac{3}{4}$%.*

Since $\frac{3}{4}$ is less than 1, $\frac{3}{4}$% is less than 1% or 0.01. However, 0.075 is greater than 0.01

Error Intervention

If students do no understand the diagram for $\frac{1}{4}$%,

then create a 100 by 100 grid out of grid paper and shade 25 squares.

If You Have More Time

Have students create flash cards that include percents on the front and the decimal and fraction equivalents on the back. Include percents that are greater than 100% and others that are less than 1%. Have students quiz each other with the flashcards.

© Pearson Education, Inc.

Estimating Percent of a Number

Name _____

Estimating Percent of a Number

Benchmark percents can be used to estimate the percent of a number.

1. Fill in the table of benchmark percents and simplified fraction equivalents.

Percent	10%	25%	$33\frac{1}{3}$%	50%	$66\frac{2}{3}$%	75%
Fraction	$\frac{1}{10}$	$\frac{1}{4}$	$\frac{1}{3}$	$\frac{1}{2}$	$\frac{2}{3}$	$\frac{3}{4}$

The circle graph shows the types of tickets sold at a museum during a week. A total of 212 tickets sold during that week.

Estimate the number of adult tickets sold by answering 2 to 6.

Museum Tickets Sold

Child 31%   Adult 48%   Senior 21%

2. According to the graph, what percent represents adult tickets?   **48%**

3. What benchmark percent is closest to 48%?   **50%**

4. What fraction is equal to 50%?   **$\frac{1}{2}$**

5. What is $\frac{1}{2} \times 212$?   **106**

6. About how many adult tickets were sold?   **106 tickets**

Estimate the number of child tickets by answering 7 to 12.

7. According to the graph, what percent represents child tickets?   **31%**

8. What benchmark percent is the closest to 31%?   **$33\frac{1}{3}$**

9. What fraction is equal to $33\frac{1}{3}$%?   **$\frac{1}{3}$**

10. What is 212 rounded to the nearest compatible number, that is, to the nearest number that is easy to divide by 3?   **210**

11. What is $\frac{1}{3} \times 210$?   **70**

12. About how many child tickets were sold?   **70 tickets**

Intervention Lesson H81   **245**

Name _____

Estimating Percent of a Number (continued)

Estimate the number of senior tickets sold by answering 13 to 18.

13. According to the graph, what percent represents senior tickets?   **21%**

14. What benchmark percent is the closest to 21%?   **25%**

15. What fraction is equal to 25%?   **$\frac{1}{4}$**

16. What is 212 rounded to the nearest hundred?   **200**

17. What is $\frac{1}{4} \times 200$?   **50**

18. About how many senior tickets were sold?   **50 tickets**

Estimate.

19. 13% of 34   **3**

20. 37% of 58   **20**

21. 68% of $32   **$20**

22. 72% of $18.03   **15**

23. 31% of 94   **30**

24. 27% of 59   **15**

25. 51% of 795   **400**

26. 48% of 8   **4**

27. 12% of 230   **23**

Use this information for Exercise 28 and 29.

A store is offering a discount of 22% on all its items for customers who own a special discount card.

28. Jackson uses his discount card to buy a sweater that originally cost $29. Estimate his discount.   **$7**

29. Patricia uses her discount card to buy a pair of shoes that cost $52 and a pair of jeans that cost $39. Estimate her discount on the jeans.   **$10**

30. Reasoning Does an estimate 29% of 43 as $\frac{1}{4}$ of 40 give an overestimate or an underestimate? Explain.

An underestimate, since both 29% and 43 were rounded down.

246   Intervention Lesson H81

© Pearson Education, Inc.

Teacher Notes

Ongoing Assessment

Ask: *What numbers can you multiply to estimate 30% of 15?* Sample answers: $\frac{1}{3} \times 120$, $\frac{1}{4} \times 120$, $\frac{1}{4} \times 100$

Error Intervention

If students have trouble multiplying a fraction and a whole number,

then use H45: Multiplying Fractions by Whole Numbers.

If You Have More Time

Take a survey of the class. For example, ask students how many pets each has. Collect the data and analyze it yourself. Put the data into 3 or 4 categories. Give students the percentage breakdowns of each category and the total number of students who answered the survey. Have students estimate how many students gave each response.

Finding the Percent of a Whole Number

Name _____

Math Diagnosis and
Intervention System
Intervention Lesson   H82

Finding the Percent of a Whole Number

Of the students in the fifth grade, 65% signed up to participate in the
band. If there are 120 students in the fifth grade, find the number that
signed up to participate by answering 1 to 4.

1. What is 65% written in decimal form?   0.65

2. To find 65% of 120, multiply the decimal form by 120.
Write an expression that can be used to find 65% of 120. 0.65×120

3. What is 0.65×120?   78

4. How many students signed up to participate in band?   78 students

Of the 78 students who signed up to participate in band, about 15%
chose to play the clarinet. Find the number of students that chose to
play the clarinet by answering 5 to 9.

5. What is 15% written in decimal form?   0.15

6. To find 15% of 78, multiply the decimal form by 78.
Write an expression that can be used to find 15% of 78. 0.15×78

7. What is 0.15×78?   11.7

8. Because 15% of 78 is a number of students,
the final answer should be a whole number.
What is 11.7 rounded to the nearest whole number?   12

9. How many students chose to play the clarinet?   12 students

Of the 12 clarinet players, 25% are girls. Find the number of
girls that play the clarinet by answering 10 to 12.

10. To find 25% of 12, multiply the decimal form by 12.
Write an expression that can be used to find 25% of 12. 0.25×12

11. What is 0.25×12?   3

12. How many clarinet players are girls?   3 girls

Intervention Lesson H82   **247**

Teacher Notes

Ongoing Assessment

Ask: *How can you use benchmark fractions to find 60% of a number?* You can find 50% or $\frac{1}{2}$ of the number and 10% or $\frac{1}{10}$ of the number and then add the two amounts together to find 60% of the number.

Error Intervention

If students have trouble multiplying a decimal and a whole number,

then use H58: Multiplying with Decimals and Whole Numbers and H60: Multiplying Decimals by Whole Numbers.

If You Have More Time

Give students the breakdown for the percentage of students in each grade in the school and the total number of students in the school. Have them find the number of students in each grade.

Name _____

Math Diagnosis and
Intervention System
Intervention Lesson   H82

Finding the Percent of a Whole Number (continued)

Find each amount.

13. 40% of 15	**14.** 5% of 60	**15.** 67% of 20
6	3	13.4
16. 76% of 80	**17.** 30% of 400	**18.** 53% of 120
60.8	120	63.6
19. 80% of 45	**20.** 30% of 79	**21.** 2% of 50
36	23.7	1
22. 75% of 150	**23.** 10% of 6	**24.** 19% of 40
112.5	0.6	7.6
25. 5% of 99	**26.** 25% of 260	**27.** 48% of 65
4.95	65	31.2
28. 71% of 90	**29.** 49% of 200	**30.** 55% of 24
63.9	98	13.2
31. 80% of 50	**32.** 30% of 400	**33.** 18% of 75
40	120	13.5

34. A store offers a 25% discount on all purchases. If you buy
an item costing $30, how much is the discount? $7.50

35. Reasoning Since 10% of $45 is $4.50, how can you use the result to
find 20% of $45?

Since 20% is twice 10%, double $4.50. So 20% of
$45 is $9.00.

248   Intervention Lesson H82

© Pearson Education, Inc.

Tips and Sales Tax

Name _____

Tips and Sales Tax

Ivan was charged $27 for a haircut. The sales tax is 7.5% and Ivan tipped 15% on the amount after tax. What is the total amount Ivan paid for his haircut?

Find the cost with sales tax by answering 1 to 5.

1. What is 7.5% written in decimal form? **0.075**

2. To find 7.5% of $27, multiply the decimal form by 27. Write an expression that can be used to find 7.5% of 27. **0.075 × 27**

3. What is 0.075 × 27? **2.025**

4. Sales tax is always rounded up to the nearest cent. What is the amount of sales tax? $ **2.03**

5. What is the cost of the haircut with tax? $ **29.03**

Find the amount of the tip by answering 6 to 10.

6. What is 15% written in decimal form? **0.15**

7. To find 15% of $29.03, multiply the decimal form by 29.03. Write an expression that can be used to find 15% of 29.03. **0.15 × 29.03**

8. What is 0.15 × 29.03? **4.3545**

9. What is the tip amount rounded to the nearest dollar? $ **4**

10. What is the cost of the haircut with tax and a 15% tip? $ **33.03**

11. If Ivan decided to tip 20% rather than 15%, what would be the total cost of his haircut? $ **35.03**

12. **Reasoning** Will the tip amount be more or less if it is figured on the amount before tax rather than the amount after tax? Explain.

The tip will be less if it is figured on the amount before tax because it involves a percent of a smaller number.

© Pearson Education, Inc.

Name _____

Tips and Sales Tax (continued)

Find the sales tax and the total cost. Round the sales tax to the nearest cent.

13. cost: $65
rate of sales tax: 6%
$3.90; $68.90

14. cost: $18
rate of sales tax: 7%
$1.26; $19.26

15. cost: $24.50
rate of sales tax: 8%
$1.96; $26.46

16. cost: $10.85
rate of sales tax: 4.5%
$0.49; $11.34

Find the amount of tip and the total cost. Round the tip amount to the nearest dollar.

17. cost: $15.75
rate of tip: 15%
$2; $17.75

18. cost: $72
rate of tip: 10%
$7; $79

19. cost: $41.80
rate of tip: 20%
$8; $49.80

20. cost: $6.25
rate of tip: 10%
$1; $7.25

21. In one city, the sales is 8%. If you buy an item costing $40, how much sales tax would you pay? **$3.20**

22. A restaurant requires diners to leave a 15% tip for the waiters. If the cost of the meal is $35, how much should the tip be? **$5.25**

Use the following information for Exercises 23 to 25.

Jose and George spend $18.50 at a restaurant for two meals. The sales tax rate is 5%. They want to leave a 15% tip, to the nearest dollar.

23. What is the cost of the meal with tax? **$19.43**

24. How much tip should they leave? **$3.00**

25. What is the total cost with sales tax and tip? **$22.43**

© Pearson Education, Inc.

Teacher Notes

Ongoing Assessment

Ask: *Why is the amount of tax rounded to two decimal places?* Because the smallest amount in the U.S. money system is a penny; represented by the hundredths place or two decimal places.

Error Intervention

If students have trouble adding money,

then use G14: Adding and Subtracting Money.

If students have trouble multiplying decimals by decimals,

then use H62: Multiplying Decimals by Decimals.

If You Have More Time

Have students use a menu from a local restaurant or have them create their own menu. Students can take turns playing the waiter and the customer. The waiter can take an order from the customer and find the amount of the order including tax. The customer can decide an appropriate tip to leave based on the amount of the bill.

Computing Discounts

Name _____

Math Diagnosis and
Intervention System
Intervention Lesson **H84**

Computing Discounts

A clothing store has all its merchandise on sale at a 15% discount. If Pilar chooses a shirt that regularly costs $18.50, how much is the sale price?

Find the discount and sale price by answering 1 to 5.

1. What is 15% written in decimal form? 0.15

2. To find 15% of $18.50, multiply the decimal form by 18.5. Write an expression that can be used to find 15% of 18.5. 0.15×18.5

3. What is 0.15×18.5? 2.775

4. Round the discount to the nearest cent. What is the amount of discount? $ 2.78

5. Sale price = Regular price − Discount What is the sale price? $ 15.72

Teachers get a 30% discount on books at a local book store. A teacher buys a book regularly priced at $24.49. What is the teacher's price?

Find the teacher's price by answering 6 to 12.

6. What is 30% written in decimal form? 0.3

7. To find 30% of $24.49, multiply the decimal form by 24.49. Write an expression that can be used to find 30% of 24.49. 0.3×24.49

8. What is 0.3×24.49? 7.347

9. Round the discount to the nearest cent. What is the amount of discount? $ 7.35

10. Sale price = Regular price − Discount What is the sale price? $ 17.14

11. The teacher pays 100% − 30% = 70%. Find 70% of $24.49, rounded to the nearest cent. $ 17.14

12. Reasoning Is 70% of $24.49 to the nearest cent the same as the sale price you found by subtracting the discount? yes

---

Name _____

Math Diagnosis and
Intervention System
Intervention Lesson **H84**

Computing Discounts (continued)

Find the discount and the sale price.

13. regular price: $35
rate of discount: 10%

$3.50; $31.50

14. regular price: $24.50
rate of discount: 15%

$3.68; $20.82

15. regular price: $72
rate of discount: 25%

$18; $54

16. regular price: $60
rate of discount: 30%

$18; $42

17. regular price: $90
rate of discount: 40%

$36; $54

18. regular price: $46.80
rate of discount: 50%

$23.40; $23.40

19. William bought two CDs on sale at a 15% discount. One CD cost $15.99 and the other CD cost $14.99. How much did he pay for both CDs after the discount? $26.33

Use the following for Exercises 20–23.

Mary bought a new television for $250. The television was on sale at a 10% discount. The sales tax rate was 6%.

20. What was the discount? $25

21. What was the sale price? $225

22. What is the amount of tax? $13.50

23. What is the total cost of the television? $238.50

24. Reasoning If an item has a discount of 20%, what percent of the original price will the customer pay? How can this be used to find the discounted price?

The customer will pay 80% of the original price. Eighty percent of the original price will equal the discounted price.

Teacher Notes

Ongoing Assessment

Ask: *Why is the discounted price subtracted from the regular price rather than added as it is on taxes and tips?* Because a discount will always make the sale price less whereas taxes and tips are additional costs that have to be paid.

Error Intervention

If students have trouble multiplying decimals by decimals,

then use H62: Multiplying Decimals by Decimals.

If students have trouble finding the amount of discount,

then use H82: Finding the Percent of a Whole Number.

If You Have More Time

Have students look in the newspaper for sale advertisements. Have them figure the price of an item using the discount in the advertisement.

© Pearson Education, Inc.

Equal Parts of a Whole

Materials rectangular sheets of paper, 3 for each student;
crayons or markers

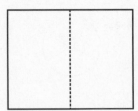

fold →

1. Fold a sheet of paper so the two shorter edges
   are on top of each other, as shown at the right.

2. Open up the piece of paper. Draw a line down the fold.
   Color each part a different color.

The table below shows special names
for the equal parts. All parts must be **equal**
before you can use these special names.

3. Are the parts you colored equal in size? _____

4. How many equal parts are there? _____

5. What is the name for the parts you colored?

   _____

Number of Equal Parts	Name of Equal Parts
2	halves
3	thirds
4	fourths
5	fifths
6	sixths
8	eighths
10	tenths
12	twelfths

6. Fold another sheet of paper like above.
   Then fold it again so that it makes a long
   slender rectangle as shown below.

7. Open up the piece of paper. Draw lines down
   the folds. Color each part a different color.

8. Are the parts you colored equal in size? _____

9. How many equal parts are there? _____

10. What is the name for the parts you colored?

    _____

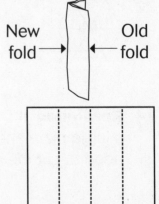

New fold → ← Old fold

11. Fold another sheet of paper into 3 parts that are
    not equal. Open it and draw lines down the folds.
    In the space below, draw your rectangle and color
    each part a different color.

© Pearson Education, Inc.

Equal Parts of a Whole (continued)

Tell if each shows parts that are equal or parts that are not equal.
If the parts are equal, name them.

12.   _____

13.   _____

14.   _____

15.   _____

16.  _____

17.   _____

18. 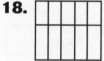 _____

19.   _____

20.   _____

21.   _____

22.   _____

23.   _____

24. Reasoning If 5 children want to equally share
a large pizza and each gets 2 pieces, will they
need to cut the pizza into fifths, eighths, or tenths? _____

© Pearson Education, Inc.

Parts of a Region

Materials crayons or markers

1. In the circle at the right, color 2 of the equal parts blue and 4 of the equal parts red.

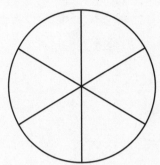

Write fractions to name the parts by answering 2 to 6.

2. How many total equal parts does the circle have? _____

3. How many of the equal parts of the circle are blue? _____

4. What fraction of the circle is blue?

$$\frac{\boxed{}}{\boxed{}} = \frac{\text{number of equal parts that are blue}}{\text{total number of equal parts}} = \frac{\text{(numerator)}}{\text{(denominator)}}$$

Two sixths of the circle is blue.

5. How many of the equal parts of the circle are red? _____

6. What fraction of the circle is red?

$$\frac{\boxed{}}{\boxed{}} = \frac{\text{number of equal parts that are red}}{\text{total number of equal parts}} = \frac{\text{(numerator)}}{\text{(denominator)}}$$

Four sixths of the circle is red.

Show the fraction $\frac{3}{8}$ by answering 7 to 9.

7. Color $\frac{3}{8}$ of the rectangle at the right.

8. How many equal parts does the rectangle have? _____

9. How many parts did you color? _____

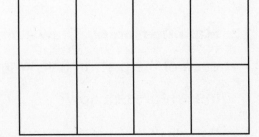

© Pearson Education, Inc.

Parts of a Region (continued)

Write the fraction for the shaded part of each region.

10.

_____

11.

_____

12.

_____

13.

_____

14.

_____

15.

_____

16.

_____

17.

_____

18.

_____

Color to show each fraction.

19. $\frac{3}{4}$

20. $\frac{5}{6}$

21. $\frac{7}{10}$

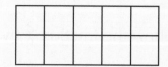

22. Math Reasoning Draw a picture to show $\frac{1}{3}$. Then divide each of the parts in half. What fraction of the parts does the $\frac{1}{3}$ represent now?

_____

23. Ben divided a pie into 8 equal pieces and ate 3 of them. How much of the pie remains?

_____

© Pearson Education, Inc.

Parts of a Set

Materials two-color counters, 20 for each pair; crayons or markers

1. Show 4 red counters and 6 yellow counters.

Write a fraction for the part that is red and the part that is yellow
by answering 2 to 6.

2. How many counters are there in all? _____

3. How many of the counters are red? _____

4. What fraction of the group of counters is red?

$$\frac{\boxed{}}{\boxed{}} = \frac{\text{number of counters that are red}}{\text{total number of counters}} = \frac{\text{(numerator)}}{\text{(denominator)}}$$

Four tenths of the group of counters is red

5. How many of the counters are yellow? _____

6. What fraction of the counters are yellow?

$$\frac{\boxed{}}{\boxed{}} = \frac{\text{number of counters that are yellow}}{\text{total number of counters}} = \frac{\text{(numerator)}}{\text{(denominator)}}$$

Six tenths of the group of counters is yellow.

Show a group of counters with $\frac{5}{6}$ red by answering 7 to 9.

7. How many counters do you need in all? _____

8. How many of the counters need to be red? _____

9. Show the counters and color below to match.

© Pearson Education, Inc.

Parts of a Set (continued)

Write the fraction for the shaded parts of each set.

10.    **11.**

_____   _____

12.   **13.**

_____   _____

14.   **15.**

_____   _____

Draw a set of shapes and shade them to show each fraction.

16. $\dfrac{5}{9}$ **17.** $\dfrac{6}{10}$

18. Reasoning If Sally has 5 yellow marbles and 7 blue
marbles. What fraction of her marbles are yellow?
Draw a picture to justify your answer.

© Pearson Education, Inc.

Fractions and Length

Materials fraction strips; crayons or markers

Fractions can be used to describe parts of lengths.

1. Use fraction strips to make what is shown below.

1					
$\frac{1}{6}$	$\frac{1}{6}$	$\frac{1}{6}$	$\frac{1}{6}$	$\frac{1}{6}$	$\frac{1}{6}$

2. How many sixth strips does it take to be the
same length as 1 whole?   _____

3. Use fraction strips to make what is shown below.

1			
$\frac{1}{6}$	$\frac{1}{6}$	$\frac{1}{6}$	$\frac{1}{6}$

4. What fraction of the length of the 1 strip do the other strips show?

$$\frac{\boxed{}}{\boxed{}} = \frac{\text{number of parts shown}}{\text{total number of parts to make 1 whole}} = \frac{\text{(numerator)}}{\text{(denominator)}}$$

5. Show the model below.

1							
$\frac{1}{8}$	$\frac{1}{8}$	$\frac{1}{8}$	$\frac{1}{8}$	$\frac{1}{8}$	$\frac{1}{8}$	$\frac{1}{8}$	$\frac{1}{8}$

6. How many eighth strips does it take to be the
same length as 1 whole?   _____

7. Show $\frac{5}{8}$ with fractions strips. Color strips above to show $\frac{5}{8}$.

© Pearson Education, Inc.

Fractions and Length (continued)

Write the fraction for the shaded part of each length.

8.

1			
$\frac{1}{4}$	$\frac{1}{4}$	$\frac{1}{4}$	$\frac{1}{4}$

_____

9.

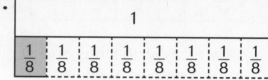

_____

10.

1				
$\frac{1}{5}$	$\frac{1}{5}$	$\frac{1}{5}$	$\frac{1}{5}$	$\frac{1}{5}$

_____

11.

1							
$\frac{1}{8}$	$\frac{1}{8}$	$\frac{1}{8}$	$\frac{1}{8}$	$\frac{1}{8}$	$\frac{1}{8}$	$\frac{1}{8}$	$\frac{1}{8}$

_____

12.

1		
$\frac{1}{3}$	$\frac{1}{3}$	$\frac{1}{3}$

_____

13.

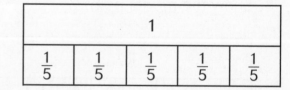

_____

Color to show each fraction.

14. $\frac{1}{2}$

1	
$\frac{1}{2}$	$\frac{1}{2}$

15. $\frac{4}{5}$

1				
$\frac{1}{5}$	$\frac{1}{5}$	$\frac{1}{5}$	$\frac{1}{5}$	$\frac{1}{5}$

16. $\frac{1}{3}$

1		
$\frac{1}{3}$	$\frac{1}{3}$	$\frac{1}{3}$

17. $\frac{7}{8}$

1							
$\frac{1}{8}$	$\frac{1}{8}$	$\frac{1}{8}$	$\frac{1}{8}$	$\frac{1}{8}$	$\frac{1}{8}$	$\frac{1}{8}$	$\frac{1}{8}$

© Pearson Education, Inc.

Name _____

Fractions on the Number Line

Each fraction names a point on a number line. Name the missing
fractions on the number line below by answering 1 to 3.

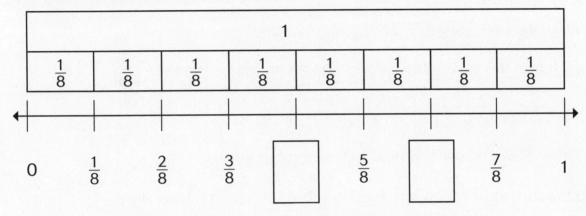

1. How many equal lengths is the distance between 0 and 1
divided into? _____

Since, the distance between 0 and 1 is divided into 8 equal

lengths, each length is $\frac{1}{8}$ of the whole length.

2. To name the first missing fraction, count by eighths. $\frac{1}{8}, \frac{2}{8}, \frac{3}{8},$ _____

Write $\frac{4}{8}$ in the first box above.

3. To name the next missing fraction, keep counting. $\frac{4}{8}, \frac{5}{8},$ _____

Write $\frac{6}{8}$ in the second box above.

Name the missing numbers on the number line below by
answering 4 to 6.

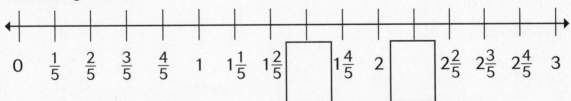

4. How many equal parts is the distance between 0 and 1
divided into? _____

Since, the distance between 0 and 1 is divided into 5 equal lengths,

each length is $\frac{1}{5}$ of the whole length.

© Pearson Education, Inc.

Fractions on the Number Line (continued)

5. To name the first missing fraction, count by fifths.

$\frac{1}{5}, \frac{2}{5}, \frac{3}{5}, \frac{4}{5}, 1, 1\frac{1}{5}, 1\frac{2}{5},$ _____

Write $1\frac{3}{5}$ in the first box on the number line.

6. To name the second missing fraction, continue counting.

$1\frac{3}{5}, 1\frac{4}{5}, 2,$ _____

Write $2\frac{1}{5}$ in the second box on the number line.

Write the missing fraction or mixed number for each number line.

7.
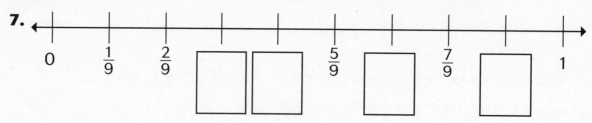

8.
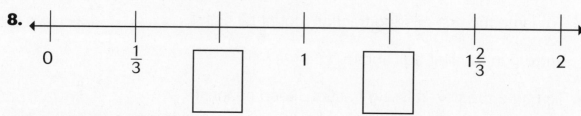

9. The number line shows how far Glen, Ned, and Lois ran in a one-mile race. Write a fraction that shows how far Ned and Lois ran.

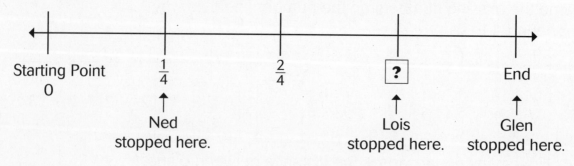

Ned _____   Lois _____

© Pearson Education, Inc.

Using Models to Compare Fractions

Materials fraction strips

Use $>$, $<$, or $=$ to compare $\frac{4}{5}$ and $\frac{2}{3}$ by answering 1 to 3.

1. Show 1, $\frac{4}{5}$, and $\frac{2}{3}$ with fraction strips.

2. Compare. Which is greater in total length, $\frac{4}{5}$ or $\frac{2}{3}$? _____

3. Since $\frac{4}{5}$ is longer than $\frac{2}{3}$, $\frac{4}{5}$ is **greater than** $\frac{2}{3}$. Write $>$, $<$, or $=$.

$\frac{4}{5} \bigcirc \frac{2}{3}$

Compare $\frac{1}{10}$ and $\frac{1}{4}$ by answering 4 to 6.

4. Show 1, $\frac{1}{10}$, and $\frac{1}{4}$ with fraction strips.

5. Compare. Which is greater in total length, $\frac{1}{10}$ or $\frac{1}{4}$? _____

6. Since $\frac{1}{10}$ is shorter than $\frac{1}{4}$, $\frac{1}{10}$ is **less than** $\frac{1}{4}$. Write $>$, $<$, or $=$.

$\frac{1}{10} \bigcirc \frac{1}{4}$

Compare $\frac{2}{5}$ and $\frac{4}{10}$ by answering 7 to 9.

7. Show 1, $\frac{2}{5}$, and $\frac{4}{10}$ with fraction strips.

8. Compare. Which is greater in total length, $\frac{2}{5}$ or $\frac{4}{10}$?

_____

9. Since $\frac{2}{5}$ and $\frac{4}{10}$ are the same length, $\frac{2}{5}$ is **equal to** $\frac{4}{10}$. Write $>$, $<$, or $=$.

$\frac{2}{5} \bigcirc \frac{4}{10}$

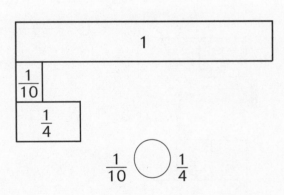

© Pearson Education, Inc.

Using Models to Compare Fractions (continued)

Compare. Write <, >, or =.

10. $\frac{1}{4}$ ◯ $\frac{3}{4}$

$\frac{1}{4}$		
$\frac{1}{4}$	$\frac{1}{4}$	$\frac{1}{4}$

11. $\frac{3}{4}$ ◯ $\frac{2}{8}$

$\frac{1}{4}$	$\frac{1}{4}$	$\frac{1}{4}$
$\frac{1}{8}$ $\frac{1}{8}$		

12. $\frac{2}{3}$ ◯ $\frac{4}{6}$

$\frac{1}{3}$		$\frac{1}{3}$	
$\frac{1}{6}$	$\frac{1}{6}$	$\frac{1}{6}$	$\frac{1}{6}$

13. $\frac{1}{5}$ ◯ $\frac{5}{10}$

$\frac{1}{5}$				
$\frac{1}{10}$	$\frac{1}{10}$	$\frac{1}{10}$	$\frac{1}{10}$	$\frac{1}{10}$

14. $\frac{1}{2}$ ◯ $\frac{1}{5}$

$\frac{1}{2}$
$\frac{1}{5}$

15. $\frac{7}{8}$ ◯ $\frac{3}{4}$

$\frac{1}{8}$	$\frac{1}{8}$	$\frac{1}{8}$	$\frac{1}{8}$	$\frac{1}{8}$	$\frac{1}{8}$	$\frac{1}{8}$
$\frac{1}{4}$		$\frac{1}{4}$		$\frac{1}{4}$		

16. $\frac{2}{6}$ ◯ $\frac{1}{2}$

$\frac{1}{6}$	$\frac{1}{6}$
$\frac{1}{2}$	

17. $\frac{3}{5}$ ◯ $\frac{1}{4}$

$\frac{1}{5}$	$\frac{1}{5}$	$\frac{1}{5}$
$\frac{1}{4}$		

18. Reasoning Give 3 fractions with different denominators that are less than $\frac{4}{6}$. _____

19. Reasoning Two students are writing stories. Eric's story is $\frac{2}{3}$ of a page. Alba's story is $\frac{4}{6}$ of a page. Whose story is longer? _____

© Pearson Education, Inc.

Using Models to Find Equivalent Fractions

Materials fraction strips

Find a fraction equivalent to $\frac{3}{4}$ by answering 1 to 3.

1. Show a 1 and $\frac{3}{4}$ with fraction strips.

2. How many $\frac{1}{8}$ strips does

it take to equal $\frac{3}{4}$?   _____

$$\frac{3}{4} = \frac{\square}{8}$$

3. So, $\frac{3}{4}$ is equal to six $\frac{1}{8}$ strips.

Find the missing number in $\frac{1}{2} = \frac{?}{10}$, by answering 4 to 7.

The denominators of the fractions tell which fraction strips to use.

4. Show 1 and $\frac{1}{2}$ with fraction strips.

5. What is the denominator of
the second fraction?   _____

6. Since the denominator of the second
fraction is 10, find the number
of $\frac{1}{10}$ strips equal to $\frac{1}{2}$.   _____

7. So, $\frac{1}{2}$ is equal to five $\frac{1}{10}$ strips.

$$\frac{1}{2} = \frac{\square}{10}$$

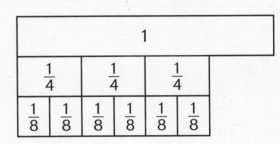

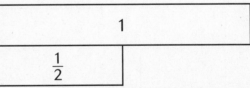

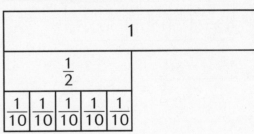

© Pearson Education, Inc.

Using Models to Find Equivalent Fractions (continued)

Complete each number sentence.

8.

1

$\frac{1}{4}$

$\frac{1}{8}$	$\frac{1}{8}$

$$\frac{1}{4} = \frac{}{8}$$

9.

1

$\frac{1}{3}$	$\frac{1}{3}$

$\frac{1}{6}$	$\frac{1}{6}$	$\frac{1}{6}$	$\frac{1}{6}$

$$\frac{2}{3} = \frac{}{6}$$

10.

1

$\frac{1}{2}$

$\frac{1}{8}$	$\frac{1}{8}$	$\frac{1}{8}$	$\frac{1}{8}$

$$\frac{1}{2} = \frac{}{8}$$

11.

1

$\frac{1}{5}$	$\frac{1}{5}$

$\frac{1}{10}$	$\frac{1}{10}$	$\frac{1}{10}$	$\frac{1}{10}$

$$\frac{2}{5} = \frac{}{10}$$

12.

1

$\frac{1}{3}$	$\frac{1}{3}$

$\frac{1}{12}$	$\frac{1}{12}$	$\frac{1}{12}$	$\frac{1}{12}$	$\frac{1}{12}$	$\frac{1}{12}$	$\frac{1}{12}$	$\frac{1}{12}$

$$\frac{2}{3} = \frac{}{12}$$

13.

1

$\frac{1}{4}$	$\frac{1}{4}$

$\frac{1}{6}$	$\frac{1}{6}$	$\frac{1}{6}$

$$\frac{2}{4} = \frac{}{6}$$

14. Reasoning On Tuesday, $\frac{2}{3}$ of the class time was spent on math projects. How many *sixths* of the class time was spent on math projects?

_____

© Pearson Education, Inc.

Comparing Fractions on the Number Line

Materials 21 index cards for each pair; crayons or markers,
13 craft sticks for each pair; 1 yard of yarn for each pair

1. Write numbers on index cards, one number on each card.
   One partner writes the following numbers.

   $0, \frac{1}{3}, \frac{2}{3}, 1, 1\frac{1}{3}, 1\frac{2}{3}, 2, 2\frac{1}{3}, 2\frac{2}{3}, 3, 3\frac{1}{3}, 3\frac{2}{3},$ and 4

   The other partner writes the following numbers.

   $\frac{1}{3}, \frac{2}{3}, 1\frac{1}{3}, 1\frac{2}{3}, 2\frac{1}{3}, 2\frac{2}{3}, 3\frac{1}{3},$ and $3\frac{2}{3}$

2. Create a number line, like the one shown below, with the yarn,
   craft sticks, and the first set of index cards.

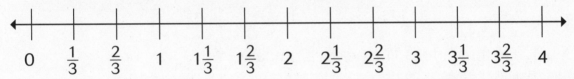

$$0 \qquad \frac{1}{3} \qquad \frac{2}{3} \qquad 1 \qquad 1\frac{1}{3} \qquad 1\frac{2}{3} \qquad 2 \qquad 2\frac{1}{3} \qquad 2\frac{2}{3} \qquad 3 \qquad 3\frac{1}{3} \qquad 3\frac{2}{3} \qquad 4$$

3. Shuffle the other set of cards. Both you and your partner
   draw a card.

4. Match the numbers on the cards you drew
   with numbers on the number line you created.

   Which number is farther to the right? _____

On the number line, fractions increase in value from
left to right. So the fraction farther to the right is greater.

5. Write a comparison of your two numbers,
   such as $2\frac{2}{3} < 3\frac{1}{3}$.   _____

   Set the first two cards aside. Continue drawing cards and writing
   comparisons until all the cards are gone.

6. _____   7. _____

8. _____   9. _____

© Pearson Education, Inc.

Comparing Fractions on the Number Line (continued)

For 10–18, use the number line below. Compare. Write <, >, or =.

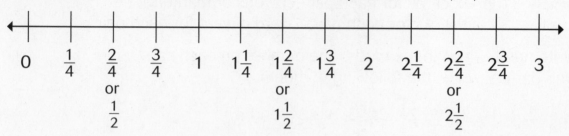

10. $\frac{3}{4}$ ◯ $\frac{1}{4}$ **11.** $1\frac{1}{4}$ ◯ $2\frac{1}{2}$ **12.** $1\frac{1}{2}$ ◯ $1\frac{3}{4}$

13. $1\frac{1}{4}$ ◯ $\frac{1}{4}$ **14.** $2\frac{3}{4}$ ◯ $2\frac{1}{4}$ **15.** $1\frac{1}{2}$ ◯ $1\frac{1}{2}$

16. $\frac{1}{4}$ ◯ $\frac{1}{2}$ **17.** $1\frac{3}{4}$ ◯ $1\frac{3}{4}$ **18.** $\frac{3}{4}$ ◯ $\frac{1}{2}$

For 19–24, use the number line below. Compare. Write <, >, or =.

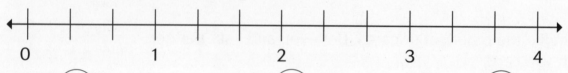

19. $\frac{2}{3}$ ◯ $\frac{1}{3}$ **20.** $2\frac{1}{3}$ ◯ $1\frac{2}{3}$ **21.** $1\frac{1}{3}$ ◯ $2\frac{1}{3}$

22. $\frac{3}{3}$ ◯ 1 **23.** $2\frac{2}{3}$ ◯ $2\frac{1}{3}$ **24.** $\frac{2}{3}$ ◯ $1\frac{1}{3}$

25. Reasoning Why is $2\frac{1}{8}$ greater than $1\frac{7}{8}$, even though $\frac{1}{8}$ is less than $\frac{7}{8}$?

26. Reasoning Explain how you can use the number line above to compare $6\frac{1}{3}$ and $6\frac{2}{3}$.

© Pearson Education, Inc.

Comparing Fractions

Materials fraction strips

Compare $\frac{3}{10}$ and $\frac{7}{8}$ by answering 1 to 3.

Compare each fraction to $\frac{1}{2}$. Write $>$ or $<$.

1. $\frac{3}{10}$ ◯ $\frac{1}{2}$

$\frac{1}{2}$

$\frac{1}{10}$	$\frac{1}{10}$	$\frac{1}{10}$

2. $\frac{7}{8}$ ◯ $\frac{1}{2}$

$\frac{1}{2}$

$\frac{1}{8}$	$\frac{1}{8}$	$\frac{1}{8}$	$\frac{1}{8}$	$\frac{1}{8}$	$\frac{1}{8}$	$\frac{1}{8}$

3. Since $\frac{3}{10} < \frac{1}{2}$ and $\frac{7}{8} > \frac{1}{2}$, then $\frac{3}{10}$ ◯ $\frac{7}{8}$.

You can compare two fractions with the same denominator just by comparing the numerators.

Use equivalent fractions to compare $\frac{1}{4}$ and $\frac{5}{12}$ by answering 4 to 6.

4. $\frac{1}{4}$ is the same as how many twelfths? _____

5. Since $\frac{1}{4} = \frac{3}{12}$, you can now compare $\frac{3}{12}$ and $\frac{5}{12}$.

Which fraction has the greater numerator? _____

6. Compare. Write $>$ or $<$. $\frac{3}{12}$ ◯ $\frac{5}{12}$

So, $\frac{1}{4}$ ◯ $\frac{5}{12}$.

7. Use fraction strips to compare $\frac{1}{8}$ and $\frac{1}{4}$. Write $>$ or $<$.

$\frac{1}{8}$ ◯ $\frac{1}{4}$

8. Which fraction has the greater denominator $\frac{1}{8}$ or $\frac{1}{4}$? _____

When both fractions have the same numerator, the fraction with the greater denominator is **less than** the other fraction.

© Pearson Education, Inc.

Comparing Fractions (continued)

Compare. Write >, <, or = for each.

9. $\frac{1}{4}$ ◯ $\frac{3}{4}$

| $\frac{1}{4}$ | | |
| $\frac{1}{4}$ | $\frac{1}{4}$ | $\frac{1}{4}$ |

10. $\frac{5}{10}$ ◯ $\frac{3}{10}$

| $\frac{1}{10}$ | $\frac{1}{10}$ | $\frac{1}{10}$ | $\frac{1}{10}$ | $\frac{1}{10}$ |
| $\frac{1}{10}$ | $\frac{1}{10}$ | $\frac{1}{10}$ | | |

11. $\frac{1}{5}$ ◯ $\frac{5}{8}$

| $\frac{1}{5}$ | | | | |
| $\frac{1}{8}$ | $\frac{1}{8}$ | $\frac{1}{8}$ | $\frac{1}{8}$ | $\frac{1}{8}$ |

12. $\frac{7}{10}$ ◯ $\frac{9}{10}$

| $\frac{1}{10}$ | $\frac{1}{10}$ | $\frac{1}{10}$ | $\frac{1}{10}$ | $\frac{1}{10}$ | $\frac{1}{10}$ | $\frac{1}{10}$ | | |
| $\frac{1}{10}$ | $\frac{1}{10}$ | $\frac{1}{10}$ | $\frac{1}{10}$ | $\frac{1}{10}$ | $\frac{1}{10}$ | $\frac{1}{10}$ | $\frac{1}{10}$ | $\frac{1}{10}$ |

13. $\frac{2}{8}$ ◯ $\frac{1}{4}$

| $\frac{1}{8}$ | $\frac{1}{8}$ |
| $\frac{1}{4}$ | |

14. $\frac{8}{12}$ ◯ $\frac{5}{6}$

| $\frac{1}{12}$ | $\frac{1}{12}$ | $\frac{1}{12}$ | $\frac{1}{12}$ | $\frac{1}{12}$ | $\frac{1}{12}$ | $\frac{1}{12}$ | $\frac{1}{12}$ |
| $\frac{1}{6}$ | $\frac{1}{6}$ | $\frac{1}{6}$ | $\frac{1}{6}$ | $\frac{1}{6}$ |

15. $\frac{6}{8}$ ◯ $\frac{6}{10}$

| $\frac{1}{8}$ | $\frac{1}{8}$ | $\frac{1}{8}$ | $\frac{1}{8}$ | $\frac{1}{8}$ | $\frac{1}{8}$ |
| $\frac{1}{10}$ | $\frac{1}{10}$ | $\frac{1}{10}$ | $\frac{1}{10}$ | $\frac{1}{10}$ | $\frac{1}{10}$ |

16. $\frac{3}{6}$ ◯ $\frac{6}{12}$

| $\frac{1}{6}$ | $\frac{1}{6}$ | $\frac{1}{6}$ |
| $\frac{1}{12}$ | $\frac{1}{12}$ | $\frac{1}{12}$ | $\frac{1}{12}$ | $\frac{1}{12}$ | $\frac{1}{12}$ |

17. $\frac{3}{5}$ ◯ $\frac{7}{12}$

| $\frac{1}{5}$ | $\frac{1}{5}$ | $\frac{1}{5}$ |
| $\frac{1}{12}$ | $\frac{1}{12}$ | $\frac{1}{12}$ | $\frac{1}{12}$ | $\frac{1}{12}$ | $\frac{1}{12}$ | $\frac{1}{12}$ |

18. $\frac{1}{2}$ ◯ $\frac{3}{8}$

| $\frac{1}{2}$ | | |
| $\frac{1}{8}$ | $\frac{1}{8}$ | $\frac{1}{8}$ |

19. $\frac{3}{5}$ ◯ $\frac{6}{10}$

| $\frac{1}{5}$ | $\frac{1}{5}$ | $\frac{1}{5}$ |
| $\frac{1}{10}$ | $\frac{1}{10}$ | $\frac{1}{10}$ | $\frac{1}{10}$ | $\frac{1}{10}$ | $\frac{1}{10}$ |

20. $\frac{1}{5}$ ◯ $\frac{1}{8}$

| $\frac{1}{5}$ |
| $\frac{1}{8}$ |

21. Reasoning Two students are timed on a math facts test.
Nathan finished $\frac{5}{6}$ of the problems. Terrell finished $\frac{5}{8}$
of the problems. Which student finished a greater part? _____

© Pearson Education, Inc.

Fractions and Decimals

Materials crayons or markers

1. Color 7 of the equal parts in the square at the right.

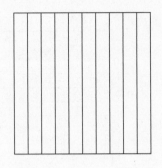

2. What fractional part of the square did you color?   _____

   The fraction $\frac{7}{10}$ can be written as a decimal.

3. How many tenths did you color? _____

4. Write a 7 in the tenths place of the place-value chart at the right.

Ones	Tenths
0 .	

   0.7 is read, "seven tenths." $\frac{7}{10} = 0.7$

5. Color 31 of the equal parts in the square at the right.

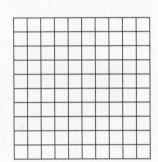

6. What fractional part of the square did you color?   _____

   The fraction $\frac{31}{100}$ can be written as a decimal.

7. How many hundredths did you color? _____

8. Write a 3 in the tenths place and a 1 in the hundredths place of the place-value chart at the right.

Ones	Tenths	Hundredths
0 .		

   0.31 is read, "thirty-one hundredths." $\frac{31}{100} = 0.31$

9. Use the place-value chart at the right to write a decimal equal to $\frac{6}{100}$.

Ones	Tenths	Hundredths
0 .		

   $\frac{6}{100} =$ _____

© Pearson Education, Inc.

Fractions and Decimals (continued)

Write a fraction and a decimal for each shaded part.

10.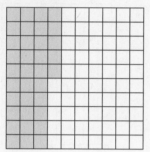

_____

11.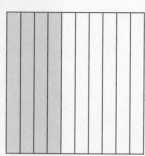

_____

12.

_____

13.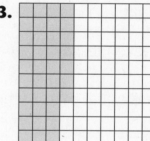

_____

14.

_____

15.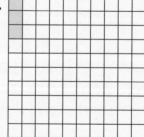

_____

16. Reasoning A pan of lasagna was cut into 10 equal
sections. A family ate 8 of the sections. Write a fraction
and a decimal to represent the amount of lasagna
the family ate.

_____

© Pearson Education, Inc.

Counting Money

Gary has a $1 bill, a quarter, 2 dimes, a nickel, and a penny.

When you count money, start with the bill or coin of greatest value. Then count on to find the total.

1. Count Gary's money.

$1.00   _____ $1.35   _____   _____   _____

2. How much money does Gary have? _____

3. Write $1.51 in words.   one dollar and _____ cents

4. Ty has a $1 bill, a half-dollar, 2 quarters, and 3 dimes. Count Ty's money.

$1.00   _____   _____   _____ $2.10   _____   _____

5. How much money does Ty have? _____

6. Who had more money, Gary or Ty? _____

© Pearson Education, Inc.

Counting Money (continued)

Write the total value in dollars and cents.

7.

_____

8. 1 five-dollar bill, 3 quarters, 1 nickel, 2 pennies

9. 1 one-dollar bill, 1 half-dollar, 4 nickels, 8 pennies

_____

_____

10. 1 one-dollar bill, 2 quarters, 4 dimes, 3 nickels, 1 penny

11. 1 five-dollar bill, 1 one-dollar bill, 1 quarter, 4 dimes, 3 nickels

_____

_____

Compare the amounts. Write <, >, or =.

12. $1.17 ◯ 4 quarters, 2 dimes

13. $0.49 ◯ 4 dimes, 1 nickel

14. 2 quarters, 6 dimes ◯ $1.10

15. 3 half-dollars, 3 nickels ◯ $1.70

16. Reasoning Anita and Ted both have $1.49, but each have different coins. What coins could each have?

© Pearson Education, Inc.

Making Change

Ivan bought a plastic dinosaur for $3.68. He paid with a $5 bill.
Answer 1 to 10 to find how much change Ivan received.

To make change, start with coins that will make it easier to skip
count. Count up to the amount you paid.

1. Start with $3.68. Count on with pennies until you get to an
amount that ends in 0 or 5.

$3.68, $3.69,   _____

2. How many pennies did you count? _____

3. How much are 2 pennies worth? $0._____ _____

4. Count on from $3.70 with dimes.

$3.70,   _____,   _____,   _____

5. How many dimes did you count? _____

6. How much is 3 dimes and 2 pennies worth? $0._____ _____

7. Count on from $4.00 with one-dollar bills until you get to
the $5.00 Ivan paid.

$4.00,   _____

8. How many dollar bills did you count? _____

9. How much is 1 dollar bill, 3 dimes
and 2 pennies worth? $_____. _____ _____

© Pearson Education, Inc.

Making Change (continued)

10. How much change did Ivan receive? _____

List the coins and bills you would use to make change.
Then write the change in dollars and cents.

11. Cost: $1.40
Amount paid: $2.00

_____

_____

12. Cost: $3.17
Amount paid: $4.00

_____

_____

13. Cost: $0.76
Amount paid: $5.00

_____

_____

14. Cost: $1.33
Amount paid: $5.00

_____

_____

_____

15. Reasoning Beverly bought a gallon of juice for $2.69.
She used three $1 bills. Give two ways to show the change.
Circle the one that uses the fewest coins.

© Pearson Education, Inc.

Using Money to Understand Decimals

1. How many dimes are
equal to one dollar?   _____

2. What fraction of a
dollar is each dime?   _____

3. What decimal shows what
part of a dollar each dime is? _____

4. How many pennies are
equal to one dollar?   _____

5. What fraction of a
dollar is each penny?   _____

6. What decimal shows what
part of a dollar each penny is? _____

7. Show $1.32 in the place-value
chart at the right.

dollars (ones	dimes (tenths)	pennies (hundredths)
.		

8. $1.32 = _____ dollar + 3 dimes

  + _____ pennies

   1.32 = _____ one + _____ tenths + 2 hundredths

9. $1.32 = _____ dollar + 32 pennies

   1.32 = _____ one + _____ hundredths

Reading decimals and money are very similar.
$1.32 is read "one dollar and thirty-two cents."
1.32 is read "one and thirty-two hundredths."

10. Show two dollars and sixty four
cents in the chart at the right.

dollars (ones	dimes (tenths)	pennies (hundredths)
.		

11. Write two and sixty-four
hundredths with a
decimal point.   _____

© Pearson Education, Inc.

Using Money to Understand Decimals (continued)

Write the values for the money amounts and the decimal numbers.

12. $4.62 = _____ dollars + _____ dimes + _____ pennies

4.62 = _____ ones + _____ tenths + _____ hundredths

13. $7.31 = _____ dollars + _____ dimes + _____ penny

7.31 = _____ ones + _____ tenths + _____ hundredth

14. $1.04 = _____ dollar + _____ dimes + _____ pennies

1.04 = _____ one + _____ tenths + _____ hundredths

15. $2.87 = _____ dollars + _____ pennies

2.87 = _____ ones + _____ hundredths

16. $9.16 = _____ dollars + _____ pennies

9.16 = _____ ones + _____ hundredths

17. $7.39 = _____ dollars + _____ pennies

7.39 = _____ ones + _____ hundredths

18. Write three and ninety-one hundredths with a
decimal point.

_____

19. Write seven and twenty-six hundredths with a
decimal point.

_____

20. Lisabeth wants to buy school supplies for $5.25. How can
she pay for them using only dollars, dimes, and pennies?

_____

21. Reasoning Explain why the 2 in $6.27 represents tenths
of a dollar.

© Pearson Education, Inc.

Equivalent Fractions

Materials crayons or markers

1					
$\frac{1}{3}$		$\frac{1}{3}$		$\frac{1}{3}$	
$\frac{1}{6}$	$\frac{1}{6}$	$\frac{1}{6}$	$\frac{1}{6}$	$\frac{1}{6}$	$\frac{1}{6}$

1. Show $\frac{2}{3}$ by coloring 2 of the $\frac{1}{3}$ strips.

2. Color as many $\frac{1}{6}$ strips as it takes to cover the same region as the $\frac{2}{3}$. How many $\frac{1}{6}$ strips did you color? _____

3. So, $\frac{2}{3}$ is equivalent to four $\frac{1}{6}$ strips. $\frac{2}{3} = \frac{\square}{6}$

You can use multiplication to find a fraction equivalent to $\frac{2}{3}$. To do this, multiply the numerator and the denominator by the same number.

4. What number is the denominator of $\frac{2}{3}$ multiplied by to get 6?

_____

5. Since the denominator was multiplied by 2, the numerator must also be multiplied by 2. Put the product of 2×2 in the numerator of the second fraction above.

Multiply the numerator and denominator of each fraction by the same number to find a fraction equivalent to each.

6.

$$\frac{2}{3} = \frac{\square}{9}$$
×3 ... ×3

7.

$$\frac{1}{2} = \frac{\square}{8}$$
×4 ... ×4

8. Show $\frac{9}{12}$ by coloring 9 of the $\frac{1}{12}$ strips.

9. Color as many $\frac{1}{4}$ strips as it takes to cover the same region as $\frac{9}{12}$. How many $\frac{1}{4}$ strips did you color? _____

1											
$\frac{1}{4}$			$\frac{1}{4}$			$\frac{1}{4}$			$\frac{1}{4}$		
$\frac{1}{12}$	$\frac{1}{12}$	$\frac{1}{12}$	$\frac{1}{12}$	$\frac{1}{12}$	$\frac{1}{12}$	$\frac{1}{12}$	$\frac{1}{12}$	$\frac{1}{12}$	$\frac{1}{12}$	$\frac{1}{12}$	$\frac{1}{12}$

© Pearson Education, Inc.

Equivalent Fractions (continued)

10. So, $\frac{9}{12}$ is equivalent to three $\frac{1}{4}$ strips. $\frac{9}{12} = \frac{\boxed{}}{4}$

You can use division to find a fraction equivalent to $\frac{9}{12}$. To do this,

divide the numerator and the denominator by the same number.

11. What number is the denominator of

$\frac{9}{12}$ divided by to get 4? _____

12. Since the denominator was divided by 3, the numerator
must also be divided by 3. Put the quotient of $9 \div 3$ in
the numerator of the second fraction above.

Divide the numerator and denominator of each fraction by
the same number to find a fraction equivalent to each.

13.

$$\overset{\div 2}{\frac{8}{10}} = \frac{\boxed{}}{5}$$
$$\div 2$$

14.

$$\overset{\div 5}{\frac{10}{15}} = \frac{\boxed{}}{3}$$
$$\div 5$$

If the numerator and denominator cannot be divided by anything
else, then the fraction is in simplest form.

15. Is $\frac{5}{12}$ in simplest form? _____   **16.** Is $\frac{6}{8}$ in simplest form? _____

Find each equivalent fraction.

17. $\frac{1}{5} = \frac{\boxed{}}{15}$ **18.** $\frac{8}{10} = \frac{\boxed{}}{5}$ **19.** $\frac{2}{8} = \frac{\boxed{}}{4}$

20. $\frac{7}{10} = \frac{\boxed{}}{20}$ **21.** $\frac{6}{14} = \frac{\boxed{}}{7}$ **22.** $\frac{8}{11} = \frac{\boxed{}}{22}$

Write each fraction in simplest form.

23. $\frac{6}{8}$ _____   **24.** $\frac{8}{12}$ _____   **25.** $\frac{7}{35}$ _____   **26.** $\frac{16}{24}$ _____

27. Reasoning Explain why $\frac{4}{6}$ is not in simplest form.

© Pearson Education, Inc.

Fractions and Division

Reg, Sal, Mac, and Ned shared 3 granola bars equally.
What fraction of a granola bar did each boy get?

Find 3 ÷ 4 by answering 1 to 5.

1. Since 4 friends shared the bars equally,
divide each bar into 4 equal sections.

2. Each boy got 1 section from each granola
bar. Write Reg in the first section of each
granola bar, Sal in the second section,
Mac in the third section, and Ned in the
fourth section.

3. How many sections total did each boy get?   _____

4. Each boy got a total of 3 sections. Each
granola bar was divided into 4 sections.
What part of a granola bar did each boy get?   _____

5. So, 3 ÷ 4 = _____ .

Mia, Val, Bea, Dee, and Kim shared 4 granola bars equally.
What fraction of a granola bar did each girl get?

Find 4 ÷ 5 by answering 6 to 10.

6. Since 5 friends shared the bars equally,
divide each bar into 5 equal sections.

7. Each girl got 1 section from each granola
bar. Write each of the girls names in
1 section of each of the granola bars.

8. How many sections total did each girl get?   _____

9. What part of a granola bar did each girl get?   _____

10. So, 4 ÷ 5 = _____ .

© Pearson Education, Inc.

Fractions and Division (continued)

11. Reasoning You found that $3 \div 4 = \frac{3}{4}$ and $4 \div 5 = \frac{4}{5}$.
What is $2 \div 9$? How do you know?

Tell what fraction each person gets when they share equally.

12. Three students share 2 packs of paper.   _____

13. Eight girls share 3 bags of balloons.   _____

14. Two sisters share 1 bag of popcorn.   _____

15. Seven family members share 3 pounds of meat. _____

16. Five brothers pay for a $3 card.   _____

Give each answer as a fraction.

17. $7 \div 8 =$ _____   **18.** $2 \div 5 =$ _____   **19.** $1 \div 9 =$ _____

20. $2 \div 6 =$ _____   **21.** $7 \div 9 =$ _____   **22.** $1 \div 5 =$ _____

23. $8 \div 9 =$ _____   **24.** $2 \div 8 =$ _____   **25.** $7 \div 10 =$ _____

26. Reasoning Mrs. Savagae baked 5 loaves of
banana bread and used 2 bananas to make
each loaf. She is dividing the loaves equally
among 7 different friends. What fraction of
a loaf does each friend get?   _____

© Pearson Education, Inc.

Estimating Fractional Amounts

Materials crayons or markers

The fractions $\frac{1}{4}$, $\frac{1}{3}$, $\frac{1}{2}$, $\frac{2}{3}$, and $\frac{3}{4}$ are all **benchmark fractions**.
Benchmark fractions can be used to estimate fractional amounts.

Paco is painting a wooden board for an art project.

Estimate what fraction of the board he has painted by answering 1 to 5.

1. Color about $\frac{1}{2}$ of the board.

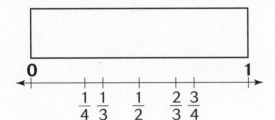

2. Color about $\frac{1}{4}$ of the board.

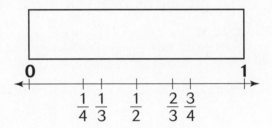

3. Color about $\frac{1}{3}$ of the board.

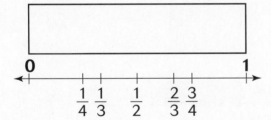

4. Color about $\frac{3}{4}$ of the board.

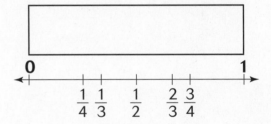

5. Paco has painted the part of the board shown at the right. About what part of the board has he painted?

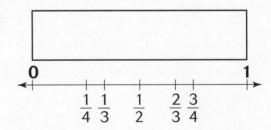

_____

6. Reasoning Why wouldn't $\frac{1}{3}$ be a good estimate for the part of the board Paco has painted in number 5?

© Pearson Education, Inc.

Estimating Fractional Amounts (continued)

Estimate the fraction that is left.

7.

8.

9.

_____   _____   _____

10. Circle the estimate of how much time has passed since 8:00.

About $\frac{1}{2}$ hour   About $\frac{1}{4}$ hour

About $\frac{1}{5}$ hour   About 1 hour

Estimate the shaded part of each.

11. _____

12. _____

13. _____

14.  _____

15. _____

16. _____

17. _____

18. _____

© Pearson Education, Inc.

Simplest Form

Anita saw that $\frac{12}{30}$ of the students in her class wore t-shirts one day.

Write $\frac{12}{30}$ in simplest form by answering 1 to 5.

To write a fraction in simplest form, you need to use the greatest
common factor (GCF) for the numerator and the denominator.

   1. What is the GCF of 12 and 30? _____

   2. Divide both the numerator and the denominator
      by the GCF to find an equivalent fraction.
      $$\frac{12 \div 6 = \boxed{}}{30 \div 6 = \ 5}$$

   3. What is the fraction that you found that is equivalent to $\frac{12}{30}$? _____

A fraction is in simplest form when the GCF of the numerator and the
denominator is 1.

   4. Is the GCF of the numerator and the
      denominator of the fraction you found 1? _____

   5. What is $\frac{12}{30}$ in simplest form? _____

Nine out of 24 girls on the cross county team went to the state finals.

   6. What fraction of the girls went to the state final?   _____

Write $\frac{9}{24}$ in simplest form by answering 7 to 11.

   7. What is the GCF of 9 and 24?   _____

   8. Divide both the numerator and the denominator
      by the GCF to find an equivalent fraction.

   9. What is the GCF of the numerator and the
      denominator of the fraction you found?   _____

   10. Is this fraction written in simplest form?   _____

   11. What fraction in simplest form represents the part of girls
      on the cross country team that went to the state finals?   _____

© Pearson Education, Inc.

Simplest Form (continued)

Write each fraction in simplest form. If it is in simplest form,
write simplest form.

12. $\frac{5}{10}$ **13.** $\frac{14}{16}$ **14.** $\frac{27}{45}$ **15.** $\frac{10}{15}$

_____   _____   _____   _____

16. $\frac{5}{20}$ **17.** $\frac{14}{18}$ **18.** $\frac{5}{11}$ **19.** $\frac{1}{15}$

_____   _____   _____   _____

20. $\frac{6}{20}$ **21.** $\frac{36}{45}$ **22.** $\frac{11}{33}$ **23.** $\frac{24}{60}$

_____   _____   _____   _____

24. $\frac{18}{24}$ **25.** $\frac{12}{160}$ **26.** $\frac{6}{12}$ **27.** $\frac{9}{81}$

_____   _____   _____   _____

28. $\frac{16}{48}$ **29.** $\frac{7}{13}$ **30.** $\frac{21}{25}$ **31.** $\frac{14}{35}$

_____   _____   _____   _____

32. Reasoning Explain how to tell $\frac{100}{105}$ is not in simplest form without
finding all the factors.

© Pearson Education, Inc.

Mixed Numbers

Materials fraction strips

A mixed number is a number written with a whole number and a fraction. An improper fraction is a fraction in which the numerator is greater than or equal to the denominator.

1. Circle the number that is a mixed number. 3 $4\frac{1}{3}$ $\frac{8}{5}$

2. Circle the number that is an improper fraction. $\frac{3}{4}$ $2\frac{3}{5}$ $\frac{9}{4}$

Write the improper fraction $\frac{7}{3}$ as a mixed number by answering 3 to 6.

3. Show seven $\frac{1}{3}$ fraction strips.

| $\frac{1}{3}$ | $\frac{1}{3}$ | $\frac{1}{3}$ | $\frac{1}{3}$ | $\frac{1}{3}$ | $\frac{1}{3}$ | $\frac{1}{3}$ |

4. Use fraction strips. How many 1 strips can you make with seven $\frac{1}{3}$ strips? _____

| $\frac{1}{3}$ | $\frac{1}{3}$ | $\frac{1}{3}$ | $\frac{1}{3}$ | $\frac{1}{3}$ | $\frac{1}{3}$ | $\frac{1}{3}$ |
| 1 | | 1 | |

5. How many $\frac{1}{3}$ strips do you have left over? _____

6. Write $\frac{7}{3}$ as a mixed number. _____

| $\frac{1}{3}$ | $\frac{1}{3}$ | $\frac{1}{3}$ | $\frac{1}{3}$ | $\frac{1}{3}$ | $\frac{1}{3}$ | $\frac{1}{3}$ |
| 1 | | 1 | | $\frac{1}{3}$ |

Write $\frac{7}{3}$ as a mixed number without fraction strips by answering 7 to 9.

7. Divide 7 by 3 at the right.

8. Fill in the missing numbers below.

Quotient → ⬚ $\dfrac{\boxed{}}{3}$ ← Remainder

← Divisor

$3\overline{)7}$

$-\boxed{}$

$\boxed{}$

Notice, the quotient 2 tells how many one strips you can make. The remainder 1 tells how many $\frac{1}{3}$ strips are left over.

9. Write $\frac{7}{3}$ as a mixed number. _____

© Pearson Education, Inc.

Mixed Numbers (continued)

10. Since $14 \div 5 = 2$ R4, what is $\frac{14}{5}$ as a mixed number? _____

Write $2\frac{1}{5}$ as an improper fraction by answering 11 to 13.

11. Show $2\frac{1}{5}$ with fractions strips.

1	1	$\frac{1}{5}$

12. Use fraction strips. How many $\frac{1}{5}$ strips does it take to equal $2\frac{1}{5}$?

1	1	$\frac{1}{5}$

$\frac{1}{5}$	$\frac{1}{5}$	$\frac{1}{5}$	$\frac{1}{5}$	$\frac{1}{5}$	$\frac{1}{5}$	$\frac{1}{5}$	$\frac{1}{5}$	$\frac{1}{5}$	$\frac{1}{5}$	$\frac{1}{5}$

_____

13. What improper fraction equals $2\frac{1}{5}$? _____

Write $2\frac{1}{5}$ as an improper fraction without using fraction strips by answering 14 to 16.

14. Fill in the missing numbers.

Whole Number $\times$ Denominator $+$ Numerator

_____ $\times$ _____ $+$ _____ $=$ _____ $+$ _____ $=$ _____

15. Write the 11 you found above over the denominator, 5. _____

16. What improper fraction equals $2\frac{1}{5}$? _____

Notice, 2×5 tells how many $\frac{1}{5}$ strips equal 2 wholes. The 1 tells how many additional $\frac{1}{5}$ strips there are.

17. Since $6 \times 4 + 3 = 27$, what is $6\frac{3}{4}$ as an improper fraction? _____

Change each improper fraction to a mixed number or a whole number and change each mixed number to an improper fraction.

18. $3\frac{2}{7}$ _____   **19.** $\frac{7}{3}$ _____   **20.** $\frac{7}{2}$ _____   **21.** $1\frac{1}{10}$ _____

© Pearson Education, Inc.

Comparing and Ordering Fractions

Jen ate $\frac{7}{9}$ of a salad. Jack ate $\frac{5}{9}$ of a salad. Find out who ate the greater part of a salad by answering 1–3.

Compare $\frac{7}{9}$ and $\frac{5}{9}$.

1. Are the denominators the same? _____

If the denominators are the same, then compare the numerators. The fraction with the **greater** numerator is **greater than** the other fraction.

2. Compare. Write >, <, or =.   7 $\bigcirc$ 5

$\frac{7}{9}$ $\bigcirc$ $\frac{5}{9}$

3. Who ate the greater part of a salad, Jen or Jack? _____

Compare $\frac{3}{5}$ and $\frac{3}{4}$ by answering 4 to 6

4. Are the denominators the same? _____

5. Are the numerators the same? _____

If the numerators are the same, compare the denominators. The fraction with the **greater** denominator is **less than** the other fraction.

6. Compare. Write >, <, or =.   5 $\bigcirc$ 4

$\frac{3}{5}$ $\bigcirc$ $\frac{3}{4}$

Compare $\frac{3}{4}$ and $\frac{2}{3}$ by answering 7 to 11.

7. Are the denominators the same? _____

8. Are the numerators the same? _____

If neither the numerators or the denominators are the same, change to equivalent fractions with the same denominator.

9. What is the LCM of 3 and 4? _____

© Pearson Education, Inc.

Comparing and Ordering Fractions (continued)

10. Rewrite $\frac{2}{3}$ and $\frac{3}{4}$ as equivalent fractions with a denominator of 12.

$$\frac{3}{4} = \frac{\square}{12} \qquad \frac{2}{3} = \frac{\square}{12}$$

11. Compare. Write $>$, $<$, or $=$. $\frac{9}{12} \bigcirc \frac{8}{12}$

$$\frac{3}{4} \bigcirc \frac{2}{3}$$

Write $\frac{5}{6}$, $\frac{5}{9}$, and $\frac{1}{3}$ in order from least to greatest by answering 12 to 15.

12. Use the denominators to compare. Write $>$, $<$, or $=$. $\frac{5}{6} \bigcirc \frac{5}{9}$

13. Rewrite $\frac{1}{3}$ so that it has a denominator common with $\frac{5}{9}$. $\frac{1}{3} = \frac{\square}{9}$

14. Compare the numerators. Write $>$, $<$, or $=$. $\frac{5}{9} \bigcirc \frac{3}{9}$

$$\frac{5}{9} \bigcirc \frac{1}{3}$$

15. Use the comparisons to write $\frac{5}{9}$, $\frac{5}{6}$, and $\frac{1}{3}$ in order from least to greatest.

_____ $<$ _____ $<$ _____

Compare. Write $>$, $<$, or $=$.

16. $\frac{3}{7} \bigcirc \frac{1}{7}$ **17.** $\frac{5}{8} \bigcirc \frac{10}{16}$ **18.** $\frac{3}{11} \bigcirc \frac{4}{10}$ **19.** $\frac{3}{4} \bigcirc \frac{2}{3}$

20. $\frac{3}{5} \bigcirc \frac{9}{15}$ **21.** $\frac{5}{6} \bigcirc \frac{5}{8}$ **22.** $\frac{5}{8} \bigcirc \frac{7}{12}$ **23.** $\frac{7}{9} \bigcirc \frac{4}{9}$

24. $\frac{1}{4}, \frac{6}{7}, \frac{3}{5}$ **25.** $\frac{5}{8}, \frac{8}{10}, \frac{2}{7}$ **26.** $\frac{5}{9}, \frac{10}{12}, \frac{5}{7}$ **27.** $\frac{3}{9}, \frac{12}{15}, \frac{5}{6}$

_____   _____   _____   _____

28. Reasoning Mario has two pizzas the same size. He cuts one into 4 equal pieces and the other into 5 equal pieces. Which pizza has larger pieces? Explain.

© Pearson Education, Inc.

Comparing and Ordering Mixed Numbers

Materials crayons or markers

The table shows the distances jumped by several members of a track team. Answer 1 to 4 to find who jumped farther, Karen or Ling.

Distances in the Standing Broad Jump

Karen	Latoya	Aileen	Lupe	Ling
$3\frac{2}{3}$ feet	$2\frac{5}{6}$ feet	$2\frac{1}{2}$ feet	$3\frac{1}{8}$ feet	$2\frac{5}{6}$ feet

Compare $3\frac{2}{3}$ and $2\frac{5}{6}$.

1. Color to show each number.

$3\frac{2}{3}$ [ ]   [ ]   [ ][ ][ ]

$2\frac{5}{6}$ [ ]   [ ]   [ ][ ][ ][ ][ ][ ]

2. Compare. Write >, <, or =. $3\frac{2}{5} \bigcirc 2\frac{5}{6}$

3. Reasoning If the whole numbers in two mixed numbers are not the same, which mixed number is always greater?

4. Who jumped farther, Karen or Ling? _____

Compare $1\frac{3}{4}$ and $2\frac{1}{2}$ by answering 5 and 6.

5. Are the whole number parts the same? _____

6. Compare. Write >, <, or =. $1 \bigcirc 2$

                  $1\frac{3}{4} \bigcirc 2\frac{1}{2}$

© Pearson Education, Inc.

Comparing and Ordering Mixed Numbers (continued)

Use the Standing Broad Jump table on the previous page. Who jumped
farther Aileen or Latoya?

Compare $2\frac{1}{2}$ and $2\frac{5}{6}$ by answering 7 to 8.

7. Color to show each number.

$2\frac{1}{2}$

$2\frac{5}{6}$

8. Compare. Write $>$, $<$, or $=$. $2\frac{5}{6}$ ◯ $2\frac{1}{2}$

9. Reasoning If the whole number parts of two mixed numbers are
the same, which mixed number is greater?

Compare. Write $>$, $<$, or $=$.

10. $4\frac{5}{15}$ ◯ $3\frac{4}{7}$ **11.** $3\frac{3}{4}$ ◯ $3\frac{2}{15}$ **12.** $3\frac{2}{8}$ ◯ $3\frac{1}{4}$

13. $5\frac{4}{9}$ ◯ $5\frac{2}{7}$ **14.** $2\frac{8}{12}$ ◯ $2\frac{3}{4}$ **15.** $8\frac{1}{7}$ ◯ $8\frac{1}{5}$

Write each set of numbers in order from least to greatest.

16. $\frac{14}{9}, \frac{10}{12}, \frac{5}{3}$ **17.** $1\frac{3}{7}, 1\frac{12}{15}, 1\frac{5}{6}$ **18.** $8\frac{4}{5}, 8\frac{1}{2}, 8\frac{7}{10}$

_____   _____   _____

19. Jim's height is 4 feet, $3\frac{3}{4}$ inches. Rex's height is
4 feet, $3\frac{3}{8}$ inches. Joan's height is 4 feet, $3\frac{7}{16}$ inches.
Who is the tallest? Who is the shortest?

© Pearson Education, Inc.

Fractions and Mixed Numbers on the Number Line

Each fraction names a point on the number line below. Use the number line to answer 1 to 7.

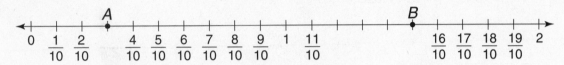

1. How many equal lengths is the distance between 0 and 1 divided into? _____

2. How many equal lengths is the distance between 1 and 2 divided into? _____

Since the distance between 0 and 1 and the distance between 1 and 2 are each divided into 10 equal lengths, each length is $\frac{1}{10}$ of the whole length.

3. To name point A, count by tenths. $\frac{1}{10}, \frac{2}{10},$ _____

4. What fraction is represented by point A on the number line above? _____

5. To name point B, continue counting.

$\frac{4}{10}, \frac{5}{10}, \frac{6}{10}, \frac{7}{10}, \frac{8}{10}, \frac{9}{10}, \frac{10}{10},$ _____, _____, _____, _____, _____

6. What improper fraction is represented by point B? _____

7. Write point B as a mixed number. _____

Plot point C at $\frac{3}{5}$ on the number line above by answering 8 and 9.

8. What fraction with a denominator of 10 is equivalent to $\frac{3}{5}$? $\qquad \frac{3}{5} = \frac{\square}{10}$

9. Plot point C at $\frac{6}{10}$. This point represents $\frac{3}{5}$.

Plot point D at $1\frac{4}{5}$ on the number line above by answering 10 and 11.

10. What improper fraction with a denominator of 10 is equivalent to $1\frac{4}{5}$?

$$1\frac{4}{5} = 1\frac{\square}{10} = \frac{\square}{10}$$

© Pearson Education, Inc.

Fractions and Mixed Numbers on the Number Line (continued)

11. Plot point D at $\frac{18}{10}$. This point represents $1\frac{4}{5}$.

12. Reasoning On a number line, numbers increase in value from left to right. Use the number line on the previous page to help you order $\frac{3}{10}$, $1\frac{1}{2}$, $\frac{3}{5}$, and $1\frac{4}{5}$ from least to greatest.

_____

Plot each point on the number line below.

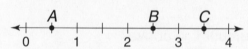

13. Point A at $\frac{3}{4}$ **14.** Point B at $1\frac{1}{4}$ **15.** Point C at $2\frac{1}{2}$ **16.** Point D at $3\frac{1}{2}$

Use the number lines below. What fraction or mixed number represents each point?

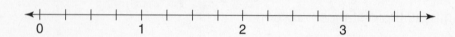

17. Point A _____   **18.** Point B _____   **19.** Point C _____

20. Point D _____   **21.** Point E _____   **22.** Point F _____

Use the number lines below. What number represents each point? If a point can be represented by both an improper fraction and a mixed number, give both.

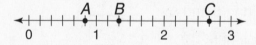

23. Point A _____   **24.** Point B _____   **25.** Point C _____

26. Point D _____   **27.** Point E _____   **28.** Point F _____

© Pearson Education, Inc.

Name _____

Place Value Through Hundredths

Materials crayons or markers

Use the grids to help you answer 1 to 7.

1. Each grid has 100 squares. Color all of the first two grids.
Then color 5 columns and 3 more squares of the third grid.

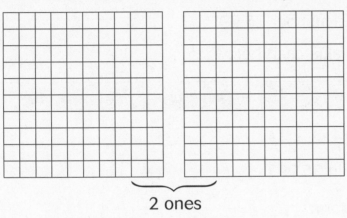

2 ones   5 tenths 3 hundredths

2. How many ones did you color? _____

Write 2 in the ones of the place-value chart below.

tens	ones		tenths	hundredths
		.		

3. After the 2 ones, how many tenths did you color?   _____

Write 5 in the tenths of the place-value chart above.

4. After the 2 ones and 5 tenths, how many
hundredths did you color?   _____

Write 3 in the hundredths place of the place-value chart above.

In 2.53, the value of the 5 is 0.5 and the value of the 3 is 0.03.

5. Write 2.53 in expanded form.

2.53 = _____ + 0.5 + _____

© Pearson Education, Inc.

Place Value Through Hundredths (continued)

6. If 1 tenth = 10 hundredths, how many
hundredths are in 5 tenths + 3 hundredths?   _____

So, the grids show 2 ones + 53 hundredths or 2.53.

7. Write 2.53 in words.   _____ and fifty-_____ hundredths

Answer 8 to 11 to examine the number 25.09.

8. Write 25.09 in the place-value chart below.

tens	ones		tenths	hundredths
		.		

9. What is the value of the 9 in 25.09? _____

10. Write 25.09 in expanded form. _____ + _____ + _____

11. Write 25.09 in words.   _____ and _____ hundredths

Write the value of the underlined digit.

12. 14.7<u>5</u>   **13.** 4.<u>2</u>9   **14.** 26.<u>4</u>6   **15.** 3.6<u>8</u>

_____   _____   _____   _____

Write each decimal in expanded form.

16. 21.97   **17.** 3.05

_____   _____

Write each decimal in words.

18. 17.81 _____

19. 0.03 _____

20. Reasoning What missing number makes the

number sentence, 28.02 = 20 + 8 = ☐ , true?   _____

© Pearson Education, Inc.

Decimals on the Number Line

Draw a point at 4.3 on the number line by answering 1 to 4.

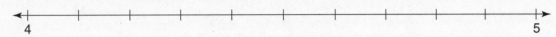

1. How many equal spaces are there between 4 and 5? _____

2. Since there are 10 equal spaces between the whole
numbers 4 and 5, each space is a tenth. One tenth more
than 4 is 4.1. The first tick mark after 4 is 4.1. Label 4.1.

3. One tenth more than 4.1 is 4.2. Continue labeling the tick
marks 4.2, 4.3, 4.4, and so on.

4. Draw a point at 4.3.

Use the number line below to answer 5 to 10.

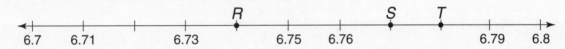

Name the decimal at point *R* by answering 5 to 8.

5. How many equal parts are there between 6.7 and 6.8? _____

6. Since there are 10 equal parts between two numbers in
the tenths, each of the parts is a hundredth. One hundredth
more than 6.7 is 6.71. One hundredth more than 6.71 is
6.72. Label 6.72.

7. Continue labeling the missing decimals by counting by
hundredths.

8. What decimal is at point *R*? _____

9. What point is at 6.77? _____

10. Reasoning If the number line continued,
what tick mark would follow 6.8?   _____

© Pearson Education, Inc.

Decimals on the Number Line (continued)

For Exercises 11–18, name the decimal that should be written at each point.

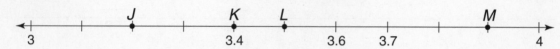

11. Point J

12. Point K

13. Point L

14. Point M

_____   _____   _____   _____

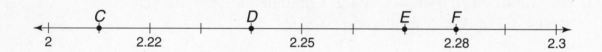

15. Point C

16. Point D

17. Point E

18. Point F

_____   _____   _____   _____

For Exercises 19–26, name the point on the number line for each decimal.

19. 9.6 _____   **20.** 9.3 _____   **21.** 10 _____   **22.** 9.1 _____

23. 5.85 _____   **24.** 5.89 _____   **25.** 5.83 _____   **26.** 5.82 _____

27. Reasoning What other decimal could be written at point 5.9 on the number line above?   _____

© Pearson Education, Inc.

Name _____

Place Value Through Thousandths

1. Write 5.739 in the place-value chart below.

ones		tenths	hundredths	thousandths
	.			

2. What is the value of the 5 in 5.739? _____

3. What is the value of the 7 in 5.739? _____

4. What is the value of the 3 in 5.739? _____

5. What is the value of the 9 in 5.739? _____

6. Write 5.739 in expanded form. _____ + 0.7 + _____ + 0.009

7. Write 5.739 in words.

_____ and seven hundred _____ thousandths

Write seven and two hundred four thousandths in standard from by answering 8 to 14.

8. How many ones are in seven and two hundred four thousandths? _____

Write 7 in the ones place of the place-value chart below.

ones		tenths	hundredths	thousandths
	.			

9. Write two hundred, thousandths as a fraction. _____

10. Write an equivalent fraction. $\dfrac{200}{1,000} = \dfrac{\square}{10}$

11. How many tenths are in seven and two hundred four thousandths? _____

Write 2 in the tenths place of the place-value chart above.

12. How many hundredths are in seven and two hundred four thousandths? _____

Write 0 in the hundredths place of the place-value chart above.

© Pearson Education, Inc.

Place Value Through Thousandths (continued)

13. How many thousandths are in seven and
two hundred four thousandths?   _____

Write 4 in the thousandths place of the place-value chart.

14. Write 7.204 in expanded form. _____ + _____ + _____

15. Reasoning What is 1 thousandth less than 7.204? _____

Write each value in standard form.

16. 507 thousandths   **17.** 5 and 6 thousandths   **18.** 9 and 62 thousandths

_____   _____   _____

Write the value of the underlined digit.

19. 2.5<u>5</u>3   **20.** 0.38<u>1</u>   **21.** 6.<u>6</u>47   **22.** 9.09<u>7</u>

_____   _____   _____   _____

Write each decimal in expanded form.

23. 4.685   **24.** 3.056

_____   _____

25. 0.735   **26.** 4.004

_____   _____

Write each decimal in word form.

27. 2.598

_____

28. 0.008

_____

29. 0.250

_____

© Pearson Education, Inc.

Place Value Through Millionths

Examine the value 4.582931 by answering 1 to 11.

1. Write 4.582931 in the place-value chart below.

Ones		Tenths	Hundredths	Thousandths	Ten Thousandths	Hundred Thousandths	Millionths
	.						

2. What is the value of the 4? _____

3. What is the value of the 5? _____

4. What is the value of the 8? _____

5. What is the value of the 2? _____

6. What is the value of the 9? _____

7. What is the value of the 3? _____

8. What is the value of the 1? _____

9. Write 4.582931 in expanded form.

_____ + 0.5 + _____ + _____ +

_____ + 0.00003 + _____

To read a decimal like 4.582931, say the whole number part and the word "and", then read the numbers to the right of the decimal as if it were a whole number. Then say the name of the place value that the last digit is in.

10. What is 4.582931 in words?

_____ and five hundred _____ thousand,

nine hundred _____ millionths

11. Write 4.582931 in short word form.   4 and _____ millionths

© Pearson Education, Inc.

Place Value Through Millionths (continued)

Write each value in standard form.

12. 35 ten thousandths

13. 5 and 3,759 millionths

14. 65,983 millionths

_____   _____   _____

Write the value of the underlined digit.

15. 0.475823

16. 2.652004

17. 1.883926

18. 0.000349

_____   _____   _____   _____

19. 2.909095

20. 1.003045

21. 0.650007

22. 0.123608

_____   _____   _____   _____

Write each decimal in expanded form.

23. 1.009671   _____

24. 0.050076   _____

25. 0.500429   _____

Write each decimal in word form.

26. 0.125456

27. 1.00058

28. Reasoning What is 1 ten thousandths more than 0.347568?   _____

29. Reasoning What is 1 hundred thousandths more than 0.347568?   _____

30. Reasoning What is 1 millionth more than 0.347598?   _____

© Pearson Education, Inc.

Rounding Decimals Through Hundredths

Round 58.21 to the nearest whole number by answering 1 to 5.

1. What digit is in the ones place? _____

2. What digit is to the right of the 8? _____

3. Is the digit to the right of the 8 less than 5, or is it 5 or greater?

_____

If the digit to the right of the 8 is 5 or more, the number rounds
up. If the digit is less than 5, the number rounds down.

4. Do you need to round up or down? _____

5. So, keep the 8. Since you are rounding to a whole
number, you do not need to keep the decimal point
or any digits to the right of the decimal point.

What is 58.21 rounded to the nearest whole number? _____

6. What is 82.62 rounded to the nearest whole number? _____

Round 27.35 to the nearest tenth by answering 7 to 11.

7. Which digit is in the tenths place? _____

8. What digit is to the right of the 3? _____

9. Is the digit to the right of the 3 less than 5, or is it 5 or greater?

_____

10. Do you need to round up or down? _____

11. So, change the 3 to the next highest digit. Since you
are rounding to the tenths, you do not need a digit
in hundredths place.

What is 27.35 rounded to the nearest tenth? _____

12. What is 36.82 rounded the nearest tenth? _____

© Pearson Education, Inc.

Rounding Decimals Through Hundredths (continued)

Round each decimal to the nearest whole number.

13. 41.4   **14.** 5.63   **15.** 5.8   **16.** 78.78   **17.** 0.96

_____   _____   _____   _____   _____

18. 47.05   **19.** 1.75   **20.** 0.5   **21.** 83.41   **22.** 6.70

_____   _____   _____   _____   _____

Round each decimal to the nearest tenth.

23. 22.79   **24.** 59.34   **25.** 0.85   **26.** 2.55   **27.** 12.86

_____   _____   _____   _____   _____

28. 38.35   **29.** 91.05   **30.** 0.62   **31.** 17.96   **32.** 28.11

_____   _____   _____   _____   _____

33. When rounded to the nearest whole number, which of these decimals round to 18?

18.5, 17.8, 18.43, 18.07, 17.58, 17.4, 17.63, 18.25, 17.49

_____

34. When rounded to the nearest tenth, which of these decimals round to 7.5?

6.9, 7.48, 7.59, 7.51, 7.43, 8.1, 7.53, 7.45, 7.65

_____

35. Reasoning When rounding to the nearest whole number, why do 5.43 and 4.68 both round to 5?

© Pearson Education, Inc.

Rounding Decimals Through Thousandths

Round 24.683 to the nearest tenth by answering 1 to 5.

1. What digit is in the tenths place? _____

2. What digit is to the right of the 6? _____

3. Is the digit to the right of the 6 less than 5, or is it 5 or greater?

  _____

If the digit to the right of the 6 is 5 or more, the number rounds up. If the digit is less than 5, the number rounds down.

4. Do you need to round up or down? _____

5. So, change the 6 to the next highest digit. Since you are rounding to the tenths, you do not need any digits to the right of the tenths.

  What is 24.683 rounded to the nearest tenth? _____

Round 0.973 to the nearest hundredth by answering 6 to 10.

6. Which digit is in the hundredths place? _____

7. What digit is to the right of the 7? _____

8. Is the digit to the right of the 7 less than 5, or is it 5 or greater?

  _____

9. Do you need to round up or down? _____

10. So, keep the 7. Since you are rounding to the hundredths, you do not need any digits to the right of the hundredths.

  What is 0.973 rounded to the nearest hundredth? _____

Round 15.136 to the nearest whole number by answering 11 to 14.

11. Which digit is in the ones place? _____

12. What digit is to the right of the 5? _____

13. Do you need to round up or down? _____

14. So, keep the 5. What is 15.136 rounded to the nearest whole number? _____

© Pearson Education, Inc.

Rounding Decimals Through Thousandths (continued)

Round 82.946 to the given place.

15. Nearest hundredth **16.** Nearest tenth   **17.** Nearest one   **18.** Nearest ten

_____   _____   _____   _____

Round 37.054 to the given place.

19. Nearest hundredth **20.** Nearest tenth   **21.** Nearest one   **22.** Nearest ten

_____   _____   _____   _____

Round each number to the nearest hundredth.

23. 0.873 _____   **24.** 23.892 _____

25. 456.134 _____   **26.** 1.006 _____

Round each number to the nearest tenth.

27. 34.276 _____   **28.** 729.35 _____

29. 0.524 _____   **30.** 10.478 _____

Round each number to the nearest whole number.

31. 184.535 _____   **32.** 50.345 _____

33. 23.297 _____   **34.** 6.767 _____

Round each number to the nearest ten.

35. 345.893 _____   **36.** 19.34 _____

37. 1,784.34 _____   **38.** 9.457 _____

39. When rounded to the nearest hundredth, which of these decimals round to 5.43?

5.44, 5.431, 5.425, 5.435, 5.434, 5.428, 5.438, 5.437, 5.429

_____

40. Reasoning When rounding to the nearest tenth, why do 8.783 and 8.839 both round to 8.8?

© Pearson Education, Inc.

Comparing and Ordering Decimals Through Hundredths

Jackson's puppy weighs 8.42 pounds. Benjamin's puppy weighs 8.48 pounds. Find whose puppy weighs more by answering 1 to 6.

1. Write 8.42 and 8.48 in the place-value chart.

ones		tenths	hundredths
	•		
	•		

For Exercises 2–5, write $<$, $>$, or $=$.

2. Start on the left. Compare the ones.   8 _____ 8

3. Since the ones are equal, compare the tenths.   0.4 _____ 0.4

4. Since the tenths are equal, compare the hundredths.   0.02 _____ 0.08

5. Since $0.02 < 0.08$, 8.42 _____ 8.48.

6. Whose dog weighs more? _____

Order 3.56; 3.67; and 2.59 from least to greatest by answering 7 to 12.

7. Write the decimals so the decimal points line up.

_____ • _____ _____

_____ • _____ _____

_____ • _____ _____

8. Start on the left. Compare the ones. 2 _____ 3

9. Since $2 < 3$, which decimal is the least? _____

10. Compare the tenths of the two other decimals. 0.5 _____ 0.6

© Pearson Education, Inc.

Comparing and Ordering Decimals Through Hundredths (continued)

11. Since 0.5 < 0.6, which decimal is the least? _____

12. Write the decimals in order from least to greatest. _____ _____ _____

Compare. Write >, <, or = for each.

13.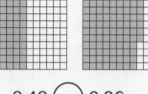

0.40 ◯ 0.86

14.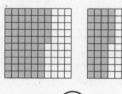

0.65 ◯ 0.35

15.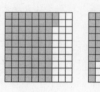

0.72 ◯ 0.17

16. 0.45 ◯ 0.14   **17.** 6.78 ◯ 6.25   **18.** 8.02 ◯ 8.2

19. 5.37 ◯ 3.5   **20.** 0.12 ◯ 0.22   **21.** 2.5 ◯ 2.50

22. 0.89 ◯ 8.09   **23.** 0.45 ◯ 0.86   **24.** 0.72 ◯ 0.17

25. 0.3 ◯ 0.30   **26.** 7.75 ◯ 7.76   **27.** 2.5 ◯ 2.41

Order the numbers from least to greatest.

28. 0.45, 0.30, 0.40   **29.** 0.05, 0.50, 0.15

_____   _____

30. 8.45, 9.56, 8.42   **31.** 3.56, 3.21, 3.72

_____   _____

32. 9.34, 9.25, 9.37, 9.3   **33.** 0.67, 6.77, 6.67, 0.76

_____   _____

34. Reasoning A green parakeet weighs 0.74
pound. A blue parakeet weighs 0.69 pound.
Which parakeet weighs more?   _____

© Pearson Education, Inc.

Comparing and Ordering Decimals Through Thousandths

Compare 3.761 and 3.766 by answering 1 to 6.

1. Write the decimals so the decimal points line up.

_____ • _____ _____ _____

_____ • _____ _____ _____

For Exercises 2–6, write <, >, or =.

2. Start on the left. Compare the ones.   3 _____ 3

3. Since the ones are equal, compare the tenths.   0.7 _____ 0.7

4. Since the tenths are equal, compare the hundredths.   0.06 _____ 0.06

5. Since the hundredths are equal, compare the thousandths.   0.001 _____ 0.006

6. So, 3.761 _____ 3.766.

Order these numbers from least to greatest by answering 7 to 13.

5.432; 5.45; 5.437

7. Write the decimals so the decimal points are lined up. You can place zeros so that all of the decimals have digits to the same place value.

_____ • _____ _____ _____

_____ • _____ _____ _____

_____ • _____ _____ _____

8. Starting on the left, in the ones place, compare the digits in each place. In what place do the digits become different?   _____

9. Compare the hundredths.   0.03 _____ 0.05

10. Since 0.03 < 0.05, which decimal is the greatest? _____

© Pearson Education, Inc.

Comparing and Ordering Decimals Through Thousandths (continued)

11. Compare the thousandths of the two other decimals.   0.002 _____ 0.007

12. Since 0.002 < 0.007, which decimal is the least? _____

13. Write the numbers in order from least to greatest.

_____   _____   _____

Compare, use >, <, or = for each .

14. 3.75 ◯ 3.750   **15.** 79.6 ◯ 79.06   **16.** 48.97 ◯ 49.87

17. 0.287 ◯ 0.278   **18.** 1.382 ◯ 1.823   **19.** 85.271 ◯ 85.27

20. 29.699 ◯ 29.700   **21.** 8.95 ◯ 8.950   **22.** 16.050 ◯ 16.005

23. 0.54 ◯ 0.549   **24.** 21.603 ◯ 21.63   **25.** 7.93 ◯ 7.9

Write the numbers in each set from least to greatest.

26. 84.44, 84.444, 84.4

27. 4.05, 4.005, 4.500

_____   _____

28. 10.56, 10.165, 10.156, 10.615

29. 7.29, 7.199, 7.129, 7.219

_____   _____

30. If a table tennis ball weighs 0.085 ounce and a squash
ball weighs 0.821 ounce, which ball weighs more?   _____

31. If a northern elephant seal weighs 3.35 tons and a southern
elephant seal weighs 3.54 tons, which seal weighs less?

_____

32. Reasoning Write three numbers between 50.1 and 50.2.

© Pearson Education, Inc.

Name _____

Relating Fractions and Decimals

Materials crayons or markers

1. How many equal parts are
   in the rectangle on the right? _____

2. Color 3 equal parts of the
   rectangle.

3. What fractional part of the
   rectangle did you color?

4. The fraction $\frac{3}{10}$ is read "three tenths",
   what is three tenths written in decimal form? _____

So, $\frac{3}{10}$ and 0.3 are both three tenths. They are the same amount.

$$\frac{3}{10} = 0.3$$

5. How many equal parts are
   in the grid on the right? _____

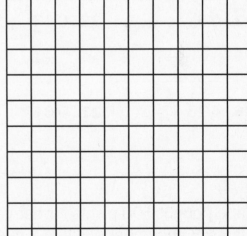

6. Color 4 columns and 3 more
   squares in the grid. How
   many small squares did you
   color? _____

7. What decimal represents the
   part of the grid you colored? _____

8. Write 0.43 in words.

_____

9. What is 43 hundredths written as a fraction?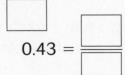

10. So, 0.43 and $\frac{43}{100}$ are the same amount. $0.43 = $

© Pearson Education, Inc.

Relating Fractions and Decimals (continued)

Write a fraction and a decimal for each shaded part.

11. 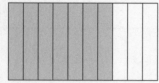   **12.**   **13.**

_____   _____   _____

Write each fraction as a decimal.

14. $\frac{8}{10}$ **15.** $\frac{56}{100}$ **16.** $\frac{7}{10}$ **17.** $\frac{13}{100}$

_____   _____   _____   _____

18. $\frac{85}{100}$ **19.** $\frac{77}{100}$ **20.** $\frac{6}{100}$ **21.** $3\frac{5}{10}$

_____   _____   _____   _____

Write each decimal as a fraction or mixed number.

22. 0.3   **23.** 0.63   **24.** 6.9   **25.** 0.17

_____   _____   _____   _____

26. 4.23   **27.** 0.01   **28.** 0.33   **29.** 1.1

_____   _____   _____   _____

Katie bought 100 plants for her garden. She bought 37 tomato plants, 8 cucumber plants, 12 pumpkin plants, and the rest of her plants were onions.

30. Write a fraction and a decimal to express the part of the plants that are tomatoes.   _____

31. Reasoning Write a fraction and a decimal to express the part of the plants that are onions.   _____

© Pearson Education, Inc.

Decimals to Fractions

Materials crayons, markers, or colored pencils

Write 0.45 as a fraction by answering 1 to 5.

1. Color the grid to show 0.45.

2. How small squares did you color?   _____

3. How many squares are in the grid?   _____

4. What fraction represents the
part of the grid that you colored?   _____

5. Write a fraction equal to 0.45.   0.45 = _____

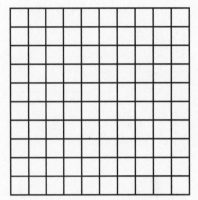

You can also use place value to change a decimal to a fraction.

Write 0.3 as a fraction by answering 6 to 9

6. Write 0.3 in words.   _____

7. What is the place value of the 3 in 0.3?   _____

8. What fraction represents three tenths?   _____

Since the 3 is in the tenths place, you write 3 over 10.

9. Write a fraction equal to 0.3.   0.3 = _____

Write 3.07 as a mixed number by answering 10 to 13.

10. What is the whole number part of the decimal 3.07?   _____

11. What is the place value of the last digit in 3.07? _____

12. Write the place value as the denominator $3.07 = 3\dfrac{7}{\boxed{}}$
and write 7 as the numerator.

13. Write a mixed number equal to 3.07.   3.07 = _____

© Pearson Education, Inc.

Name _____

Decimals to Fractions (continued)

Write each decimal as a fraction or mixed number.

14. 0.4

15. 3.7

16. 5.27

_____   _____   _____

17. 0.8

18. 1.2

19. 4.03

_____   _____   _____

20. 0.12

21. 10.5

22. 0.19

_____   _____   _____

23. 0.42

24. 5.75

25. 8.6

_____   _____   _____

26. 19.09

27. 0.01

28. 28.37

_____   _____   _____

29. Jaime put 13.9 gallons of gas in the car.
What is 13.9 written as a mixed number?   _____

30. Candice ran 2.75 miles.
What is 2.75 written as a mixed number?   _____

31. Justin's mom bought a 12.57 pound turkey.
What is 12.57 written as a mixed number?   _____

32. Reasoning Marco says $0.08 = \frac{8}{10}$. Is he correct? Explain why.

33. Reasoning $2.37 = 2\frac{37}{100}$ and $2.3 = 2\frac{3}{10}$. Explain why the 3 in
2.37 represents $\frac{3}{10}$.

© Pearson Education, Inc.

Fractions to Decimals

Materials crayons, markers, or colored pencils

In the Princeton Middle School marching band, 3 of the 100 students play the tuba.

Write $\frac{3}{100}$ as a decimal by answering 1 to 3.

1. Color the grid to show $\frac{3}{100}$.

2. What decimal represents the part of the grid you colored? _____

3. What decimal is equal to $\frac{3}{100}$? $\frac{3}{100} =$ _____

4. What decimal is equal to $5\frac{3}{100}$? _____

5. How many zeros are in the denominator of $\frac{3}{100}$? _____

6. How many digits are to the right of the decimal point in 0.03? _____

When the denominator is a power of 10, like 10 or 100, the number of zeros in the denominator matches the number of digits to the right of the decimal point in the equivalent decimal.

7. Complete the table.

Fraction	Number of Zeros in Denominator	Number of Digits to Right of Decimal Point	Equivalent Decimal
$\frac{2}{10}$	1	1	0.2
$\frac{2}{100}$	2		
$\frac{20}{100}$			0.20

8. How many zeros are in the denominator of $\frac{67}{100}$? _____

So what decimal is equal to $\frac{67}{100}$? $\frac{67}{100} =$ _____

You can also change a fraction to a decimal by dividing the numerator by the denominator.

9. Write $\frac{3}{20}$ as a decimal. Find the quotient of $\frac{3}{20}$ or 3 ÷ 20, at the right.

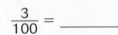

$20\overline{)3.00}$

10. What decimal is equal to $\frac{3}{20}$? $\frac{3}{20} =$ _____

© Pearson Education, Inc.

Fractions to Decimals (continued)

Write each fraction as a decimal.

11. $\frac{1}{5}$ **12.** $\frac{7}{10}$ **13.** $\frac{1}{2}$ **14.** $\frac{63}{100}$

_____   _____   _____   _____

15. $\frac{47}{100}$ **16.** $\frac{3}{4}$ **17.** $\frac{84}{100}$ **18.** $\frac{77}{100}$

_____   _____   _____   _____

19. $\frac{6}{100}$ **20.** $\frac{29}{100}$ **21.** $\frac{51}{100}$ **22.** $\frac{40}{100}$

_____   _____   _____   _____

The picture at the right shows the books Jason read in September.
Use the picture for Exercises 23 and 24.

23. Write a fraction and a decimal to describe the
part of the books that Jason read that were fiction.

$\frac{\boxed{}}{10}$, _____

24. Write a fraction and a decimal to describe the
part of the books that Jason read that were
nonfiction.

$\frac{\boxed{}}{10}$, _____

Katie bought 100 plants for her garden. She bought 37 tomato plants,
8 cucumber plants, 12 pumpkin plants, and the rest of her plants were
onions. Use this information for Exercises 25 to 27.

25. Write a fraction and a decimal to express the part of
the plants that are tomatoes.

$\frac{\boxed{}}{100}$, _____

26. What part of her plants are cucumbers and pumpkins?
Express your answer as a decimal.

_____

27. Reasoning Explain the difference between the decimal
equivalents of $\frac{9}{10}$ and $\frac{9}{100}$.

© Pearson Education, Inc.

Name _____

Relating Fractions and Decimals to Thousandths

Wyatt lost a swim race by 0.065 second. Answer 1 to 4 to learn how to write this value as a fraction.

1. In the decimal 0.065, 0 is in the tenths place, 6 is in the hundreths

place and 5 is in the _____ place.

2. Write the value of 0.065 in words.   _____

3. To write sixty-five thousandths as a fraction, what value
goes in the numerator?   _____

What value goes in the denominator?   _____

4. Write a fraction equal to 0.065 second.   0.065 = _____ second

To write a fraction as a decimal, first look at the denominator of the fraction.

When the denominator is a power of 10, like 10, 100, or 1,000, the number of zeros in the denominator matches the number of digits to the right of the decimal point in the equivalent decimal.

5. Complete the table.

Fraction	Number of Zeros in Denominator	Number of Digits to Right of Decimal Point	Decimal
$\frac{4}{10}$	1	1	0.4
$\frac{45}{100}$		2	0.45
$\frac{455}{1000}$		3	0.455
$\frac{485}{1000}$			

6. How many zeros are in the denominator of $\frac{285}{1000}$?   _____

So, what decimal is equal to $\frac{285}{1000}$? $\frac{285}{1000}$ = _____

7. **Reasoning** Janet beat her opponent by one hundred and sixteen thousandths second. Write this value as a fraction and a decimal.   _____

© Pearson Education, Inc.

Relating Fractions and Decimals to Thousandths (continued)

Write each decimal as a fraction.

8. 0.345　　　　**9.** 0.043　　　　**10.** 0.002　　　　**11.** 0.507

_____　　_____　　_____　　_____

12. 0.201　　　　**13.** 0.011　　　　**14.** 0.999　　　　**15.** 0.058

_____　　_____　　_____　　_____

16. A major league baseball player has a batting
average of 0.385. What is his batting average
written as a fraction?　　　　　　　　_____

Write each fraction as a decimal.

17. $\dfrac{4}{1000}$　　　　**18.** $\dfrac{56}{1000}$　　　　**19.** $\dfrac{702}{1000}$　　　　**20.** $\dfrac{23}{1000}$

_____　　_____　　_____　　_____

21. $\dfrac{545}{1000}$　　　　**22.** $\dfrac{757}{1000}$　　　　**23.** $\dfrac{67}{1000}$　　　　**24.** $\dfrac{1}{1000}$

_____　　_____　　_____　　_____

A local ballet theater can seat 1,000 patrons. There are 64 seats in the
private balcony sections, 225 seats in the orchestra section, 300 seats
in the lower level, and the rest of the seats are located in the upper
level. Use this information for Exercises 25 and 26.

25. Write a fraction and a decimal to represent
the part of the seats that are balcony seats.　　　_____

26. Reasoning Write a fraction and a decimal
to represent the part of the seats that are
in the upper level.　　　　　　　　　　　_____

© Pearson Education, Inc.

Using Models to Compare Fractions and Decimals

Materials crayons, markers, or colored pencils

Brigette walks $\frac{6}{10}$ of a mile to school and Ronnie walks 0.9 of a mile. Which student walks farther to school?

Compare $\frac{6}{10}$ and 0.9 by answering 1 to 4.

1. Color $\frac{6}{10}$ of the grid.

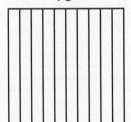

2. Color 0.9 of the grid.

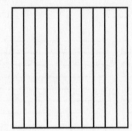

3. Compare. Write >, <, or =. $\frac{6}{10}$ ◯ 0.9

4. Which student walks farther to school? _____

Compare $\frac{35}{100}$ and 0.3 by answering 5 to 7.

5. Color $\frac{35}{100}$ of the grid.

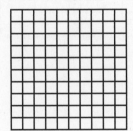

6. Color 0.3 of the grid.
(Color whole columns.)

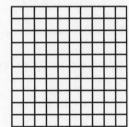

7. Compare. Write >, <, or =. $\frac{35}{100}$ ◯ 0.3

8. Reasoning How can you compare $\frac{35}{100}$ and 0.3 without using grids?

© Pearson Education, Inc.

Name

Using Models to Compare Fractions and Decimals (continued)

Color the grids to compare. Write >, <, or =.

9. 0.5 ◯ $\frac{3}{10}$

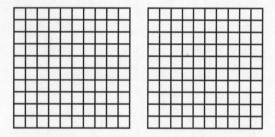

10. $\frac{44}{100}$ ◯ 0.8

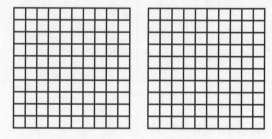

11. 0.2 ◯ $\frac{12}{100}$

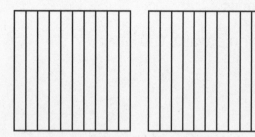

12. $\frac{8}{100}$ ◯ 0.08

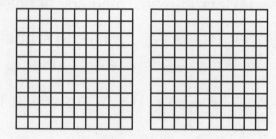

13. 0.53 ◯ $\frac{57}{100}$

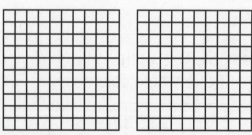

14. $\frac{45}{100}$ ◯ 0.54

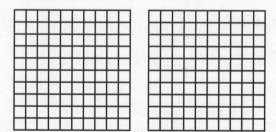

15. Maria has 100 flowers in a garden. If 0.43 of the flowers are roses and $\frac{9}{100}$ of the flowers are daisies, does Maria have more roses or daisies? _____

16. Reasoning Without coloring a grid, how can you tell that 0.7 and $\frac{70}{100}$ are equal?

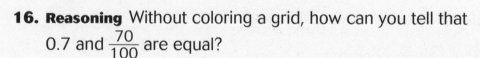

© Pearson Education, Inc.

Fractions, Decimals, and the Number Line

The points on a number line may be identified using a fraction, decimal, or both.

Plot point *A* at 3.4, point *B* at $3\frac{1}{10}$, and point *C* at 4.15 on the number line below by answering 1 to 9.

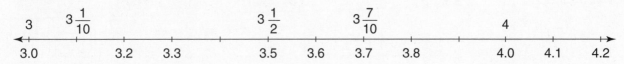

1. How many equal lengths is the distance
between 3.0 and 4.0 divided into?   _____

2. Find 3.4 on the number line. Plot the point and label it *A*.

3. What mixed number is equivalent to 3.4? _____

4. Find $3\frac{1}{10}$ on the number line. Plot the point and label it *B*.

5. What decimal is equivalent to $3\frac{1}{10}$? _____

6. Is 4.15 greater than 4.1? _____

7. Is 4.15 greater than 4.2? _____

8. Since 4.15 is between 4.1 and 4.2, locate 4.15 on the
enlarged number line below.

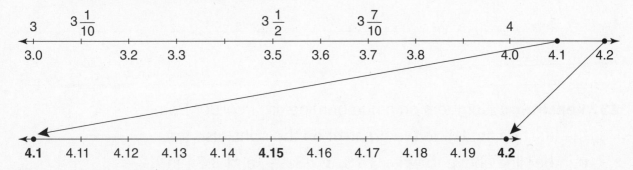

9. Describe the location of 4.15
on the enlarged number line. _____

10. Plot 4.15 on both number lines and label each point *C*.

© Pearson Education, Inc.

Fractions, Decimals, and the Number Line (continued)

For Exercises 11 to 14, name the decimal and mixed number that should be written at each point on the number line below.

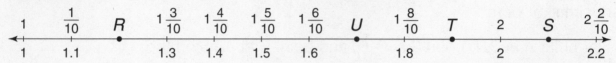

11. R   **12.** S   **13.** T   **14.** U

_____   _____   _____   _____

_____   _____   _____   _____

For Exercises 15 to 18, name the point on the number line below that represents each decimal or mixed number.

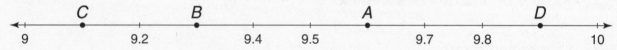

15. 9.6   **16.** $9\frac{3}{10}$ **17.** $9\frac{9}{10}$ **18.** 9.1

_____   _____   _____   _____

For Exercises 19 to 22, name the decimal and mixed number that should be written at each point on the number line below.

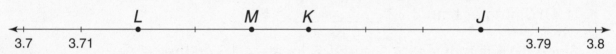

19. J   **20.** K   **21.** L   **22.** M

_____   _____   _____   _____

_____   _____   _____   _____

23. Reasoning Numbers on a number line are in order from the least on the left to the greatest on the right. Use the number line above to write 3.78, $3\frac{3}{4}$, $3\frac{72}{100}$, and 3.74 in order from least to greatest.

_____

© Pearson Education, Inc.

Name _____

Adding Fractions with Like Denominators

Materials crayons or markers

Nur wove $\frac{2}{5}$ of a rug in February and $\frac{1}{5}$ of it in March. Find what part of the rug she has finished in all by answering 1 to 4.

1. Color $\frac{2}{5}$ of the rectangle on the right.

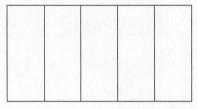

2. Color $\frac{1}{5}$ more of the rectangle on the right.

3. How much of the rectangle did you color in all?

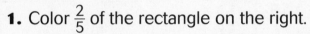

       This is the sum of $\frac{2}{5}$ and $\frac{1}{5}$. So, $\frac{2}{5} + \frac{1}{5} = \frac{3}{5}$.

4. What part of her rug has Nur finished in all? _____

Jamal wove $\frac{2}{6}$ of a rug in February and $\frac{2}{6}$ in March. Find what part of the rug he has finished in all by answering 5 to 11.

5. Color $\frac{2}{6}$ of the rectangle on the right.

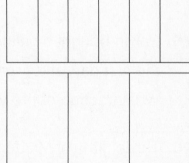

6. Color $\frac{2}{6}$ more of the rectangle on the right.

7. How much of the rectangle did you color in all?

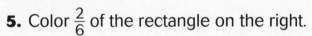

8. What is $\frac{2}{6} + \frac{2}{6}$? _____

9. What is a fraction equivalent to $\frac{4}{6}$, but with smaller numbers? Color the second rectangle to find out.

$\frac{4}{6} = \dfrac{\square}{\square}$

10. So, $\frac{2}{6} + \frac{2}{6} = \frac{4}{6} = \dfrac{\square}{\square}$.

11. What part of his rug has Jamal finished in all? _____

© Pearson Education, Inc.

Adding Fractions with Like Denominators (continued)

12. Reasoning Explain how to add $\frac{1}{9} + \frac{4}{9}$.

Add.

13.

$\frac{1}{3} + \frac{1}{3} =$ _____

14.

$\frac{1}{5} + \frac{3}{5} =$ _____

15.

$\frac{1}{4} + \frac{2}{4} =$ _____

16.

$\frac{2}{6} + \frac{3}{6} =$ _____

17. $\frac{2}{8} + \frac{5}{8} =$ _____

18. $\frac{3}{10} + \frac{2}{10} =$ _____ = _____

19. Calvin bought a gallon of yogurt. He ate $\frac{1}{6}$ gallon
the first day, and $\frac{2}{6}$ gallon the second day.
What fraction of the yogurt did he eat?   _____

20. Three-fifths of Mr. James' class are wearing blue jeans
and white shirts. One-fifth of the class are wearing blue
jeans and red shirts. One-fifth of the class are wearing
brown pants and white shirts. What fraction of Mr. James'
class are wearing white shirts?   _____

21. Reasoning What fraction would you add to $\frac{1}{3}$ to get $\frac{3}{3}$?   _____

© Pearson Education, Inc.

Subtracting Fractions with Like Denominators

Materials crayons or markers

Tammy loves tuna bake. When she came home from school, she found $\frac{6}{8}$ of a tuna bake on the stove. She ate $\frac{1}{8}$ of it. Find how much of the tuna bake was left by answering 1 to 5.

1. Color $\frac{6}{8}$ of the rectangle on the right.

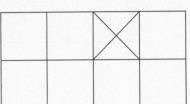

2. Cross out $\frac{1}{8}$ of the part you colored.

3. How much of the rectangle you colored is not crossed out? $\frac{\boxed{}}{\boxed{}}$

4. What is $\frac{6}{8} - \frac{1}{8}$? $\frac{\boxed{}}{\boxed{}}$

5. How much of the tuna bake was left after Tammy ate? _____

Brad found $\frac{3}{4}$ of a submarine sandwich when he came home from school. He ate $\frac{1}{4}$ of the sandwich. Find how much of the sandwich was left by answering 6 to 12.

6. Color $\frac{3}{4}$ of the rectangle on the right.

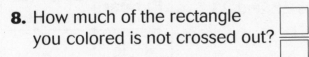

7. Cross out $\frac{1}{4}$ of the part you colored.

8. How much of the rectangle you colored is not crossed out? $\frac{\boxed{}}{\boxed{}}$

9. What is $\frac{3}{4} - \frac{1}{4}$? $\frac{\boxed{}}{\boxed{}}$

10. What is a fraction equivalent to $\frac{2}{4}$, but with smaller numbers? Color the second rectangle to find out. $\frac{2}{4} = \frac{\boxed{}}{\boxed{}}$

11. So, $\frac{3}{4} - \frac{1}{4} = \frac{2}{4} = \frac{\boxed{}}{\boxed{}}$.

12. How much of the sandwich was left after Brad ate? _____

© Pearson Education, Inc.

Subtracting Fractions with Like Denominators (continued)

13. Reasoning Explain how to subtract $\frac{5}{10} - \frac{2}{10}$.

Subtract.

14.

$$\frac{5}{6} - \frac{3}{6} = \underline{\hspace{1cm}}$$

15.

$$\frac{3}{5} - \frac{1}{5} = \underline{\hspace{1cm}}$$

16.

$$\frac{3}{4} - \frac{1}{4} = \underline{\hspace{1cm}}$$

17.

$$\frac{4}{5} - \frac{2}{5} = \underline{\hspace{1cm}}$$

18. $\frac{4}{7} - \frac{3}{7} = \underline{\hspace{1cm}}$

19. $\frac{5}{9} - \frac{4}{9} = \underline{\hspace{1cm}}$

20. $\frac{7}{8} - \frac{1}{8} = \underline{\hspace{1cm}} = \underline{\hspace{1cm}}$

21. $\frac{4}{6} - \frac{1}{6} = \underline{\hspace{1cm}} = \underline{\hspace{1cm}}$

The table shows the distances run by members of
a track team. Use the table for Exercises 22 and 23.

22. How much farther did
Rosie run than Tricia?   _____

23. How much farther did
Caro run than Tricia?   _____

24. Reasoning Why would it be more difficult

to subtract $\frac{2}{3} - \frac{1}{6}$ than $\frac{2}{3} - \frac{1}{3}$?

Runner	Distance in miles
Rosie	$\frac{7}{8}$
Tricia	$\frac{4}{8}$
Amy	$\frac{5}{8}$
Caro	$\frac{6}{8}$

© Pearson Education, Inc.

Adding and Subtracting Fractions with Like Denominators

Carlos spent $\frac{3}{4}$ hour writing email and another $\frac{3}{4}$ hour surfing the internet. How much time did he spend on his computer in all?

Find $\frac{3}{4} + \frac{3}{4}$ by answering 1 to 4.

1. Show $\frac{3}{4} + \frac{3}{4}$ with fraction strips.

2. What is $\frac{3}{4} + \frac{3}{4}$? _____

3. Use the fraction strips to find $\frac{6}{4}$ as a mixed number in simplest form.

$$\frac{3}{4} + \frac{3}{4} = \frac{6}{4} = 1\frac{\boxed{}}{4} = \text{_____}$$

4. How much time did Carlos spend on his computer in all? _____

5. Reasoning Explain how to find $\frac{7}{10} + \frac{9}{10}$.

Connie had $\frac{5}{6}$ hour to surf the internet. She finished with one site in $\frac{1}{6}$ hour. How much time did she have left?

Find $\frac{5}{6} - \frac{1}{6}$ by answering 6 to 11.

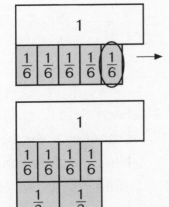

6. Show $\frac{5}{6}$ with fraction strips.

7. Take away $\frac{1}{6}$.

8. What is $\frac{5}{6} - \frac{1}{6}$? _____

9. Write the difference in simplest form. $\frac{4}{6} = $ _____

10. So, $\frac{5}{6} - \frac{1}{6} = \frac{4}{6} = $ _____.

11. How much time did Connie have left to surf the internet? _____

© Pearson Education, Inc.

Adding and Subtracting Fractions with Like Denominators (continued)

12. Reasoning Explain how to find $\frac{7}{8} - \frac{1}{8}$.

Add. Write the sum in simplest form.

13. $\frac{5}{12} + \frac{1}{12}$ **14.** $\frac{5}{9} + \frac{1}{9}$ **15.** $\frac{4}{15} + \frac{8}{15}$

_____   _____   _____

16. $\frac{3}{5} + \frac{4}{5}$ **17.** $\frac{6}{7} + \frac{4}{7}$ **18.** $\frac{2}{3} + \frac{2}{3}$

_____   _____   _____

19. $\frac{7}{10} + \frac{9}{10}$ **20.** $\frac{7}{8} + \frac{5}{8}$ **21.** $\frac{11}{12} + \frac{5}{12}$

_____   _____   _____

Subtract. Write the difference in simplest form.

22. $\frac{2}{3} - \frac{1}{3}$ **23.** $\frac{11}{12} - \frac{1}{12}$ **24.** $\frac{7}{9} - \frac{1}{9}$

_____   _____   _____

25. $\frac{7}{8} - \frac{1}{8}$ **26.** $\frac{9}{10} - \frac{3}{10}$ **27.** $\frac{3}{4} - \frac{1}{4}$

_____   _____   _____

28. Each class is making a friendship chain the length of the school gym, for the end of year party. The fifth grade class has $\frac{7}{10}$ of their chain finished. The sixth grade class has $\frac{9}{10}$ of theirs finished. How much more of the sixth grade chain is finished than the fifth grade chain?

_____

29. Reasoning Richard gathered $\frac{7}{12}$ of a dozen eggs and Karina gathered $\frac{5}{12}$ of a dozen. What part of a dozen did they gather in all? Explain.

© Pearson Education, Inc.

Adding and Subtracting Fractions on a Number Line

Materials place-value blocks, for each student

Sarah walks $\frac{1}{12}$ of the way to school. Then, she rides a bus $\frac{3}{4}$ or $\frac{9}{12}$ of the way. Finally, she has to walk the rest of the way. When she gets off the bus, what part of the way to school is she?

Find $\frac{1}{12} + \frac{9}{12}$ by answering 1 to 4.

1. The number line below has an arrow from 0 to $\frac{1}{12}$ to show how far Sarah walks before she catches the bus. Draw another arrow that is $\frac{9}{12}$ units long, starting at $\frac{1}{12}$.

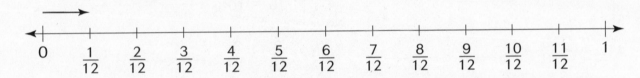

2. At what fraction does your arrow end? _____

The two arrows show that $\frac{1}{12} + \frac{9}{12} = \frac{10}{12}$.

3. What is $\frac{10}{12}$ in simplest form?   _____

4. When Sarah gets off the bus, what part of the way to school is she? _____

When Sarah gets off the bus, how much farther does she need to walk to get to school?

Find $\frac{12}{12} - \frac{10}{12}$ by answering 5 to 8.

5. Draw an arrow that is $\frac{10}{12}$ units long, from $\frac{12}{12}$ or 1 back toward zero.

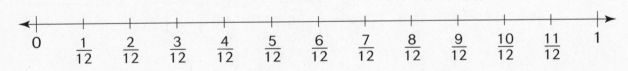

6. At what fraction does your arrow end? _____

The number line shows that $\frac{12}{12} - \frac{10}{12} = \frac{2}{12}$.

© Pearson Education, Inc.

Adding and Subtracting Fractions on a Number Line (continued)

7. What is $\frac{2}{12}$ in simplest form? _____

8. When Sarah gets off the bus, how much farther
does she need to walk to get to school? _____ of the way

Use the number line to add or subtract. Write answers in simplest form.

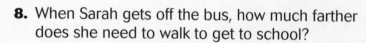

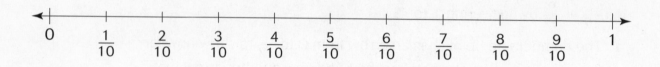

9. $\frac{3}{10} + \frac{4}{10} = $ _____

10. $\frac{7}{10} + \frac{1}{10} = $ _____ = _____

11. $\frac{9}{10} - \frac{3}{10} = $ _____ = _____

12. $\frac{8}{10} - \frac{3}{10} = $ _____ = _____

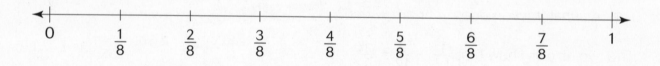

13. $\frac{1}{8} + \frac{4}{8} = $ _____

14. $\frac{3}{8} + \frac{1}{8} = $ _____ = _____

15. $\frac{7}{8} - \frac{1}{8} = $ _____ = _____

16. $\frac{5}{8} - \frac{3}{8} = $ _____ = _____

17. Rodney mixed $\frac{2}{9}$ of a bottle of apple juice with $\frac{4}{9}$ of a bottle
of cranberry juice. How much juice was in the mixture? _____

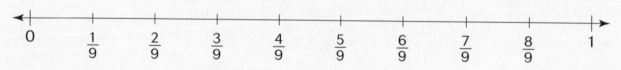

18. Reasoning What is $\frac{4}{9} + \frac{2}{9} - \frac{1}{9}$? _____

© Pearson Education, Inc.

Name _____

Adding Fractions with Unlike Denominators

Materials fraction strips

Tamika and Li are painting a mural. Tamika has painted $\frac{1}{3}$ of the mural and
Li has painted $\frac{1}{6}$ of it. What part of the mural have they painted in all?

Find $\frac{1}{3} + \frac{1}{6}$ by answering 1 to 6.

1. Show a $\frac{1}{3}$ and a $\frac{1}{6}$ strip on a one strip.

| $\frac{1}{3}$ | $\frac{1}{6}$ | |

Since it is difficult to tell what part of the
one strip is covered, change the $\frac{1}{3}$ to sixths.

2. $\frac{1}{3} = \frac{\square}{6}$

| $\frac{1}{3}$ | $\frac{1}{6}$ | |
| $\frac{1}{6}$ | $\frac{1}{6}$ | |

3. Put $\frac{1}{6}$ strips on top of the $\frac{1}{3}$ strip.

| $\frac{1}{6}$ | $\frac{1}{6}$ | $\frac{1}{6}$ | |

What is $\frac{2}{6} + \frac{1}{6}$? _____

4. What is $\frac{1}{3} + \frac{1}{6}$? _____

| $\frac{1}{6}$ | $\frac{1}{6}$ | $\frac{1}{6}$ | $\frac{1}{6}$ | $\frac{1}{6}$ | |
| $\frac{1}{2}$ | | | | | |

5. What is $\frac{3}{6}$ in simplest form? _____

So, $\frac{1}{3} + \frac{1}{6} = \frac{2}{6} + \frac{1}{6} = \frac{3}{6} = \frac{1}{2}$.

At the right is another way to write the addition.

6. What part of the mural have
Tamika and Li painted in all? _____

$$\begin{array}{r} \frac{1}{3} = \frac{2}{6} \\ + \frac{1}{6} = \frac{1}{6} \\ \hline \frac{3}{6} = \frac{1}{2} \end{array}$$

7. Use fraction strips and fill in the missing
numbers at the right to find $\frac{1}{2} + \frac{2}{5}$.

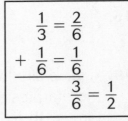

$$\begin{array}{r} \frac{1}{2} = \frac{\square}{10} \\ + \frac{2}{5} = \frac{\square}{10} \\ \hline \square \end{array}$$

| $\frac{1}{2}$ | | | | | $\frac{1}{5}$ | $\frac{1}{5}$ | |
| $\frac{1}{10}$ | $\frac{1}{10}$ | $\frac{1}{10}$ | $\frac{1}{10}$ | $\frac{1}{10}$ | $\frac{1}{10}$ | $\frac{1}{10}$ | $\frac{1}{10}$ | $\frac{1}{10}$ |

© Pearson Education, Inc.

Adding Fractions with Unlike Denominators (continued)

Find each sum. Use fraction strips, if you like.

8.

$$\frac{4}{8} = \frac{4}{8}$$

$$+ \frac{1}{4} = \frac{\boxed{}}{8}$$

$\frac{1}{8}$	$\frac{1}{8}$	$\frac{1}{8}$	$\frac{1}{8}$	$\frac{1}{4}$	
$\frac{1}{8}$	$\frac{1}{8}$	$\frac{1}{8}$	$\frac{1}{8}$	$\frac{1}{8}$	$\frac{1}{8}$
$\frac{1}{4}$		$\frac{1}{4}$		$\frac{1}{4}$	

9.

$$\frac{1}{2} = \frac{\boxed{}}{6}$$

$$+ \frac{1}{3} = \frac{\boxed{}}{6}$$

| $\frac{1}{2}$ | | $\frac{1}{3}$ | |
| $\frac{1}{6}$ | $\frac{1}{6}$ | $\frac{1}{6}$ | $\frac{1}{6}$ | $\frac{1}{6}$ |

10. $\frac{2}{3} + \frac{1}{6} =$ _____

11. $\frac{1}{5} + \frac{3}{10} =$ _____

12. $\frac{3}{8} + \frac{2}{4} =$ _____

13. $\frac{3}{4} + \frac{2}{8} =$ _____

14. $\frac{1}{6} + \frac{5}{12} =$ _____

15. $\frac{1}{8} + \frac{1}{2} =$ _____

16. $\frac{2}{6} + \frac{1}{3} =$ _____

17. $\frac{2}{4} + \frac{1}{8} =$ _____

18. $\frac{3}{8} + \frac{1}{2} =$ _____

19. A jar is filled with red, blue, and green marbles. Half of the marbles are red. One-third of the marbles are blue. One-sixth of the marbles are green. What fraction of the marbles are either red or blue?

_____

20. **Reasoning** Could you change both fractions to a denominator of 9 to add $\frac{1}{3}$ and $\frac{1}{4}$? Explain.

© Pearson Education, Inc.

Name _____

Subtracting Fractions with Unlike Denominators

Materials fraction strips

Marion climbed $\frac{3}{4}$ of the way to the top of the climbing wall in the gym. Rober climbed $\frac{2}{3}$ of the way. Answer 1 to 6 to find what fraction farther Marion climbed than Rober.

Find $\frac{3}{4} - \frac{2}{3}$.

1. Show a one strip, three $\frac{1}{4}$ strips, and two $\frac{1}{3}$ strips.

Since it is difficult to tell how much longer $\frac{3}{4}$ is than $\frac{2}{3}$, change both fractions to twelfths.

2. $\frac{3}{4} = \frac{\square}{12}$

3. $\frac{2}{3} = \frac{\square}{12}$

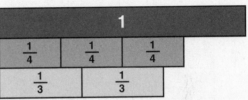

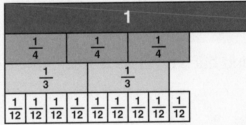

4. What is $\frac{9}{12} - \frac{8}{12}$? _____

5. So, $\frac{3}{4} - \frac{2}{3} = \frac{9}{12} - \frac{8}{12} = \frac{\square}{\square}$

$$\frac{3}{4} = \frac{9}{12}$$
$$-\frac{2}{3} = \frac{8}{12}$$
$$\overline{\quad\frac{1}{12}}$$

At the right is another way to write the subtraction.

6. What fraction farther did Marion climb than Rober? _____

7. Use fraction strips and fill in the missing numbers below to find $\frac{1}{2} - \frac{1}{6}$.

$\frac{1}{2} = \dfrac{\square}{6}$

$-\ \frac{1}{6} = \dfrac{\square}{6}$

$\dfrac{\square}{\square} = \dfrac{\square}{\square}$

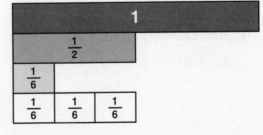

© Pearson Education, Inc.

Name _____

Subtracting Fractions with Unlike Denominators (continued)

Find each difference. Use fraction strips, if you like.

8. $\dfrac{9}{10} = \dfrac{9}{10}$

$-\ \dfrac{2}{5} = \dfrac{\square}{10}$

$\dfrac{\square}{\square} = \dfrac{\square}{\square}$

9. $\dfrac{1}{2} = \dfrac{\square}{6}$

$-\ \dfrac{1}{3} = \dfrac{\square}{6}$

$\dfrac{\square}{\square}$

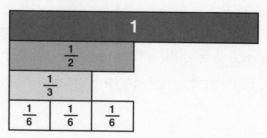

Find each difference. You may use fraction strips to help.

10. $\dfrac{5}{6} - \dfrac{2}{3} =$ _____

11. $\dfrac{3}{5} - \dfrac{1}{10} =$ _____

12. $\dfrac{3}{4} - \dfrac{1}{2} =$ _____

13. $\dfrac{1}{2} - \dfrac{1}{4} =$ _____

14. $\dfrac{2}{3} - \dfrac{2}{12} =$ _____

15. $\dfrac{7}{8} - \dfrac{3}{4} =$ _____

16. $\dfrac{3}{4} - \dfrac{3}{8} =$ _____

17. $\dfrac{5}{6} - \dfrac{1}{3} =$ _____

18. $\dfrac{9}{10} - \dfrac{2}{5} =$ _____

19. Renee watched $\dfrac{2}{3}$ of the movie and Timothy watched $\dfrac{3}{6}$ of the movie. How much more did Renee watch than Timothy? _____

20. Reasoning Could you change to a denominator of 20 to subtract $\dfrac{2}{5}$ from $\dfrac{9}{10}$? Explain.

© Pearson Education, Inc.

Estimating Sums and Differences of Mixed Numbers

Last week, Dwayne spent $4\frac{1}{3}$ hours playing basketball and $1\frac{2}{3}$ hours playing soccer. Answer 1 to 9 to estimate how much time Dwayne spent in all playing these two sports.

Estimate $4\frac{1}{3} + 1\frac{2}{3}$.

1. What two whole numbers is $4\frac{1}{3}$ between? _____ and _____

2. Use the number line.
Is $4\frac{1}{3}$ closer to 4 or 5? _____

$4\frac{1}{3}$

```
←┼─────┼─────┼─────┼─────┼─────┼─────┼→
 4    4 1/6  4 2/6  4 3/6  4 4/6  4 5/6   5
```

3. What is the number halfway between 4 and 5? _____

4. Compare. Write >, <, or =. $\frac{1}{3} \bigcirc \frac{1}{2}$

By comparing $\frac{1}{3}$ and $\frac{1}{2}$, you can tell that $4\frac{1}{3}$ is closer to 4 than 5, without using a number line. So, $4\frac{1}{3}$ rounded to the nearest whole number is 4.

5. What two whole numbers is $1\frac{2}{3}$ between? _____ and _____

6. Compare. Write >, <, or =. $\frac{2}{3} \bigcirc \frac{1}{2}$

7. What is $1\frac{2}{3}$ rounded to the nearest whole number? _____

$4\frac{1}{3} \rightarrow 4$

8. Use the rounded numbers to estimate $4\frac{1}{3} + 1\frac{2}{3}$.

$+ 1\frac{2}{3} \rightarrow + 2$

9. About how much time did Dwayne spend playing basketball and soccer? _____

About how much more time did Dwayne spend playing basketball than soccer?

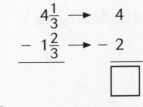

10. Estimate $4\frac{1}{3} - 1\frac{2}{3}$ at the right.

11. About how much more time did Dwayne spend playing basketball than soccer? _____

© Pearson Education, Inc.

Estimating Sums and Differences of Mixed Numbers (continued)

Estimate each sum or difference.

12. $2\frac{2}{3}$
$- 1\frac{1}{3}$

_____

13. $2\frac{9}{10}$
$- 1\frac{5}{10}$

_____

14. 5
$+ 4\frac{2}{4}$

_____

15. $6\frac{4}{6}$
$+ 1\frac{5}{6}$

_____

16. $6\frac{7}{8}$
$- 5\frac{3}{8}$

_____

17. 6
$- 3\frac{3}{9}$

_____

18. $4\frac{9}{14}$
$+ 2\frac{11}{14}$

_____

19. 6
$+ 4\frac{2}{16}$

_____

20. $2\frac{3}{4} - 1$

_____

21. $7\frac{2}{6} + 6\frac{5}{6}$

_____

22. $3\frac{2}{5} + 1\frac{2}{5}$

_____

23. $6\frac{1}{8} - 1\frac{5}{8}$

_____

24. $7 - 2\frac{3}{7}$

_____

25. $3\frac{4}{8} + 1\frac{7}{8}$

_____

26. Yolanda walked $2\frac{3}{5}$ miles on Monday, $1\frac{1}{5}$ miles on Tuesday, and $3\frac{4}{5}$ miles on Wednesday. Estimate her total distance walked.

_____

27. Chris was going to add $2\frac{1}{4}$ cups of a chemical to the swimming pool until he found out that Richard already added $1\frac{1}{8}$ cups of the chemical. Estimate how much more Chris should add so that the total is his original amount.

_____

28. Reasoning Is $3\frac{1}{2}$ closer to 3 or 4? Explain.

© Pearson Education, Inc.

Name _____

Adding Mixed Numbers

Materials fraction strips

Caroline is painting the ceiling border of her room. On Saturday, she painted $1\frac{3}{4}$ feet. On Sunday, she painted $1\frac{7}{8}$ feet. How much did she paint in the two days combined?

Find $1\frac{3}{4} + 1\frac{7}{8}$ by answering 1 to 10.

1. Estimate. $1\frac{3}{4} + 1\frac{7}{8}$ is about _____ + _____ = _____.

2. Show $1\frac{3}{4} + 1\frac{7}{8}$ with fraction strips.

3. Put the ones together and the fractions together. Change $\frac{3}{4}$ to eighths.

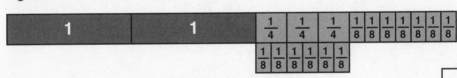

4. How many eighths equal $\frac{3}{4}$? Write the number in the box at the right.

5. Add the ones and write the sum at the right. Add $\frac{6}{8}$ and $\frac{7}{8}$ and write the sum at the right.

$$1\frac{3}{4} = 1\frac{\boxed{}}{8}$$
$$+ 1\frac{7}{8} = 1\frac{7}{8}$$
$$\rule{3cm}{0.4pt}$$
$$\boxed{}\,\frac{\boxed{}}{8}$$

6. Is $\frac{13}{8}$ a proper fraction? _____

7. Since $\frac{13}{8}$ is improper, simplify. What is $\frac{13}{8}$ as a mixed number? _____

8. Fill in the blank. $2\frac{13}{8} = 2 + \frac{13}{8} = 2 + 1\frac{5}{8} =$ _____

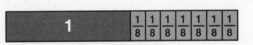

9. What is $1\frac{3}{4} + 1\frac{7}{8}$? _____

10. How much border did Caroline paint in the two days combined? _____

© Pearson Education, Inc.

Adding Mixed Numbers (continued)

11. Is the answer $3\frac{5}{8}$ close to the estimate of 4? _____

Since $3\frac{5}{8}$ is close to the estimate of 4, $3\frac{5}{8}$ is a reasonable answer.

Add. Write the sum as a simplified fraction.
Estimate to check.

12. $2\frac{1}{2}$
       $+ 1\frac{1}{3}$
       _____

13. $1\frac{1}{5}$
       $+ 3\frac{3}{10}$
       _____

14. $1\frac{3}{4}$
       $+ \frac{2}{5}$
       _____

15. $2\frac{5}{12}$
       $+ 3\frac{5}{6}$
       _____

16. $6\frac{5}{6}$
       $+ 5\frac{3}{8}$
       _____

17. $6\frac{1}{9}$
       $+ 3\frac{2}{3}$
       _____

18. $4\frac{3}{4}$
       $+ 7\frac{5}{6}$
       _____

19. $6\frac{1}{16}$
       $+ 4\frac{3}{8}$
       _____

20. $6\frac{7}{8} + 1\frac{5}{6}$

21. $7\frac{1}{2} + 2\frac{3}{7}$

22. $3\frac{1}{10} + 1\frac{5}{8}$

23. Ramona bought $1\frac{2}{3}$ pounds of strawberries,
$2\frac{1}{4}$ pounds of apples, and $2\frac{1}{2}$ pounds of oranges
at the store. What was the total weight of
Ramona's purchase?   _____

24. Reasoning Rhonda needs 4 gallons of green paint to decorate
her room. If she mixes $2\frac{1}{3}$ gallons of blue paint with $1\frac{1}{2}$ gallons of
yellow paint, will she have enough? Explain.

© Pearson Education, Inc.

Subtracting Mixed Numbers

Materials fraction strips

On Monday, Carmen swam $2\frac{3}{4}$ miles and Katie swam $1\frac{5}{8}$ miles. Answer
1 to 8 to find how much farther Carmen swam than Katie.

Find $2\frac{3}{4} - 1\frac{5}{8}$.

1. Estimate. $2\frac{3}{4} - 1\frac{5}{8}$ is about _____ – _____ = _____.

2. Show $2\frac{3}{4}$ and $1\frac{5}{8}$ with fraction strips.

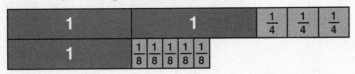

3. How many eighths equal $\frac{3}{4}$? Write the number
in the box at the right.

$$2\frac{3}{4} = 2\frac{\square}{8}$$

$$-\,1\frac{5}{8} = 1\frac{5}{8}$$

4. Subtract the ones and subtract the fractions.
Fill in the boxes at the right.

$$\dfrac{\boxed{}\ \dfrac{\boxed{}}{8}}{}$$

5. What is $2\frac{3}{4} - 1\frac{5}{8}$? _____

6. How much farther did Carmen swim than Katie? _____

7. Is $1\frac{1}{8}$ close to the estimate of 1? _____

8. Is $1\frac{1}{8}$ a reasonable answer? _____

On Wednesday, Carmen swam $2\frac{1}{8}$ miles and Katie swam $1\frac{3}{4}$ miles.
Answer 9 to 18 to find how much farther Carmen swam than Katie.

Find $2\frac{1}{8} - 1\frac{3}{4}$.

9. Show $2\frac{1}{8}$ and $1\frac{3}{4}$ with fraction strips.

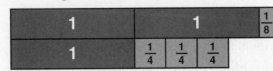

10. What is the least common denominator of $\frac{1}{8}$ and $\frac{3}{4}$? _____

© Pearson Education, Inc.

Subtracting Mixed Numbers (continued)

11. How many eighths equal $\frac{3}{4}$? Write the number in
the box at the right.

12. Compare. Write $>$, $<$, or $=$. $\frac{1}{8}$ ◯ $\frac{6}{8}$

Since $\frac{1}{8}$ is less than $\frac{6}{8}$, you need to regroup.

$$2\frac{1}{8} = 2\frac{1}{8}$$
$$-1\frac{3}{4} = 1\frac{\Box}{8}$$

13. What is $1\frac{1}{8}$ as an improper fraction? _____

14. What is the missing number?

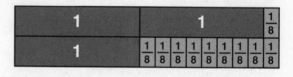

$2\frac{1}{8} = 1 + 1\frac{1}{8} = 1 + \dfrac{\Box}{8}$
Write this number at the right.

15. Subtract the ones. What is $1 - 1$? _____

$$2\frac{1}{8} = 2\frac{1}{8} = 1\frac{\Box}{8}$$

16. Subtract the fractions. What is $\frac{9}{8} - \frac{6}{8}$? _____
Write 3 at the right.

$$-1\frac{3}{4} = 1\frac{6}{8} = 1\frac{6}{8}$$
$$\dfrac{\Box}{8}$$

17. What is $2\frac{1}{8} - 1\frac{3}{4}$? _____

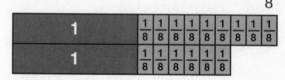

18. How much farther did Carmen
swim than Katie on Wednesday? _____

Subtract. Simplify, if possible. Estimate to check.

19. $2\frac{2}{3}$
       $-1\frac{1}{6}$
       _____

20. $2\frac{4}{10}$
       $-1\frac{3}{5}$
       _____

21. $5\frac{1}{4}$
       $-\frac{2}{5}$
       _____

22. $6\frac{7}{8}$
       $-1\frac{5}{6}$
       _____

23. To make a dress, $1\frac{1}{6}$ yards of blue material is needed and $\frac{3}{4}$ yard
of red material is needed. How much more blue material is
needed than red material?

_____

24. Reasoning If you have $7\frac{3}{16}$ and you subtract $\frac{3}{16}$, how much
do you have?

_____

© Pearson Education, Inc.

Name _____

Multiplying Fractions by Whole Numbers

Materials counters, 24 for each student or pair, a loop of yarn

Brianna has 15 model cars in her collection. Of the 15, $\frac{2}{3}$ are vintage cars. How many of her cars are vintage?

Find $\frac{2}{3}$ of 15 or $\frac{2}{3} \times 15$ by answering 1 to 5.

1. Show 15 counters in 3 equal rows.

2. Each row has $\frac{1}{3}$ of the counters. Put the loop of yarn around 2 rows to find $\frac{2}{3}$. Circle 2 rows of counters at the right.

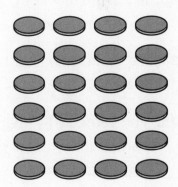

3. How many counters did you circle? _____

4. What is $\frac{2}{3}$ of 15 or $\frac{2}{3} \times 15$? _____

5. How many of Brianna's cars are vintage? _____

When you put the 15 counters into 3 rows, you found 15 ÷ 3. This can also be shown as: $\frac{2}{\overset{1}{\cancel{3}}} \times \frac{\overset{5}{\cancel{15}}}{1}$

6. What is left is 2 × 5. What is the product? _____

Find $\frac{5}{6} \times 24$ by answering 7 to 10.

7. Show the product with counters and yarn. Circle the counters at the right.

8. What is 24 ÷ 6? _____
   Show this by crossing out and changing numbers below.

   $\frac{5}{6} \times \frac{24}{1}$

   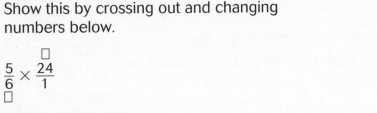

9. What product is left? _____ × _____ = _____

10. What is $\frac{5}{6} \times 24$? _____

© Pearson Education, Inc.

Multiplying Fractions by Whole Numbers (continued)

Find each product.

11. $\frac{8}{9} \times 45$ **12.** $42 \times \frac{3}{7}$ **13.** $\frac{7}{12}$ of 96   **14.** $\frac{2}{11} \times 77$

_____   _____   _____   _____

15. $\frac{3}{8} \times 64$ **16.** $\frac{1}{6}$ of 102   **17.** $\frac{2}{9} \times 72$ **18.** $\frac{3}{4} \times 168$

_____   _____   _____   _____

19. $\frac{2}{5}$ of 25   **20.** $\frac{7}{9} \times 81$ **21.** $\frac{1}{2} \times 52$ **22.** $\frac{2}{3}$ of 66

_____   _____   _____   _____

Use the information in the table for Exercises 23 and 24.

Zoo Animals	Population	Zoo Animals	Population
Wild Dogs	10	Elephants	3
Monkeys	21	Tigers	8
Bears	18	Giraffes	5

23. If $\frac{2}{7}$ of the monkey population are spider monkeys, how many spider monkeys are at the zoo? _____

24. If $\frac{3}{5}$ of the animals listed are female, how many females are in the list? _____

25. You earned $141 babysitting last month. You told your parents that you will saved $\frac{2}{3}$ of your earnings. How much did you save last month? _____

26. Emperor penguins are approximately 45 inches tall, while rockhopper penguins are about $\frac{5}{9}$ of that height. How tall is a typical rockhopper penguin? _____

27. Reasoning If you know that $\frac{3}{4}$ of a number is 18, what is $\frac{1}{4}$ of the same number? _____

© Pearson Education, Inc.

Name _____

Multiplying Two Fractions

Materials crayons, markers, or colored pencils, paper to fold

Pablo's yard is $\frac{3}{4}$ of an acre. One-half of the yard is woods. What part of an acre is wooded?

Find $\frac{1}{2}$ of $\frac{3}{4}$ or $\frac{1}{2} \times \frac{3}{4}$ by answering 1 to 5.

1. Fold a sheet of paper into 4 equal parts, as shown at the right. Color 3 parts with slanted lines to show $\frac{3}{4}$. Color the rectangle at the right to show what you did.

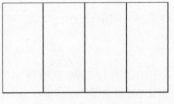

2. Now fold the paper in half the other way. Shade one half with lines slanted the opposite direction of the first set. Color the rectangle at the right to show what you did.

3. What fraction of the paper is shaded with crisscrossed lines?   _____

4. The part shaded with crisscrossed lines shows $\frac{1}{2}$ of $\frac{3}{4}$ or $\frac{1}{2} \times \frac{3}{4}$.

So, what is $\frac{1}{2} \times \frac{3}{4}$?   _____

5. In Pablo's yard, what part of his $\frac{3}{4}$ acre is wooded?   _____

6. To find $\frac{1}{2} \times \frac{3}{4}$, how many sections did you divide the paper into?   _____

7. What is the product of the denominators in $\frac{1}{2} \times \frac{3}{4}$? $2 \times 4 = $ _____

8. To find $\frac{1}{2} \times \frac{3}{4}$, how many sections did you crisscross?   _____

9. What is the product of the numerators in $\frac{1}{2} \times \frac{3}{4}$? $1 \times 3 = $ _____

10. Write the product of the numerators over the product of the denominators. $\dfrac{1 \times 3}{2 \times 4} = \dfrac{\square}{\square}$

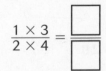

11. Is your answer to item 9 the same as item 4?   _____

12. Use paper folding to find $\frac{2}{3} \times \frac{3}{4}$. Color the rectangle at the right to show what you did. So, $\frac{2}{3} \times \frac{3}{4} = $ _____ .

13. To find $\frac{2}{3} \times \frac{3}{4}$, how many sections did you divide the paper into?   _____

© Pearson Education, Inc.

Multiplying Two Fractions (continued)

14. What is the product of the denominators in $\frac{2}{3} \times \frac{3}{4}$? $3 \times 4 =$ _____

15. To find $\frac{2}{3} \times \frac{3}{4}$ how many sections did you crisscross?   _____

16. What is the product of the numerators in $\frac{2}{3} \times \frac{3}{4}$? $2 \times 3 =$ _____

17. Complete: $\frac{2}{3} \times \frac{3}{4} = \frac{2 \times 3}{3 \times 4} = \dfrac{\square}{\square}$

To multiply two fractions, you can multiply the numerators and then the denominators. Then simplify, if possible.

$$\frac{2}{3} \times \frac{3}{4} = \frac{2 \times 3}{3 \times 4} = \frac{6}{12} = \frac{1}{2}$$

18. Reasoning Shari found $\frac{3}{10} \times \frac{5}{9}$ as shown at the right. Why does Shari's method work?

$$\frac{3}{10} \times \frac{5}{9} = \frac{\overset{1}{\cancel{3}} \times \overset{1}{\cancel{5}}}{\underset{2}{\cancel{10}} \times \underset{3}{\cancel{9}}} = \frac{1}{6}$$

Multiply. Simplify, if possible.

19. $\frac{1}{8} \times \frac{2}{3} =$ _____

20. $\frac{5}{6} \times \frac{1}{2} =$ _____

21. $\frac{1}{4} \times \frac{3}{5} =$ _____

22. $\frac{6}{7} \times \frac{1}{3} =$ _____

23. $\frac{3}{4} \times \frac{3}{8} =$ _____

24. $\frac{1}{5} \times \frac{4}{5} =$ _____

25. $\frac{2}{3} \times \frac{4}{7} =$ _____

26. $\frac{3}{7} \times \frac{3}{10} =$ _____

27. $\frac{4}{9} \times \frac{3}{4} =$ _____

28. $\frac{5}{8} \times \frac{4}{5} =$ _____

29. $\frac{7}{9} \times \frac{3}{5} =$ _____

30. $\frac{1}{10} \times \frac{5}{7} =$ _____

31. $\frac{7}{8} \times \frac{5}{14} =$ _____

32. $\frac{3}{11} \times \frac{1}{9} =$ _____

33. $\frac{1}{12} \times \frac{4}{5} =$ _____

34. There are 45 tents at the summer camp. Girls will use $\frac{2}{3}$ of the tents. How many tents will the girls use?

_____

© Pearson Education, Inc.

Understanding Division with Fractions

Materials crayons, markers, or colored pencils

Donna has 3 kilograms of clay. She uses $\frac{1}{2}$ kilogram for each vase.
Answer 1 to 3 to find the number of vases she can make.

Find $3 \div \frac{1}{2}$.

1. Color each half of a rectangle at the right a
different color. How many $\frac{1}{2}$'s are in 3? _____

2. What is $3 \div \frac{1}{2}$? _____

3. How many vases can Donna make? _____

You could also find $3 \div \frac{1}{2}$ by multiplying $3 \times \frac{2}{1}$.

The numbers $\frac{1}{2}$ and $\frac{2}{1}$ or 2 have a special relationship because $\frac{1}{2} \times 2 = 1$. The
numbers $\frac{1}{2}$ and 2 are reciprocals. Similarly, $\frac{3}{4}$ and $\frac{4}{3}$ are reciprocals. Note that $\frac{3}{4} \times \frac{4}{3} = 1$.

4. What is the reciprocal of $\frac{1}{3}$? _____

5. What is the reciprocal of $\frac{5}{7}$? _____

So, $3 \div \frac{1}{2}$ can be written as 3×2, because 2 is the reciprocal of $\frac{1}{2}$.

Thomas has $\frac{9}{10}$ kilogram of clay. He uses $\frac{3}{10}$ kilogram for each small
bowl. Answer 6 to 8 to find how many small bowls Thomas can make.

Find $\frac{9}{10} \div \frac{3}{10}$ using a model.

6. Color each $\frac{3}{10}$ of the rectangle at the right a
different color. How many $\frac{3}{10}$'s are in $\frac{9}{10}$? _____

7. What is $\frac{9}{10} \div \frac{3}{10}$? _____

8. How many small bowls can Thomas make? _____

Find $\frac{9}{10} \div \frac{3}{10}$ by using the reciprocal.

9. What is the reciprocal of $\frac{3}{10}$? _____

© Pearson Education, Inc.

Understanding Division with Fractions (continued)

10. To find $\frac{9}{10} \div \frac{3}{10}$, can you multiply $\frac{9}{10}$ by the reciprocal of $\frac{3}{10}$? _____

11. Complete: $\frac{9}{10} \times \frac{10}{3} = \frac{9 \times 10}{10 \times \boxed{}} = \frac{90}{\boxed{}} = \boxed{}$

12. Is the answer to item 11 the same as item 8? _____

Find the reciprocal of each number.

13. $\frac{3}{4}$ _____   **14.** $\frac{1}{15}$ _____   **15.** $\frac{7}{9}$ _____   **16.** $1\frac{3}{7}$ _____

Find each quotient.

17. How many $\frac{1}{4}$ are in 2? _____   **18.** How many $\frac{1}{2}$ are in 3? _____

19. How many $\frac{1}{4}$ are in 4? _____   **20.** How many $\frac{3}{4}$ are in 3? _____

21. How many $\frac{1}{8}$ are in 2? _____   **22.** How many $\frac{2}{8}$ are in 1? _____

23. How many $\frac{3}{8}$ are in 3? _____   **24.** How many $\frac{6}{8}$ are in 3? _____

25. $3 \div \frac{1}{6}$ _____   **26.** $9 \div \frac{3}{5}$ _____   **27.** $4 \div \frac{1}{4}$ _____

28. $10 \div \frac{5}{6}$ _____   **29.** $9 \div \frac{3}{4}$ _____   **30.** $6 \div \frac{1}{3}$ _____

31. $2 \div \frac{1}{7}$ _____   **32.** $6 \div \frac{3}{5}$ _____   **33.** $10 \div \frac{1}{10}$ _____

34. Bonnie is cutting 7 apples. Each apple is cut into eighths.
How many slices of apple will she have?   _____

35. **Reasoning** Explain how to find $\frac{3}{4} \div \frac{3}{8}$ by using the reciprocal of $\frac{3}{8}$.

© Pearson Education, Inc.

Name _____

Dividing Fractions

A serving of juice is $\frac{1}{16}$ of a gallon. Answer 1 to 6 to find how many servings are in $\frac{7}{8}$ of a gallon.

Find $\frac{7}{8} \div \frac{1}{16}$.

1. What is the reciprocal of $\frac{1}{16}$? _____

2. Write $\frac{7}{8} \div \frac{1}{16}$ as $\frac{7}{8}$ times the reciprocal of $\frac{1}{16}$.　　$\frac{7}{8} \div \frac{1}{16} = \frac{7}{8} \times$ _____

3. Does $16 = \frac{16}{1}$? _____

4. Multiply. Remove common factors first.　　$\frac{7}{8} \times \frac{16}{1} = \frac{7 \times \overset{2}{\cancel{16}}}{\underset{1}{\cancel{8}} \times 1} = \frac{\boxed{}}{1}$

5. What is $\frac{7}{8} \div \frac{1}{16}$?　　$\frac{7}{8} \div \frac{1}{16} = \frac{7}{8} \times 16 =$ _____

6. How many $\frac{1}{16}$ gallon servings are in $\frac{7}{8}$ gallon of juice? _____

Answer 7 to 11 to find how many $\frac{3}{8}$ gallon servings are in $\frac{1}{2}$ gallon of water.

Find $\frac{1}{2} \div \frac{3}{8}$.

7. What is the reciprocal of $\frac{3}{8}$? _____

8. Write $\frac{1}{2} \div \frac{3}{8}$ as $\frac{1}{2}$ times the reciprocal of $\frac{3}{8}$.　　$\frac{1}{2} \div \frac{3}{8} = \frac{1}{2} \times$ _____

9. Multiply. Remove common factors first.　　$\frac{1}{2} \times \frac{8}{3} = \frac{1 \times \overset{4}{\cancel{8}}}{\underset{1}{\cancel{2}} \times 3} = \frac{\boxed{}}{\boxed{}}$

10. Write the answer in simplest form. So, $\frac{1}{2} \div \frac{3}{8} = \frac{1}{2} \times \frac{8}{3} =$ _____ = _____

11. How many $\frac{3}{8}$ gallon servings are in $\frac{1}{2}$ gallon of water? _____

12. Fill in the missing numbers to divide. Remove common factors before multiplying.

$\frac{2}{3} \div \frac{5}{12} = \frac{2}{3} \times$ _____ $= \frac{8}{5} =$ _____

© Pearson Education, Inc.

Dividing Fractions (continued)

Divide. Simplify, if possible.

13. $\frac{1}{8} \div \frac{2}{3} =$ _____

14. $\frac{5}{6} \div \frac{1}{2} =$ _____

15. $\frac{1}{4} \div \frac{3}{5} =$ _____

16. $\frac{6}{7} \div \frac{3}{4} =$ _____

17. $\frac{3}{4} \div \frac{3}{8} =$ _____

18. $\frac{1}{5} \div \frac{4}{5} =$ _____

19. $\frac{2}{3} \div \frac{4}{7} =$ _____

20. $\frac{3}{7} \div \frac{3}{10} =$ _____

21. $\frac{4}{9} \div \frac{3}{4} =$ _____

22. $\frac{5}{8} \div \frac{4}{5} =$ _____

23. $\frac{7}{9} \div \frac{3}{5} =$ _____

24. $\frac{1}{10} \div \frac{5}{7} =$ _____

25. $\frac{7}{8} \div \frac{5}{14} =$ _____

26. $\frac{3}{11} \div \frac{1}{9} =$ _____

27. $\frac{1}{12} \div \frac{4}{5} =$ _____

28. $\frac{2}{5} \div \frac{5}{7} =$ _____

29. $\frac{1}{3} \div \frac{3}{8} =$ _____

30. $\frac{1}{4} \div \frac{1}{4} =$ _____

31. $\frac{5}{12} \div \frac{3}{5} =$ _____

32. $\frac{9}{10} \div \frac{5}{7} =$ _____

33. $\frac{4}{5} \div \frac{5}{9} =$ _____

34. Reasoning For the school cafeteria, 15 pounds of vegetables
were ordered by the chef. If each student usually gets $\frac{3}{8}$ of
a pound of vegetables each day for lunch, how many students
could be fed with the vegetables in one day?   _____

35. Draw a picture to show $\frac{7}{8} \div \frac{1}{16} = 14$.

© Pearson Education, Inc.

Name _____

Estimating Products and Quotients of Mixed Numbers

Karina's recipe for tacos uses $1\frac{3}{4}$ pounds of beef. She needs to make $3\frac{1}{3}$ times the recipe for a party. About how many pounds of beef does she need?

Estimate $3\frac{1}{3} \times 1\frac{3}{4}$ by answering 1 to 9.

1. What two whole numbers is $3\frac{1}{3}$ between? _____ and _____

2. Use the number line below. Is $3\frac{1}{3}$ closer to 3 or 4? _____

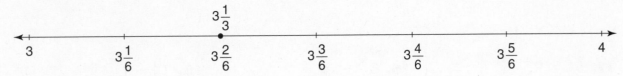

3. What number is halfway between 3 and 4? _____

4. Compare. Write $>$, $<$, or $=$. $\frac{1}{3}\bigcirc\frac{1}{2}$

By comparing $\frac{1}{3}$ and $\frac{1}{2}$, you can tell that $3\frac{1}{3}$ is closer to 3 than 4, without using a number line.

$3\frac{1}{3}$ rounded to the nearest whole number is 3.

5. What two whole numbers is $1\frac{3}{4}$ between? _____ and _____

6. Compare. Write $>$, $<$, or $=$. $\frac{3}{4}\bigcirc\frac{1}{2}$

7. What is $1\frac{3}{4}$ rounded to the nearest whole number? _____

8. Use the rounded numbers to estimate.

$3\frac{1}{3} \times 1\frac{3}{4}$ is about _____ $\times$ _____ = _____

9. About how many pounds of beef does Karina need?   About _____

Marco is making $12\frac{2}{3}$ pounds of lasagna. Each pan can hold $2\frac{3}{4}$ pounds. About how many pans does he need?

Estimate $12\frac{2}{3} \div 2\frac{3}{4}$ by answering 10 to 13.

10. What is $12\frac{2}{3}$ rounded to the nearest whole number? _____

© Pearson Education, Inc.

Estimating Products and Quotients of Mixed Numbers (continued)

11. What is $2\frac{3}{4}$ rounded to the nearest whole number? _____

12. Since $13 \div 3$ is not easy to divide, use compatible numbers.
What numbers are close to $12\frac{2}{3} \div 2\frac{3}{4}$ and easy to divide?

$12\frac{2}{3} \div 2\frac{3}{4}$ is about _____ ÷ _____ = _____.

13. About how many pans does Marco need?   About _____

Estimate.

14. $2\frac{7}{8} \times 7\frac{3}{5}$

15. $6\frac{1}{5} \times 8\frac{3}{4}$

16. $5\frac{7}{12} \div 1\frac{1}{5}$

_____   _____   _____

17. $5\frac{2}{7} \times 9\frac{4}{5}$

18. $8\frac{5}{7} \div 2\frac{2}{3}$

19. $7\frac{5}{7} \div 1\frac{9}{10}$

_____   _____   _____

20. $3\frac{5}{12} \times 1\frac{3}{5}$

21. $1\frac{5}{9} \times 7\frac{1}{2}$

22. $1\frac{1}{3} \times 5\frac{2}{9}$

_____   _____   _____

23. $4\frac{3}{12} \times 7$

24. $25 \div 4\frac{7}{9}$

25. $9\frac{1}{10} \div 3\frac{1}{12}$

_____   _____   _____

26. The Hummingbird Trail at Camp Redlands is $1\frac{7}{8}$ miles long.
Surinder, a camp counselor, hikes the train $2\frac{1}{4}$ times a day.
About how far does he hike each day?   About _____

27. Tammy needs to hike $15\frac{1}{4}$ miles to win an award. About how
many times does she need to hike a trail that is $2\frac{7}{8}$ miles long? About _____

28. Reasoning Explain how to use compatible numbers to find
$17\frac{2}{3} \div 5\frac{9}{10}$.

© Pearson Education, Inc.

Name _____

Multiplying Mixed Numbers

Materials crayons, markers, or colored pencils

George made a rectangular quilt that is $2\frac{1}{2}$ yards long and $1\frac{2}{3}$ yards wide. Answer 1 to 6 to find the area of the quilt.

Find $1\frac{2}{3} \times 2\frac{1}{2}$.

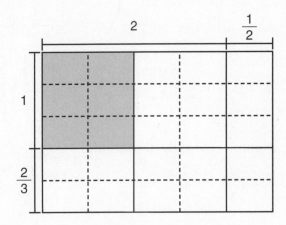

1. The rectangular quilt at the right is $2\frac{1}{2}$ units by $1\frac{2}{3}$ units. The shaded area represents one whole yard. Shade another region that is equal to one whole yard.

2. The quilt is divided into equal parts. Six equal parts equal one whole yard. Each part is what fraction of one whole yard?   _____

3. Color another whole yard with a different color. Then another, as many times as you can. How many total whole yards are there in the quilt?   _____

4. What part of a whole yard is left over?   _____

5. So, what is $1\frac{2}{3} \times 2\frac{1}{2}$?   _____

6. What is the area of George's quilt?   _____ square yards

Find $1\frac{2}{3} \times 2\frac{1}{2}$ another way by answering 7 to 9.

7. Write $1\frac{2}{3}$ as an improper fraction.   _____

8. Write $2\frac{1}{2}$ as an improper fraction.   _____

9. Now find $\frac{5}{3} \times \frac{5}{2}$.   _____ = _____

Notice that the product of the numerators, $5 \times 5 = 25$, is the number of equal parts in the rectangle. Also, the products of the denominators, $3 \times 2 = 6$, is the number of equal parts in each whole.

© Pearson Education, Inc.

Name _____

Multiplying Mixed Numbers (continued)

Fill in the blanks to find each product. Change mixed numbers to
improper fractions. Write whole numbers over 1. Remove common
factors before multiplying to make the computations easier.

10. $\frac{2}{3} \times 1\frac{3}{8} = \frac{2}{3} \times \frac{\square}{\square} = \frac{\overset{1}{2} \times \square}{3 \times \underset{4}{\square}} = \frac{\square}{\square}$

11. $5 \times 1\frac{3}{10} = \frac{5}{1} \times \frac{\square}{\square} = \frac{\overset{1}{5} \times \square}{1 \times \underset{2}{\square}} = \frac{\square}{\square} = \frac{\square}{\square}$

Multiply. Simplify, if possible.

12. $2\frac{6}{7} \times 1\frac{3}{4} =$

13. $\frac{3}{4} \times 3\frac{1}{5} =$

14. $3\frac{2}{5} \times \frac{5}{7} =$

_____   _____   _____

15. $5\frac{5}{8} \times 3\frac{4}{5} =$

16. $2\frac{2}{7} \times 5\frac{3}{5} =$

17. $2\frac{1}{10} \times 2\frac{1}{7} =$

_____   _____   _____

18. $4\frac{1}{12} \times \frac{4}{5} =$

19. $2\frac{1}{10} \times 6\frac{5}{7} =$

20. $3\frac{4}{5} \times 5 =$

_____   _____   _____

21. Pam is making a cake. The recipe calls for $2\frac{1}{8}$ cups
of flour. How much flour is needed for 4 cakes?   _____ cups

22. Reasoning Find each product and compare it to $2\frac{1}{2}$. What is true
when multiplying by numbers less than 1 and when multiplying by
numbers greater than 1?

$\frac{1}{3} \times 2\frac{1}{2} =$ _____ $1\frac{1}{3} \times 2\frac{1}{2} =$ _____ $\frac{2}{3} \times 2\frac{1}{2} =$ _____ $1\frac{2}{3} \times 2\frac{1}{2} =$ _____

© Pearson Education, Inc.

Name _____

Dividing Mixed Numbers

Materials crayons, markers, or colored pencils

Sierra used $3\frac{1}{2}$ cups of shredded paper and $1\frac{1}{6}$ cups of paste to make paper mache. Answer 1 to 6 to find how many times more paper than paste Sierra used.

1. If Sierra used 6 cups of paper and 3 cups of paste, what computation would you do to solve the problem? _____

Find $3\frac{1}{2} \div 1\frac{1}{6}$.

2. Four large rectangles are shown below. Color $3\frac{1}{2}$ rectangles.

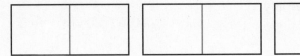

3. Write $1\frac{1}{6}$ as an improper fraction. _____

4. To find how many times $1\frac{1}{6}$ goes into $3\frac{1}{2}$, each rectangle below is divided into 6 equal parts. Color $1\frac{1}{6}$ or $\frac{7}{6}$ of the rectangles. Now color another $\frac{7}{6}$ with a different color. Repeat as many times as you can.

5. What is $3\frac{1}{2} \div 1\frac{1}{6}$? _____

6. How many times more paper than paste did Sierra use? _____

Find $3\frac{1}{2} \div 1\frac{1}{6}$ another way by writing the missing numbers.

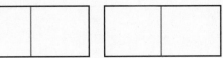

7. $3\frac{1}{2} \div 1\frac{1}{6} = \dfrac{\square}{2} \div \dfrac{\square}{6}$ Change to improper fractions.

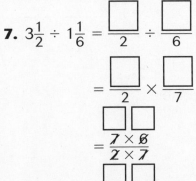

$= \dfrac{\square}{2} \times \dfrac{\square}{7}$ Multiply by the reciprocal.

$= \dfrac{\square\square}{7 \times \cancel{6}}{2 \times 7}$ Multiply numerators and denominators and remove common factors.

$\dfrac{\square\square}{}$

$= \underline{}$ Simplify.

© Pearson Education, Inc.

Name _____

Dividing Mixed Numbers (continued)

Find $4 \div 2\frac{1}{5}$ by writing the missing numbers.

8. $4 \div 2\frac{1}{5} = \frac{4}{1} \div \frac{\boxed{}}{5}$ Change to improper fractions.

$= \frac{4}{1} \times \dfrac{\boxed{}}{\boxed{}}$ Multiply by the reciprocal.

$= \dfrac{\boxed{} \times \boxed{}}{\boxed{} \times \boxed{}}$ Multiply numerators and denominators and remove common factors.

$= \dfrac{\boxed{}}{11} = 1\dfrac{\boxed{}}{11}$ Simplify.

Divide. Simplify if possible.

9. $7 \div 3\frac{4}{10} =$ _____

10. $3\frac{4}{5} \div 5 =$ _____

11. $3\frac{1}{4} \div 4\frac{1}{4} =$ _____

12. $3\frac{5}{12} \div 1\frac{3}{5} =$ _____

13. $2\frac{6}{7} \div 1\frac{3}{4} =$ _____

14. $1\frac{4}{9} \div 4 =$ _____

15. $3\frac{7}{9} \div 5\frac{5}{3} =$ _____

16. $2\frac{7}{8} \div 5\frac{5}{14} =$ _____

17. $1 \div 2\frac{2}{3} =$ _____

18. Horatio is making a necklace. He has large beads that are $1\frac{1}{8}$ inches long. How many beads are needed to make a necklace 18 inches long?

19. Reasoning If $3 \times 2\frac{1}{2} = 7\frac{1}{2}$, what is $7\frac{1}{2} \div 2\frac{1}{2}$?   _____

20. Reasoning Use estimation to explain why 6 is a reasonable solution for $10\frac{1}{2} \div 1\frac{3}{4}$.

© Pearson Education, Inc.

Using Models to Add and Subtract Decimals

Materials crayons, markers, or colored pencils

Mr. Mantini bought 0.45 pound of apples and 0.37 pound of oranges. Answer 1 to 7 to find the total weight of the fruit.

Find 0.45 + 0.37.

1. How many squares are in the grid shown below?   _____

2. If the entire grid represents one unit, how many squares represent 0.45? Color in 4 columns and 5 squares.   _____

3. How many squares represent 0.37? Color in 3 columns and 7 squares a different color.   _____

4. How many squares are colored all together? _____

5. What part of the grid did you color in all?   _____

6. What is 0.45 + 0.37?   _____

7. What is the total weight of the fruit?   _____ pound

Answer 8 to 12 to find how much more the apples weigh than the oranges.

Find 0.45 − 0.37.

8. Color 0.45 of the grid.

9. Cross out 37 of the squares that are colored. This represents 0.37, the weight of the oranges.

10. How many squares are colored in but not crossed out?   _____

11. What is 0.45 − 0.37?   _____

12. How much more do the apples weigh than the oranges?   _____ pound

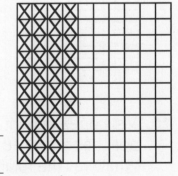

© Pearson Education, Inc.

Using Models to Add and Subtract Decimals (continued)

13. Reasoning How can the sum $45 + 37 = 82$ be used to
find that $0.45 + 0.37 = 0.82$?

Use the grids to find the sum or difference.

14. $0.28 + 0.56 =$ _____

15. $0.77 + 0.19 =$ _____

16. $0.72 - 0.16 =$ _____

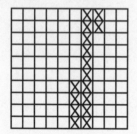

17. $0.6 - 0.34 =$ _____

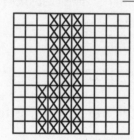

18. $0.85 + 0.77 =$ _____

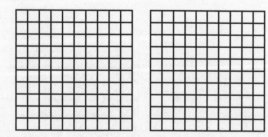

19. $1.23 - 0.45 =$ _____

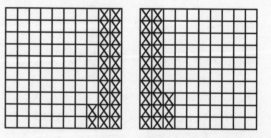

20. Ms. Lopez bought 0.5 pound of
peaches and 0.48 pound of grapes.
What was the total weight of the fruit? _____

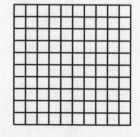

© Pearson Education, Inc.

Estimating Decimal Sums and Differences

A recipe calls for 20.8 ounces of pineapple and 16.2 ounces of mandarin oranges. Answer 1 to 6 to find how many ounces of fruit the recipe calls for.

1. What word in the question indicates
that an estimate is enough?   _____

Estimate 20.8 + 16.2.

2. What is 20.8 rounded to the nearest whole number?   _____

3. What is 16.2 rounded to the nearest whole number?   _____

4. Find the sum of the two rounded whole numbers.   21 + 16 = _____

5. So, what is a good estimate for 20.8 + 16.2?   _____

6. About how many ounces of fruit does the
recipe call for?   About _____ ounces

In a fishing derby, Starla caught a 5.7 pound fish and Roberto caught a 2.43 pound fish. Answer 7 to 11 to find about how many more pounds Starla's fish weighed than Roberto's.

Estimate 5.7 − 2.43.

7. What is 5.7 rounded to the nearest whole number?   _____

8. What is 2.43 rounded to the nearest whole number?   _____

9. Find the difference of the two rounded whole numbers.   6 − 2 = _____

10. So, what is a good estimate for 5.7 − 2.43?   _____

11. About how many more pounds did Starla's
fish weigh than Roberto's?   About _____ pounds

© Pearson Education, Inc.

Estimating Decimal Sums and Differences (continued)

Estimate each sum or difference.

12. 4.6 + 5.2   **13.** 99.6 − 21.7   **14.** 89.7 − 42.4   **15.** 9.1 + 5.8

_____   _____   _____   _____

16. 0.61 + 0.91   **17.** 5.21 − 0.7   **18.** 14.23 + 1.82   **19.** 31.6 − 10.5

_____   _____   _____   _____

20.   7.06   **21.**   5.39   **22.**   33.7   **23.**   16.18
    + 3.72   − 1.74   − 10.08   + 10.02

24.   10.7   **25.**   57.09   **26.**   47   **27.**   6.1
    + 2.38   + 12.62   − 12.43   − 0.85

Use the table at the right for Exercises 28 to 30.

28. About how much taller is Derek than Peppe? _____

29. What is the approximate combined measure of Amy and Barnaby? _____

30. Who is about 10 inches taller than Peppe? _____

Heights of Students	
Jozie	46.5 in.
Derek	52.25 in.
Peppe	41.4 in.
Amy	53.75 in.
Barnaby	50.5 in.

31. Reasoning Explain how to estimate 3.85 + 5.27.

© Pearson Education, Inc.

Name _____

Adding Decimals to Hundredths

Materials place-value blocks: 3 ones, 9 tenths, 13 hundredths
per pair or group

It rained 2.36 inches in May and 1.57 inches in June. Answer 1
to 11 to find the total amount of rainfall in May and June.

Find 2.36 + 1.57.

Let the block at the right represent one unit, or 1.0.

1.0

So, 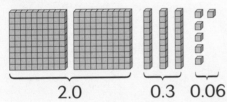 represents one tenth, or 0.1 and ▱ represents
one hundredth or 0.01.

1. Show 2.36 and 1.57 using place-value blocks.

2.36:   1.57:

⎣___2.0___⎦ ⎣0.3⎦ ⎣0.06⎦   ⎣__1.0__⎦ ⎣_0.5_⎦ ⎣0.07⎦

2. To add the hundredths, combine the small cubes.

6 hundredths + 7 hundredths = _____ hundredths

3. Trade 10 hundredths for 1 tenth.

13 hundredths = _____ tenth and _____ hundredths

4. Record the 3 hundredths in the
hundredths column of the place-
value chart. Record the 1 tenth
at the top of the tenths column.

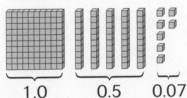

Ones		Tenths	Hundredths
	.		
2	.	3	6
+ 1	.	5	7
	.		

© Pearson Education, Inc.

Adding Decimals to Hundredths (continued)

5. Combine the tenths.
1 tenth + 3 tenths + 5 tenths =

_____ tenths

Ones		Tenths	Hundredths
		1	
2	.	3	6
+ 1	.	5	7
	.		3

6. Record the 9 tenths in the tenths column of the place-value chart.

7. Add the ones.
2 ones + 1 one = _____ ones

8. Record the 3 ones in the ones column of the place-value chart.

9. So, what is 2.36 + 1.57? _____

10. What was the total rainfall in May and June? _____ inches

11. Reasoning Estimate 2.36 + 1.57 and use the estimate to explain why the sum 3.93 is reasonable.

Add.

12.   6.28
      + 1.47

13.   3.55
      + 4.69

14.   8.6
      + 2.7

15.   5.4
      + 3.3

16.   2.6
      + 3.1

17.   0.58
      + 6.13

18.   5.1
      + 3.97

19.   8.9
      + 2.2

20.   5.18
      + 3.24

21.   9.37
      + 0.44

22.   13.8
      + 5.71

23. $1.75
      + 5.15

24. Ramon bought 2.4 yards of blue fabric and 3.25 yards of red fabric for a craft project. How many total yards of fabric did he buy? _____

© Pearson Education, Inc.

Subtracting Decimals to Hundredths

Materials place-value blocks: 2 ones, 11 tenths, 5 hundredths per pair or group

Cable jumped 2.15 meters and Pedro jumped 1.72 meters. Answer 1 to 11 to find how much farther Cable jumped than Pedro.

Find 2.15 − 1.72.

Let the block at the right represent one unit, or 1.0.

1.0

So, ▯ represents one tenth, or 0.1 and ▱ represents one hundredth or 0.01.

1. Show 2.15 using place-value blocks.

2. Do you have enough hundredths to take away 2 hundredths? _____

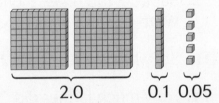

2.0   0.1 0.05

3. Subtract the hundredths.
5 hundredths − 2 hundredths =

_____ hundredths

Write 3 in the hundredths column of the place-value chart.

4. Do you have enough tenths to take away 7 tenths? _____

Ones		Tenths	Hundredths
	.		
2	.	1	5
− 1	.	7	2
	.		

5. Regroup. Trade 1 one for 10 tenths.

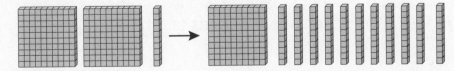

© Pearson Education, Inc.

Subtracting Decimals to Hundredths (continued)

6. How many ones do you
have left? _____
Record this value in the
chart. Cross out the 2 ones
and write 1 above it.

Ones		Tenths	Hundredths
2	.	1	5
− 1	.	7	2
	.		3

7. How many tenths do you
have now? _____
Record this value in the
chart. Cross out the 1 tenth
and write 11 above it.

8. Subtract the tenths. 11 tenths − 7 tenths = _____ tenths
Write 4 in the tenths column of the chart.

9. Subtract the ones. 1 one − 1 one = _____ ones
Write 0 in the ones column of the chart.

10. So, what is 2.15 − 1.72? _____

11. How much farther did Cable jump than Pedro? _____ meters

Subtract.

12.   7.34
     − 2.18

13.   5.27
     − 4.58

14.   6.7
     − 1.5

15.   9.2
     − 2.7

16.   7.4
     − 3.8

17.   3.68
     − 1.93

18.   3.4
     − 2.2

19.   5.69
     − 4.35

20. Paulie caught two fish. One weighed 1.43 pounds
and the other weighed 5.7 pounds. Janice caught
one 7.09 pound fish. Who caught more pounds of fish? _____

How much more? _____

21. Reasoning What regrouping do you need to do to subtract 8 − 5.43?

© Pearson Education, Inc.

**Math Diagnosis and
Intervention System**

Intervention Lesson   **H56**

More Estimation of Decimal Sums and Differences

Ryan used 12.56 liters of saline solution (salt water) for a chemistry
experiment and 7.815 liters of saline solution for another experiment.
What is the approximate amount of saline solution he used all together?

1. What word in the question indicates
that an estimate is enough?   _____

Estimate 12.56 + 7.815 by answering 2 to 6.

2. What is 12.56 rounded to the nearest whole number?   _____

3. What is 7.815 rounded to the nearest whole number?   _____

4. Find the sum of the two rounded numbers.   13 + 8 = _____

5. So, what is a good estimate for 12.56 + 7.815?   _____

6. What is the approximate amount of saline
solution Ryan used all together?   About _____ liters

Estimate 12.56 + 7.815 using compatible numbers, by answering
7 to 9.

7. What are two compatible numbers, numbers that
are easy to add, close to 12.56 and 7.815?   _____ and _____

8. What is the sum of the compatible numbers you chose?   _____

9. What is another good estimate for 12.56 + 7.815?   _____

About how much more saline was used in the first experiment than in
the second experiment?

Estimate 12.56 − 7.815 by answering 10 to 12. Use the rounded
numbers 13 and 8 found above.

10. What is the difference of the rounded numbers?   13 − 8 = _____

11. What is a good estimate for 12.56 − 7.815?   _____

12. About how much more saline solution was used in
the first experiment than in the second experiment?   About _____ liters

© Pearson Education, Inc.

More Estimation of Decimal Sums and Differences (continued)

Estimate each sum or difference.

13. 5.68 + 28.5

14. 67.415 − 8.62

15. 32.912 + 47.622

16. 16.225 − 0.92

17. 0.89 + 2.4

18. 77.561 − 1.944

19. 45.61 + 36.2

20. 85.3 + 4.937

21. 17.5 − 11.289

22. 15.8 + 35.9

23. 14.822 − 8.1

24. 5.96 + 7.25

25. 16.1 − 3.81

26. 5.83 + 0.83

27. 16.854 − 2.1

28.   42.83
      − 19.116

29.   81.674
      − 2.52

30.   22
      + 10.3

31.   51.3
      + 22.68

32.   33.8
      + 8.223

33.   12.54
      + 86.142

34.   6.882
      − 0.52

35.   37.65
      − 22.9

36. Jean is 2.4 inches taller than Stefano. If Stefano
is 48.125 inches tall, about how tall is Jean? _____

37. Reasoning Are the estimates always the same when you use
rounding to the nearest whole number and compatible numbers?

© Pearson Education, Inc.

Adding and Subtracting Decimals to Thousandths

At a gymnastics competition Claudia earned a score of 7.75 on the uneven parallel bars. She scored 1.465 points higher on the beam. Answer 1 to 9 to find how many points she earned on the beam.

Find 7.75 + 1.465.

1. How many thousandths are in 7.75?

_____

2. Add 0 thousandths and 5 thousandths and record the value in the place-value chart.

Ones		Tenths	Hundredths	Thousandths
7	.	7	5	
+ 1	.	4	6	5
	.			

3. Add the hundredths.   5 hundredths + 6 hundredths = _____ hundredths

4. Regroup the hundredths. 11 hundredths = _____ tenth and _____ hundredth

Record the 1 hundredth at the bottom of the hundredths column and the 1 tenth at the top of the tenths column.

5. Add the tenths.   1 tenth + 7 tenths + 4 tenths = _____ tenths

6. Regroup the tenths.   12 tenths = _____ one and _____ tenths

Record the 2 tenths at the bottom of the tenths column and the 1 one at the top of the ones column.

7. Add the ones and record.   1 one + 7 ones + 1 one = _____ ones

8. So, what is 7.75 + 1.465?   _____

9. How many points did Claudia earn on the beam?   _____ points

Claudia also earned a score of 6.825 on her floor routine. How many more points did she earn on the uneven parallel bars than the floor routine?

Find 7.75 − 6.825 by answering 10 to 18.

10. Since 7.75 has 0 thousandths, write a zero in the place-value chart on the next page, to change 7.75 to 7.750.

© Pearson Education, Inc.

Adding and Subtracting Decimals to Thousandths (continued)

11. Regroup. Trade
1 hundredth for
10 thousandths. In the
chart, cross out the
5 hundredths and
write 4 above it. Cross
out the 0 thousandths
and write 10 above it.

Ones		Tenths	Hundredths	Thousandths
	.			
7	.	7	5	
− 6	.	8	2	5
	.			

12. Subtract the thousandths. 10 thousandths − 5 thousandths = _____ thousandths

Record the 5 in the thousandths column.

13. Subtract the hundredths. 4 hundredths − 2 hundredths = _____ hundredths

Record the 2 in the hundredths column.

14. Regroup. Trade 1 one for 10 tenths. Cross out the 7 ones and
write 6 above it. Cross out the 7 tenths and write 17 above it.

15. Subtract the tenths.   17 tenths − 8 tenths = _____ tenths

Record the 9 in the tenths column.

16. Subtract the ones and record the value in the ones column.

17. So, what is 7.75 − 6.825?   _____

18. How many more points did Claudia earn on the uneven
parallel bars than the floor routine?   _____ point

Find each sum or difference.

19.   43.72
       − 18.68

20.   25.83
       + 14.76

21.   75.77
       − 64.89

22.   865.80
        + 74.95

23.   0.951
       − 0.678

24.   0.810
       + 0.125

25.   7.618
       − 4.909

26.   6.234
       + 5.195

27. Bart is 1.486 meters tall and Sergio is 1.817 meters tall.
What is the difference in their heights?   _____

© Pearson Education, Inc.

Name ______________________________

Multiplying with Decimals and Whole Numbers

Materials place-value blocks: 1 one, 15 tenths, 12 hundredths per pair or group

A small jar of spice weighs 0.54 ounce. What is the weight of three jars?

Find 3 × 0.54 by answering 1 to 10.

Let the block at the right represent one unit, or 1.0.

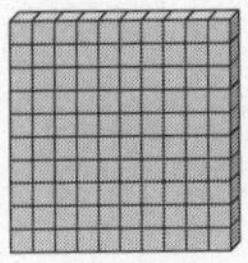

1.0

So,  represents one tenth, or 0.1 and  represents one hundredth or 0.01.

1. Show three groups of 0.54 using place-value blocks.

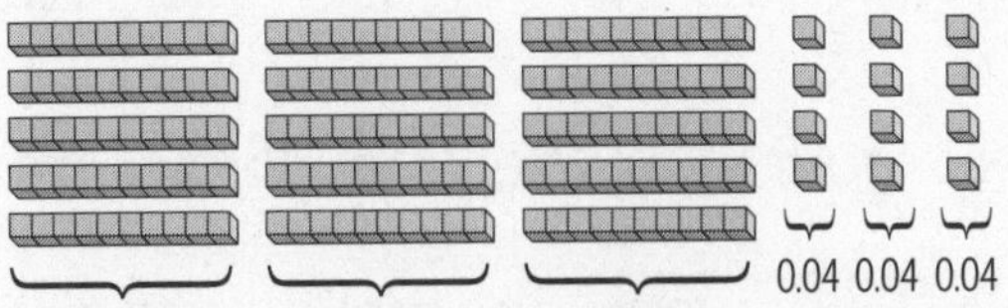
0.5
0.5
0.5
0.04
0.04
0.04

2. Multiply the hundredths.

3 × 4 hundredths = _______ hundredths

3. Trade 10 hundredths for one tenth.

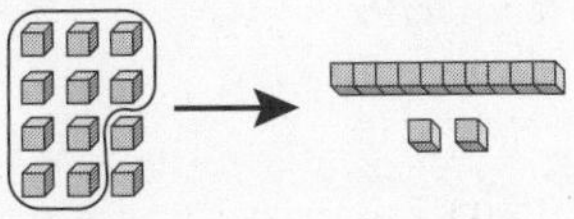

12 hundredths = _______ tenth

and _______ hundredths

	Ones		Tenths	Hundredths
	0	.	5	4
×		.		3

Record the 2 at the bottom of the hundredths column and the 1 at the top of the tenths column.

4. Multiply the tenths.

3 × 5 tenths = _______ tenths

© Pearson Education, Inc.

Multiplying with Decimals and Whole Numbers (continued)

5. Add the regrouped tenth.   15 tenths + 1 tenth = _____ tenths

6. Trade 10 tenths for 1 one.   16 tenths = _____ one and _____ tenths

Record the 6 at the bottom of the tenths column and
the 1 at the top of the ones column.

7. Multiply the ones. 3×0 ones = _____ ones

8. Add the regrouped one.   0 one + 1 one = _____ one

Record the 1 at the bottom of the ones column.

9. What is 3×0.54?   _____

10. What is the weight of three jars?   _____

11. How many decimal places are there in 0.54?   _____

12. How many decimal places are there in 3?   _____

13. How many decimal places are there in both factors combined?   _____

14. How many decimal places are in the product of $0.54 \times 3 = 1.62$?   _____

The total number of decimal places in the factors always equals
the number of decimal places in the product.

15. Reasoning If $5 \times 83 = 415$, what is 5×0.83? Explain.

Find each product.

16.   8.6
      $\times\ 4$

17.   42.5
      $\times\ 6$

18.   40
      $\times 1.3$

19. $9.12
      $\times\quad 3$

© Pearson Education, Inc.

20. Louis bought 5 pens that cost $0.79 each.
    How much did he pay for them?   _____

21. A small bottle of perfume holds 0.25 ounce.
    How many ounces would 5 of these bottles hold?   _____

Multiplying Decimals by 10, 100, or, 1,000

1. What is the value of 1 nickel? $1 \times \$0.05 =$ _____

2. What is the value of 10 nickels? $10 \times \$0.05 =$ _____

3. What is the value of 100 nickels? $100 \times \$0.05 =$ _____

4. What is the value of 1 quarter? $1 \times \$0.25 =$ _____

5. What is the value of 10 quarters? $10 \times \$0.25 =$ _____

6. What is the value of 100 quarters? $100 \times \$0.25 =$ _____

7. Reasoning What do you notice about the decimal point as a decimal is multiplied by a multiple of 10?

8. Use the pattern to fill in the table and to find $1,000 \times 0.945$.

Multiply by	Expression	Product	Move the decimal point to the right:
1	1×0.945	0.945	0 places
10	10×0.945	9.45	
100	100×0.945		2 places
1,000	$1,000 \times 0.945$		

9. What is $1,000 \times 0.945$? _____

Find 2.8×100 by answering 10 and 11.

10. How many places to the right do you need to move the decimal point when multiplying a decimal by 100? _____

To multiply 2.8×100, you need to move the decimal point two places to the right, but 2.8 only has one digit to the right of the decimal point. When this happens, use zeroes as place holders.

11. What is 2.8×100? _____

© Pearson Education, Inc.

Multiplying Decimals by 10, 100, or 1,000 (continued)

Use mental math to find each product.

12. $6.74 \times 1 =$ _____

$6.74 \times 10 =$ _____

$6.74 \times 100 =$ _____

$6.74 \times 1,000 =$ _____

13. $42.19 \times 1 =$ _____

$42.19 \times 10 =$ _____

$42.19 \times 100 =$ _____

$42.19 \times 1,000 =$ _____

14. $0.0125 \times 1 =$ _____

$0.0125 \times 10 =$ _____

$0.0125 \times 100 =$ _____

$0.0125 \times 1,000 =$ _____

15. $295.81 \times 1 =$ _____

$295.81 \times 10 =$ _____

$295.81 \times 100 =$ _____

$295.81 \times 1,000 =$ _____

16. $0.0007 \times 1 =$ _____

$0.0007 \times 10 =$ _____

$0.0007 \times 100 =$ _____

$0.0007 \times 1,000 =$ _____

17. $1,400 \times 1 =$ _____

$1,400 \times 10 =$ _____

$1,400 \times 100 =$ _____

$1,400 \times 1,000 =$ _____

18. One box weighs 3.25 pounds. What is the weight of 10 boxes?

_____

19. Reasoning How is multiplying a decimal by 100 the same as multiplying a whole number by 100? How is it different?

© Pearson Education, Inc.

Estimating the Product of a Whole Number and a Decimal

A paving stone is 7.25 inches long. If 68 of the stones are placed end to end to form a border for a flower bed, about how long is the border?

Estimate 68 × 7.25 by answering 1 to 5.

Round each factor to the greatest place that has a non-zero digit.

1. What is 7.25 rounded to the nearest one?   _____

2. What is 68 rounded to the nearest ten?   _____

3. Find the product of the two rounded factors.   7 × 70 = _____

4. So, what is a good estimate for 68 × 7.25?   _____

5. About how long is the border?   About _____ inches

A bead is 0.375 inch wide. If 32 beads are put on a necklace, about how long is the necklace?

Estimate 32 × 0.375 by answering 6 to 11.

6. What is 32 rounded to the nearest ten?   _____

7. What is 0.375 rounded to the nearest tenth?   _____

8. Find the product of the rounded factors by filling in the blanks.

30 × 0.4 = 3 × (10 × 0.4) = 3 × _____ = _____

9. So, what is a good estimate for 32 × 0.375?   _____

10. About how long is the necklace?   About _____ inches

11. Reasoning How can number sense be used to explain that 120 inches is not a reasonable estimate for the product of 32 × 0.375?

© Pearson Education, Inc.

Estimating the Product of a Whole Number and a Decimal (continued)

Estimate each product.

12. 2.6 × 4 _____

13. 7.8 × 5 _____

14. 0.34 × 9 _____

15. 0.051 × 6 _____

16. 18 × 1.07 _____

17. 23 × 5.69 _____

18. 4 × 0.081 _____

19. 56 × 0.19 _____

20. 6.21 × 5 _____

21. 8.05 × 7 _____

22. 1.7 × 6 _____

23. 0.82 × 4 _____

24. 0.074 × 3 _____

25. 26 × 2.51 _____

26. 32 × 8.9 _____

27. 45 × 0.036 _____

28. 26 × 0.89 _____

29. 13 × 1.25 _____

30. 74 × 3.3 _____

31. 0.046 × 159 _____

32. 89 × 0.25 _____

33. 14 × 3.47 _____

34. 5.39 × 24 _____

35. 6.54 × 76 _____

36. A bobcat weighs about 17.5 pounds. About how much would 2 bobcats weigh? _____

37. Erik needs 12 pieces of posterboard to make signs for a car wash. Each posterboard costs $0.36. About how much money will it cost him? _____

38. A golf ball weighs about 1.62 ounces. If a package of 6 golf balls is purchased for $5.59, about how much does the package weigh? _____

39. Reasoning When estimating by rounding, if both numbers to be multiplied are rounded up, will the actual answer be greater than or less than the estimate? _____

© Pearson Education, Inc.

Multiplying Decimals Using Grids

Materials crayons, markers, or colored pencils

Find 0.4×0.2 by answering 1 to 5.

1. Color 0.4 of the grid by coloring 4 vertical columns.

2. Use another color. Color 0.2 of the grid by coloring 2 horizontal rows.

3. How many small squares have both colors? _____

4. Write the decimal that represents the part of the grid that has both colors. This decimal represents the product. _____

5. So, what is 0.4×0.2? _____

6. How many decimal places does 0.4 have? _____

7. How many decimal places does 0.2 have? _____

8. How many decimal places do 0.4 and 0.2 have together? _____

9. How many decimal places does the product of $0.4 \times 0.2 = 0.08$ have? _____

The total number of decimal places in the factors always equals the number of decimal places in the product.

10. **Reasoning** What is 0.05×0.007? _____

Find 2.5×1.6 by answering 11 to 15.

You can use a grid to find partial products and add them together as you did to find 25×16

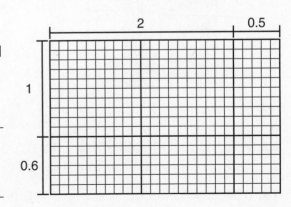

11. Color the area of the grid that shows 1×2. What is 1×2? _____

12. Color the area of the grid that shows 1×0.5 a different color. What is 1×0.5? _____

© Pearson Education, Inc.

Multiplying Decimals Using Grids (continued)

13. Color the area of the grid that shows 0.6×2 a third color. What is 0.6×2? _____

14. Color the area of the grid that shows 0.6×0.5 a fourth color. What is 0.6×0.5? _____

15. Add the partial products to find 2.5×1.6.

16. What is 2.5×1.6? _____

$$\begin{array}{r} 2.0 \\ 0.5 \\ 1.2 \\ + \ 0.30 \\ \hline \end{array}$$

Write a multiplication sentence to describe the shaded areas of each grid.

17.

_____

18.

_____

19.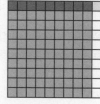

_____

20.

_____

21.

_____

22.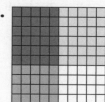

_____

23.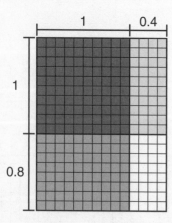

_____

24.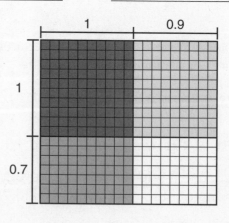

_____

25. A small can of cat food weighs 0.5 pound. Mollie's cat ate 0.3 can of food. How much food did Mollie's cat eat? _____

26. The new trail around a lake is 0.6 miles long. Rich ran 2 tenths of the trail. How far did he run? _____

© Pearson Education, Inc.

Multiplying Decimals by Decimals

Hans lives 2.35 miles from school. Jamal lives 1.2 times as far. How far from school does Jamal live?

Find 1.2×2.35 by answering 1 to 7.

$$\begin{array}{r} 235 \\ \times\ 12 \\ \hline \end{array}$$

   1. Multiply 1.2×2.35 as you would with whole numbers. What is 12×235?   _____

   2. How many decimal places are in 1.2?   _____

   3. How many decimal places are in 2.35?   _____

   4. How many decimal places are in both factors together?   _____

The number of decimal places in the product equals the total number of decimal places in the factors.

   5. How many decimal places should be in the product 1.2×2.35?   _____

   6. So, what is 1.2×2.35?   _____

   7. How far from the school does Jamal live?   _____ miles

   8. Reasoning Why are there only 2 decimal places in the correct answer of 2.82 when 1.2 and 2.35 have 3 decimal places altogether?

Rico lives 0.03 as far from the school as Hans. How far from the school does Rico live?

Find 0.03×2.35 by answering 9 to 13.

$$\begin{array}{r} 235 \\ \times\ 3 \\ \hline \end{array}$$

   9. What is 3×235?   _____

   10. How many decimal places are in both factors, 0.03 and 2.35, together?   _____

   11. How many decimal places should be in the product?   _____

© Pearson Education, Inc.

Multiplying Decimals by Decimals (continued)

If necessary, zeros may need to be added at the beginning of the number to place the decimal point correctly.

12. So, what is 0.03×2.35?   _____

13. How far from the school does Rico live?   _____ miles

Find each product.

14. 0.8×0.01 **15.** 1.5×0.02 **16.** 6.7×0.005 **17.** 0.2×0.03

_____   _____   _____   _____

18. 0.5×0.05 **19.** 1.2×0.03 **20.** 0.9×0.08 **21.** 0.3×0.3

_____   _____   _____   _____

22. 0.06×0.3 **23.** 1.2×0.07 **24.** 0.04×0.09 **25.** 0.7×0.09

_____   _____   _____   _____

26. $\begin{array}{r} 9.8 \\ \times\ 1.2 \\ \hline \end{array}$ **27.** $\begin{array}{r} 5.6 \\ \times\ 3.7 \\ \hline \end{array}$ **28.** $\begin{array}{r} 0.4 \\ \times\ 0.6 \\ \hline \end{array}$ **29.** $\begin{array}{r} 0.85 \\ \times\ 0.2 \\ \hline \end{array}$ **30.** $\begin{array}{r} 1.95 \\ \times\ 0.4 \\ \hline \end{array}$

31. $\begin{array}{r} 17.6 \\ \times\ 0.23 \\ \hline \end{array}$ **32.** $\begin{array}{r} 4.05 \\ \times\ 8.1 \\ \hline \end{array}$ **33.** $\begin{array}{r} 6.10 \\ \times\ 5.2 \\ \hline \end{array}$ **34.** $\begin{array}{r} 2.09 \\ \times\ 0.7 \\ \hline \end{array}$ **35.** $\begin{array}{r} 0.49 \\ \times\ 0.3 \\ \hline \end{array}$

36. An inch is 2.54 centimeters. How many centimeters are in 6.5 inches?   _____

37. A cell phone company offers telephone calls for $0.05 for one minute. How much should it cost to make a cell phone call for 0.5 minute?   _____

38. **Reasoning** Is the product 1.01×1.01 less than or greater than 1? Explain.

© Pearson Education, Inc.

Name _____

Dividing with Decimals and Whole Numbers

Materials place-value blocks: 5 ones, 13 tenths and
12 hundredths for each pair or group

Danica has 5.32 yards of ribbon to use on a craft project. If she
divides the ribbon into 4 equal parts, how long is each part?

Find 5.32 ÷ 4 by answering 1 to 20 and completing
the division problem below.

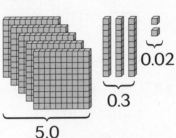

1. Use place-value blocks to show 5.32.

2. Divide the 5 ones evenly into 4 equal groups.

3. How many ones can go into each group? _____

4. Record the 1 above the 5 in 5.32, at the right.

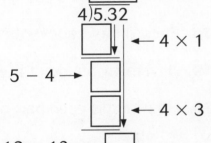

5. How many ones were used?

   4 × 1 one = _____ ones

6. Record the ones used below the
   5 in 5.32, at the right.

7. How many ones are leftover? 5 − 4 = _____ ones

8. Record the ones left below the 4 and the line.

9. Regroup the one into tenths and
   add the other 3 tenths.

   _____ one + 3 tenths =

   _____ tenths

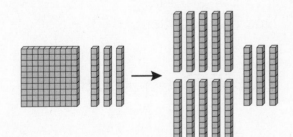

10. Bring down the 3 next to the 1,
    to show the 13 regrouped tenths.

11. Divide the 13 tenths evenly into the 4 groups.
    How many tenths can go in each group? _____

12. Record the 3 above the 3 in 5.32.

© Pearson Education, Inc.

Dividing with Decimals and Whole Numbers (continued)

13. How many tenths were used?   4 × 3 tenths = _____ tenths

14. Record the tenths used below the 3 in 5.32, and subtract to
find the tenths left over.

15. Regroup the tenths into hundredths
and add the other 2 hundredths.

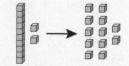

_____ tenth + 2 hundredths = _____ hundredths

16. Bring down the 2 next to the 1, to show the 12 regrouped
hundredths.

17. Divide the 12 hundredths evenly into the 4 groups.
How many ones can go in each group?   _____

18. Record the 3 above the 2 in 5.32.

19. How many hundredths were used? 4 × 3 hundredths = _____ hundredths

20. How long is each part of the ribbon?   _____

21. Reasoning Where is the decimal point placed in the quotient
when a decimal is divided by a whole number?

Find each quotient.

22. $8\overline{)36.08}$ **23.** $5\overline{)6.15}$ **24.** $6\overline{)36.12}$ **25.** $7\overline{)49.21}$

26. $7\overline{)56.98}$ **27.** $3\overline{)56.88}$ **28.** $6\overline{)18.84}$ **29.** $7\overline{)63.84}$

30. Three friends are equally sharing a 19.5 ounce drink.
How many ounces does each friend get?   _____

© Pearson Education, Inc.

Name _____

Dividing Decimals by 10, 100, or 1,000

1. If $250 is divided evenly by 10 people,
how much does each person get?   _____

2. If $250 is divided evenly by 100 people,
how much does each person get?   _____

3. If $250 is divided evenly by 1,000 people,
how much does each person get?   _____

4. What do you notice about the decimal point
as a decimal is divided by multiples of 10?   _____

5. Use the pattern to fill in the table and to find 873.2 ÷ 1,000.

Divide by	Expression	Answer	Move the decimal point to the left
1	873.2 ÷ 1	873.2	0 places
10	873.2 ÷ 10	87.32	
100	873.2 ÷ 100		2 places
1,000	873.2 ÷ 1,000		

6. What is 873.2 ÷ 1,000?   _____

Find 3.6 ÷ 100 by answering 7 to 9.

7. How many places to the left does the decimal
point move when dividing by 100?   _____

To divide 3.6 ÷ 100, you need to move the decimal point two places
to the left, but 3.6 only has one digit to the left of the decimal point.
When this happens, use zeroes as place holders.

8. What is 3.6 ÷ 100?   _____

9. Reasoning How can you check your answer?

© Pearson Education, Inc.

Dividing Decimals by 10, 100, or 1,000 (continued)

Use mental math to find each quotient.

10. 18.4 ÷ 1 = _____   **11.** 73 ÷ 1 = _____   **12.** 106.2 ÷ 1 = _____

18.4 ÷ 10 = _____   73 ÷ 10 = _____   106.2 ÷ 10 = _____

18.4 ÷ 100 = _____   73 ÷ 100 = _____   106.2 ÷ 100 = _____

18.4 ÷ 1,000 = _____   73 ÷ 1,000 = _____   106.2 ÷ 1,000 = _____

13. 9 ÷ 1 = _____   **14.** 45.3 ÷ 1 = _____   **15.** 575 ÷ 1 = _____

9 ÷ 10 = _____   45.3 ÷ 10 = _____   575 ÷ 10 = _____

9 ÷ 100 = _____   45.3 ÷ 100 = _____   575 ÷ 100 = _____

9 ÷ 1,000 = _____   45.3 ÷ 1,000 = _____   575 ÷ 1,000 = _____

16. 6.2 ÷ 10   **17.** 83.9 ÷ 100   **18.** 27.5 ÷ 1,000   **19.** 375 ÷ 1,000

_____   _____   _____   _____

20. 93.3 ÷ 100   **21.** 12.4 ÷ 10   **22.** 214 ÷ 1,000   **23.** 5.04 ÷ 100

_____   _____   _____   _____

24. 37 ÷ 10   **25.** 564 ÷ 10   **26.** 72.9 ÷ 1,000   **27.** 4.1 ÷ 100

_____   _____   _____   _____

28. 97.6 ÷ 100   **29.** 813 ÷ 1,000   **30.** 3.7 ÷ 10   **31.** 8 ÷ 100

_____   _____   _____   _____

32. 17.65 ÷ 10   **33.** 3,175 ÷ 1,000   **34.** 0.54 ÷ 10   **35.** 2.06 ÷ 100

_____   _____   _____   _____

36. A 220-foot long coil of rope is to be divided into 10 equal
pieces. How long will each piece be?

_____

37. A 40-acre plot of land is to be subdivided into
100 equal size plots. How large will each plot be?

_____

© Pearson Education, Inc.

Name _____

Dividing a Decimal by a Whole Number

A plot of land that is 29.4 acres is divided into 12 equal parts. How many acres is each part?

Find 29.4 ÷ 12 by answering 1 to 11 and completing the long division problem at the right.

1. How many groups of 12 are there in 29? _____

   Record the 2 above the 9 in 29.4 at the right.

2. Multiply and subtract.
   How many ones are leftover? 29 − 24 = _____ ones

   Record this value below the 24 and the line.

3. How many tenths are 5 ones and 4 tenths? _____ tenths
   Bring down the 4 next to the 5, to show the 54 tenths.

4. How many groups of 12 are there in 54? _____

   Record the 4 above the 4 in 29.4.

5. Multiply and subtract.
   How many tenths are leftover?   54 tenths − 48 tenths = _____ tenths

   Record this value below the 48 and the line.

6. Does 29.4 = 29.40? _____ Since there is a remainder, add a zero to the dividend to change 29.4 to 29.40.

7. How many hundredths are in 6 tenths and 0 hundredths? _____ hundredths

   Bring down the 0 next to the 6, to show the 60 hundredths.

8. How many groups of 12 are there in 60? _____

   Record the 5 above the 0 in 29.40.

9. Multiply and subtract.
   How many hundredths are leftover?   60 − 60 = _____ hundredths

   Since there are no hundredths left, the division is finished.
   Notice that the decimal point in the quotient is directly above the decimal point in the dividend

10. So, what is 29.4 ÷ 12? _____

11. How many acres is each piece of land? _____

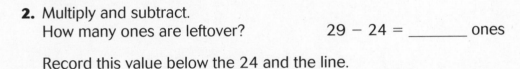

© Pearson Education, Inc.

Dividing a Decimal by a Whole Number (continued)

Find each quotient.

12. $4\overline{)12.8}$ **13.** $37\overline{)55.5}$ **14.** $35\overline{)2.1}$ **15.** $2\overline{)37.4}$

16. $11\overline{)97.9}$ **17.** $41\overline{)129.15}$ **18.** $30\overline{)13.5}$ **19.** $9\overline{)45.54}$

20. $6\overline{)72.24}$ **21.** $5\overline{)43.75}$ **22.** $3\overline{)7.41}$ **23.** $30\overline{)188.4}$

24. $9\overline{)67.86}$ **25.** $3\overline{)39.09}$ **26.** $52\overline{)72.8}$ **27.** $81\overline{)32.4}$

28. $2\overline{)621.5}$ **29.** $16\overline{)75.2}$ **30.** $24\overline{)151.2}$ **31.** $9\overline{)132.3}$

32. A 12-pack of canned juice costs $3.24. What is the cost
of each juice can?   _____

33. Reasoning How many zeros can be placed after the last digit in a
decimal without changing the value of the number?

© Pearson Education, Inc.

Estimating the Quotient of a Decimal and a Whole Number

A butcher has 62.75 pounds of ground beef. If he divides it into 34 packages of equal weight, about how many pounds should he put in each package?

Estimate 62.75 ÷ 34 by answering 1 to 6.

Round the dividend and the divisor to the greatest place that has a non-zero digit.

1. What is the greatest place in 62.75 that has a non-zero digit? _____

2. What is 62.75 rounded to the nearest ten? _____

3. What is 34 rounded to the nearest ten? _____

4. What is 60 ÷ 30? _____

5. So, what is a good estimate for 62.75 ÷ 34? _____

6. About how many pounds should
the butcher put in each package?   About _____ pounds

Compatible numbers can also be used to find an estimate. Compatible numbers are close to the actual numbers, but easy to divide.

The Delgato family drove 473.6 miles over a period of 8 hours. About how far did they drive each hour?

Estimate 473.6 ÷ 8 by answering 7 to 13.

7. What is the greatest place in 473.6 that has a non-zero digit? _____

8. What is 473.6 rounded to the nearest hundred? _____

9. Is it easy to divide 500 by 8? _____

10. What is a number close to 473.6 that is easy to divide by 8? _____

11. What is 480 ÷ 8? _____

12. So, what is a good estimate for 473.6 ÷ 8? _____

13. About how far did the Delgato family drive each hour?   About _____ miles

© Pearson Education, Inc.

Estimating the Quotient of a Decimal and a Whole Number (continued)

Estimate each quotient.

14. 352.84 ÷ 10

_____

15. 42.9 ÷ 8

_____

16. 397.52 ÷ 42

_____

17. 754.61 ÷ 74

_____

18. 84.69 ÷ 5

_____

19. 198.6 ÷ 51

_____

20. 41.9 ÷ 7

_____

21. 28.68 ÷ 9

_____

22. 225.81 ÷ 69

_____

23. 633.4 ÷ 73

_____

24. 410.88 ÷ 18

_____

25. 69.3 ÷ 8

_____

26. 159.1 ÷ 19

_____

27. 542.98 ÷ 58

_____

28. 158.6 ÷ 4

_____

29. Mr. Chen worked 148.6 hours last month.
If he worked 22 days during the month, about
how many hours did he work each day?   _____

30. Reasoning About how many 26-ounce cartons can be filled from
231 ounces of juice? Find the estimate two ways and explain how
you found each.

31. Reasoning Why is more than one answer correct when estimating
quotients?

© Pearson Education, Inc.

Dividing a Decimal by a Decimal

Materials place-value blocks: 2 ones, 21 tenths and 15 hundredths for each pair or group

Simon has 2.25 gallons of filtered water. How many 0.75 gallon servings of water does Simon have?

Find 2.25 ÷ 0.75 by answering 1 to 4.

1. Show 2.25 with place-value blocks.

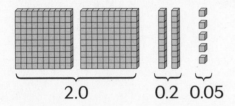

    2.0   0.2 0.05

2. Divide 2.25 into groups with 0.75 in each. Trade ones for tenths and tenths for hundredths, as needed. How many groups of 0.75 are in 2.25? _____

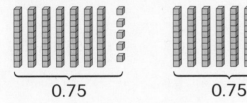

    0.75   0.75   0.75

3. So, what is 2.25 ÷ 0.75? _____

4. How many 0.75 gallon servings of water does Simon have? _____

Find 2.25 ÷ 0.75 another way by answering 5 to 8.

5. What number makes the number sentence true?   0.75 × _____ = 75

6. You can change 2.25 ÷ 0.75 to make it easier to divide. Fill in the missing number below to see how.

$$2.25 \div 0.75 = \frac{2.25}{0.75} = \frac{2.25 \times 100}{0.75 \times 100} = \frac{\boxed{}}{75} = \underline{\hspace{1cm}} \div 75$$

7. What is 225 ÷ 75? _____

© Pearson Education, Inc.

Dividing a Decimal by a Decimal (continued)

8. Since 225 ÷ 75 = 2.25 ÷ 0.75, what is 2.25 ÷ 0.75? _____

To divide decimals, multiply the divisor by 10 or 100 to make it a whole number. Multiply the dividend by the same amount. The quotient of the resulting amounts equals the quotient of the original numbers.

Find 2.96 ÷ 0.4 by answering 9 to 12.

9. What number makes the number sentence true? $0.4 \times$ _____ = 4

10. Multiply 2.96 by the same number. $2.96 \times 10 =$ _____

11. What is 29.6 ÷ 4? _____

12. What is 2.96 ÷ 0.4? _____

Divide.

13. 12.2 ÷ 6.1   **14.** 35.7 ÷ 5.1   **15.** 0.18 ÷ 0.2   **16.** 53.4 ÷ 8.9

_____   _____   _____   _____

17. 125 ÷ 0.25   **18.** 0.48 ÷ 0.16   **19.** 26.8 ÷ 6.7   **20.** 1.008 ÷ 5.6

_____   _____   _____   _____

21. Baseball card packages cost $3.50 each.
How many packages can be purchased for $17.50? _____

22. **Reasoning** When dividing a number which is greater than 1 by a number less than 1, will the quotient be greater than or less than the dividend? Explain.

© Pearson Education, Inc.

Scientific Notation

Scientific notation is a method of writing large numbers so that they are easier to write, to read, and to use, than standard form.

Find the relationship between scientific notation and standard notation by answering 1 to 3.

1. Complete the table.

Scientific Notation	Expanded Form	Standard Notation	Places Decimal Point Moved
2.1×10^2	2.1×100	210	
2.1×10^3	$2.1 \times$	2,100	3
2.1×10^4	$2.1 \times$	21,000	
2.1×10^5	$2.1 \times$	210,000	5

2. Reasoning What is the relationship between the exponent on the 10 and the number of places the decimal point moves when rewriting a number in scientific notation to standard notation?

3. Using the pattern from the table, write 2.1×10^{11} in standard notation. _____

A mole is a measurement commonly used in chemistry. One mole of an item represents about 6.023×10^{23} molecules. Write this number in standard notation by answering 4 to 6.

4. How many places do you move the decimal point? _____

5. How many zeros does 6.023×10^{23} have when written in standard form? _____

6. Write one mole of an item in standard notation.

_____

© Pearson Education, Inc.

Scientific Notation (continued)

The mass of the Earth is about 5,970,000,000,000,000,000,000,000
kilograms. Write this number in scientific notation by answering 7 to 9.

7. The first number in scientific notation is always
between 1 and 10. What is the first number?   _____

8. How many digits are between the new position
for the decimal and the end of the given number?   _____

9. $5,970,000,000,000,000,000,000,000 = 5.97 \times$ _____

10. What is the mass of the Earth in scientific notation? _____ kilograms

Write each number in standard notation.

11. 3.25×10^8

12. 6.887×10^{10}

13. 1.2×10^3

_____

_____

_____

14. 8.1×10^{12}

15. 5.7×10^5

16. 6.117×10^7

_____

_____

_____

Write each number in scientific notation.

17. 38,500,000,000

$3.85 \times 10^{\boxed{}}$

18. 577,000,000

$5.77 \times 10^{\boxed{}}$

19. 6,100,000,000

$6.1 \times 10^{\boxed{}}$

20. 116,000,000

21. 3,800,000,000,000

22. 85,000

_____

_____

_____

23. 599,000,000,000,000

24. 1,214,000

25. 46,000,000,000

_____

_____

_____

26. A light-year is the distance that light
can travel in one year. It is equal to
9,500,000,000,000 kilometers. What is
one light-year written in scientific notation?   _____ kilometers

© Pearson Education, Inc.

Understanding Ratios

A ratio is a comparison of like or unlike quantities. A ratio of 2 items to 3 items can be expressed in three different ways: 2 to 3, $\frac{2}{3}$ or 2:3.

Examine ratios in your classroom by answering 1 to 12.

1. How many boys are in the classroom?   _____

How many girls are in the classroom?   _____

2. What is the ratio of boys to girls in words?   _____ to _____

3. What is the ratio of boys to girls as a fraction?   _____

4. Write the ratio of girls to boys using a colon.   _____

5. How many students are in the classroom?   _____

6. What is the ratio of boys to students in words?   _____

7. What is the ratio of students to girls as a fraction? _____

8. Write the ratio of girls to students using a colon.   _____

9. Reasoning How does the ratio of girls to boys differ from the ratio of boys to girls?

10. How many students in the classroom have brown hair?   _____

How many students in the classroom have black hair?   _____

11. What is the ratio of students with black hair to total students as a fraction?   _____

12. Write the ratio of students with brown hair to those with black hair using a colon.   _____

© Pearson Education, Inc.

Understanding Ratios (continued)

Write each ratio in three different ways.

△ ♡ △ ☺ △ □   □
□ ♡ ♡ □ ☺ △ ♡
☺ △ □ ☺ ♡ □ △

13. hearts to triangles _____

14. smiley faces to triangles _____

15. squares to all figures _____

16. triangles to squares _____

17. all figures to smiley faces _____

18. triangles to hearts _____

19. hearts and triangles to all figures _____

For Exercises 20–24, use the information in the table to write a ratio for each comparison.

Animals on a Farm	
Animals	**Number**
Chickens	12
Goats	22
Cows	8
Sheep	9
Pigs	15
Rabbits	0

20. chickens to goats _____

21. sheep to chickens _____

22. pigs to cows _____

23. chickens to all animals _____

24. rabbits to goats _____

25. Reasoning Karina's stuffed animals are only teddy bears and dogs. The ratio of teddy bears to dogs is 5:3. What is the ratio of dogs to all stuffed animals? Explain your answer.

© Pearson Education, Inc.

Name _____

Rates and Unit Rates

A rate is a special type of ratio that compares quantities with unlike units of measure, such as hits per game.

The table shows the number of hits for some members of a baseball team. Use the table for 1 to 7.

Name	Number of Hits	Number of Games
Maurice	20	10
Wade	24	8
Alfonso	30	12

1. What is Maurice's rate of hits to games?   _____ hits in _____ games

2. To find Maurice's unit rate, divide the number of hits by the number of games.

_____ ÷ _____ = _____ hits per game

On average, Maurice gets 2 hits per game.

3. What is Wade's rate of hits to games?   _____

4. On average, how many hits per game does Wade get?

_____ ÷ _____ = _____ hits per game

5. What is Alfonso's rate of hits to games?   _____

6. On average, how many hits per game does Alfonso get?

_____ ÷ _____ = _____ hits per game

7. Reasoning Although Alfonso had the most hits, his unit rate was not the highest. Why not?

© Pearson Education, Inc.

Rates and Unit Rates (continued)

Find the unit rate.

8. 525 points in 15 games

9. 54 teachers for 6 schools

_____

_____

10. 33 apples for 11 fruit baskets

11. $1.77 for 3 pounds of bananas

_____

_____

12. 312 miles every 12 gallons

13. 185 feet in 37 seconds

_____

_____

14. 42 tennis balls in 14 cans

15. 110 calories in 4 servings

_____

_____

16. $1.50 for 3 power bars

17. 1,530 miles in 6 hours

_____

_____

18. $48 in 8 hours

19. 96 aces in 12 sets

_____

_____

20. Samantha scored 6 goals playing soccer in 18 games. What units would you use to describe her rate? What is her rate?

_____

21. A light bulb manufacturer claims that each bulb lasts at least 480 hours. Suppose you get 3,000 hours of use from 6 light bulbs. Write this information as a rate.

_____

© Pearson Education, Inc.

Comparing Rates

Larry's Market sells 6 bagels for $2.28. Sal's Convenience Mart sells the
same bagels, but charges $3.50 for 10. Find which store has the better
buy by answering 1 to 8.

1. What is Larry's rate of cost of bagels?   _____ dollars per _____ bagels

To compare two prices, find the unit price for each. The unit price is the
same as the unit rate.

2. To find the unit price, divide the price
by the number of bagels.   _____ ÷ _____ = _____

3. What is the unit price for Larry's bagels? $_____ per bagel

4. What is Sal's rate of cost to bagels?   _____ dollars per _____ bagels

5. To find the unit price, divide the price
by the number of bagels.   _____ ÷ _____ = _____

6. What is the unit price for Sal's bagels? $_____ per bagel

7. Compare. Write > or <. $0.38 ◯ $0.35

8. Which market has the better buy?   _____

The Thompson family drove 5 hours and traveled a total of 275 miles.
The Gonzalez family drove 8 hours and traveled a total of 400 miles.
Find which family traveled at a faster rate by answering 9 to 14.

To find the unit rate, divide the miles by the number of hours.

9. Divide total miles by hours to find the Thompson
family's unit rate of speed.   _____ ÷ _____ = _____

10. What was the Thompson family's unit rate of speed?   _____ miles per hour

11. Divide to find the Gonzalez family's
unit rate of speed.   _____ ÷ _____ = _____

© Pearson Education, Inc.

Comparing Rates (continued)

12. What was the Gonzalez family's unit rate of speed?   _____ miles per hour

13. Compare. Write > or <.   55 miles per hour $\bigcirc$ 50 miles per hour

14. Which family traveled at a faster rate?   _____

Find each unit price. Determine the better buy.

15. $3 for 4 baseballs or $4 for 5 baseballs

_____

16. 6 wristbands for $1.68 or 9 wristbands for $2.43

_____

17. $65 for 2 wallets or $93 for 3 wallets

_____

Find each unit rate and determine which rate is greater.

18. 12 runs in 4 games or 20 runs in 5 games

_____

_____

19. 8 feet in 4 seconds or 15 feet in 5 seconds

_____

_____

20. 6 fish in 8 hours or 7 fish in 10 hours

_____

_____

21. Your pulse rate is the number of times your heart beats
per minute. Betty counted 130 beats in 2 minutes and
Sarah counted 204 beats in 3 minutes. Who had the
higher pulse rate?   _____

22. Reasoning Suppose Store A has 28 pencils for $7.50, and Store
B has 29 pencils for $7.25. Explain without doing any calculations
why Store B has the better buy.

© Pearson Education, Inc.

Distance, Rate, and Time

The formula $d = r \times t$ relates distance, d, rate, r and time, t. Rate in this formula means average speed.

The table shows the results of practice races run by some members of a track team. Rates written as 6 meters/second are read 6 meters per second.

Complete the table by answering 1 to 13.

Name	Distance	Rate	Time
Hannah	600 meters	6 meters/second	
Mya	800 meters		160 seconds
Adrienne		5 meters/second	120 seconds

1. What is the formula that relates distance, rate and time?   _____

2. For Hannah, what is the value of d ?   _____

3. For Hannah, what is the value of r ?   _____

4. For Hannah, which variable is unknown?   _____

5. Substitute Hannah's values for d and r in the formula.

$$d \quad = \quad r \quad \times \quad t$$

$$\text{_____} = \text{_____} \times \quad t$$

6. Solve $600 = 6t$. Show your work.

$$t = \text{_____}$$

7. How fast did Hannah run the race?
Write this amount in the table.   _____ seconds

8. Substitute Mya's values for d and r in the formula.

$$d \quad = \quad r \quad \times \quad t$$

$$\text{_____} = \quad r \quad \times \text{_____}$$

© Pearson Education, Inc.

Distance, Rate, and Time (continued)

9. Solve the equation $800 = 160r$.

$r =$ _____

10. How fast did Mya run the race?
Write this amount in the table.   _____ meters/second

11. Substitute Adrienne's values for r and t in the formula.

$$d \;\; = \;\; r \;\; \times \;\; t$$

$$d \;\; = \; \underline{\quad\quad} \times \underline{\quad\quad}$$

12. What is the value of d?   _____

13. How far did Adrienne run?
Write this amount in the table.   _____

Solve the equation for the missing variable.

14. $d = 55$ miles/hour $\times$ 7 hours   **15.** 300 feet $= 15$ feet/second $\times t$

$d =$ _____ $t =$ _____

Complete the table.

	Distance	Rate	Time
16.	200 meters	2 meters/second	
17.	10 miles		4 hours
18.		8 yards/minute	10 minutes

19. Reasoning If two people run the same distance but one person takes less time than the other, how do their rates compare?

© Pearson Education, Inc.

Equal Ratios and Proportions

Equal ratios can be found by multiplying or dividing both terms of the ratio by the same number.

Rectangle A has a length of 10 centimeters and a width of 8 centimeters. The ratio of the length to the width is $\frac{10}{8}$. Find two ratios equal to $\frac{10}{8}$ by answering 1 to 4.

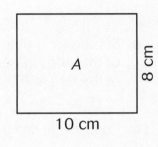

A

10 cm

8 cm

1. Try multiplying by 5.   length → $\dfrac{10}{8} = \dfrac{10 \times \square}{8 \times 5} = \dfrac{\square}{\square}$
width →

2. What is one ratio that is equal to $\frac{10}{8}$? _____

3. Try dividing by 2.   length → $\dfrac{10}{8} = \dfrac{10 \div \square}{8 \div 2} = \dfrac{\square}{\square}$
width →

4. What is another ratio equal to $\frac{10}{8}$? _____

5. Reasoning How many ratios are equal to $\frac{10}{8}$? Explain.

Rectangle B has a length of 60 cm and a width of 48 cm. Are the sides of Rectangle B proportional to the sides of Rectangle A? Find out by answering 6 to 8.

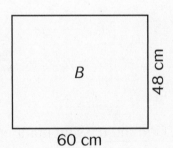

B

60 cm

48 cm

6. What is the ratio of the length to the width in Rectangle B?   _____

7. The sides of Rectangle B are proportional to the sides of Rectangle A if $\frac{10}{8}$ is equal to $\frac{60}{48}$. Try to multiply both terms of $\frac{10}{8}$ by the same number to get $\frac{60}{48}$.

$$\frac{10}{8} = \frac{10 \times \square}{8 \times \square} = \frac{\square}{\square}$$

8. Are the sides of Rectangle A proportional to the sides of Rectangle B?   _____

© Pearson Education, Inc.

Equal Ratios and Proportions (continued)

Rectangle C has a width of 24 cm. The ratio of the length to the width of Rectangle C is the same as Rectangle A. Find the length of Rectangle C by answering 9 to 11.

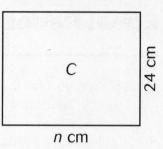

n cm

9. Set the ratio of the sides in Rectangle A equal to the ratio of the sides in Rectangle C. Use n to represent the length of Rectangle C. What is the proportion?   _____

10. Complete to find the value of n. $\dfrac{10}{8} = \dfrac{10 \times \boxed{}}{8 \times \boxed{}} = \dfrac{\boxed{}}{24}$

11. What is the length of Rectangle C?   _____

Write three ratios that are equal to each of the following.

12. $\dfrac{5}{10}$

13. $\dfrac{8}{12}$

14. $\dfrac{8}{6}$

_____   _____   _____

Tell whether each pair of ratios can form a proportion.

15. $\dfrac{5}{6}, \dfrac{15}{18}$

16. $\dfrac{8}{14}, \dfrac{4}{7}$

17. $\dfrac{5}{6}, \dfrac{30}{42}$

18. $\dfrac{6}{15}, \dfrac{30}{25}$

_____   _____   _____   _____

19. $\dfrac{5}{8}, \dfrac{25}{45}$

20. $\dfrac{16}{20}, \dfrac{4}{5}$

21. $\dfrac{27}{30}, \dfrac{9}{10}$

22. $\dfrac{16}{18}, \dfrac{2}{9}$

_____   _____   _____   _____

Find the missing number in each proportion.

23. $\dfrac{2}{5} = \dfrac{18}{n}$

24. $\dfrac{48}{64} = \dfrac{n}{4}$

25. $\dfrac{24}{n} = \dfrac{3}{7}$

26. $\dfrac{10}{45} = \dfrac{2}{n}$

_____   _____   _____   _____

27. You use a photocopy machine to enlarge a paper for school. The original is 8 inches wide and 10 inches long. The enlarged copy has a width of 12 inches. What is the length?   _____

© Pearson Education, Inc.

Solving Proportions

When thawing a turkey, it can take 12 hours of thawing time for every 3 pounds of turkey. How many hours should be allowed to thaw a 15 pound turkey? You can use a table or a proportion to find the answer.

1. Complete the ratio table to find the number of hours.

Hours of Thawing Time	12				
Pounds of Turkey	3	6	9	12	15

2. How many hours of thawing time should be allowed for a 15 pound turkey?   _____

3. You can also use a proportion to find the number of hours. Set the ratio 12 hours to 3 pounds equal to a ratio of n hours to 15 pounds.

 Write the proportion.   _____

4. What is the unit rate for thawing?   _____

5. Multiply 15 by the unit rate to find the number of hours.

 What is 15×4?   _____

6. How many hours of thawing time should be allowed for a 15 pound turkey?   _____

How many hours of thawing time should be allowed for a 20 pound turkey?

7. Can the answer be found in the ratio table above?   _____

8. So, use a proportion to find the number of hours. Set the ratio 12 hours to 3 pounds equal to a ratio of n hours to 20 pounds.

 Write the proportion.   _____

9. What is the unit rate for thawing?   _____

© Pearson Education, Inc.

Solving Proportions (continued)

10. Multiply 20 by the unit rate to find the number of hours.

What is 20×4? _____

11. How many hours of thawing time should be
allowed for a 20 pound turkey? _____

12. Rachel is paid $13 for 2 hours of babysitting. Complete the ratio
table and use the table to answer 13 to 15.

Dollar amount	13				
Hours of Babysitting	2	4	6		

13. How much money does Rachel make for 4 hours of babysitting? _____

14. How much money does Rachel make for 8 hours of babysitting? _____

15. How long does Rachel have to baby sit to make $65? _____

Use unit rates to solve the proportions.

16. $\dfrac{21 \text{ people}}{\text{class}} = \dfrac{x \text{ people}}{3 \text{ classes}}$

$x =$ _____

17. $\dfrac{36 \text{ feet}}{12 \text{ sec}} = \dfrac{n \text{ feet}}{20 \text{ sec}}$

$n =$ _____

18. $\dfrac{9 \text{ fouls}}{2 \text{ games}} = \dfrac{f \text{ fouls}}{10 \text{ games}}$

$f =$ _____

19. $\dfrac{16 \text{ pages}}{4 \text{ hours}} = \dfrac{m \text{ pages}}{24 \text{ hours}}$

$m =$ _____

20. $\dfrac{10 \text{ points}}{4 \text{ items}} = \dfrac{p \text{ points}}{18 \text{ items}}$

$p =$ _____

21. $\dfrac{8 \text{ pictures}}{\text{day}} = \dfrac{a \text{ pictures}}{7 \text{ days}}$

$a =$ _____

22. The average snow fall in a town is 22 inches per year. How much
snow would be expected to fall in this town in 4 years?

23. Reasoning Do unit rates have an advantage over ratio tables
when finding an unknown in a proportion? Explain.

© Pearson Education, Inc.

Solving Proportions Using Cross Products

The Cougars scored 5 touchdowns during the first 4 football games of the season. At this rate, how many touchdowns should the team score in a 10-game season?

Write a proportion and solve to find the number of touchdowns, by answering 1 to 5.

1. Write a proportion.

Touchdowns scored → $\dfrac{\boxed{}}{\boxed{}} = \dfrac{n}{\boxed{}}$ ← Touchdowns for season

Number of games → ← Games in season

2. Find the cross products.

$$\dfrac{5}{4} \diagup\!\!\!\!\diagup \dfrac{n}{10}$$

$4 \times n =$ _____

$5 \times 10 =$ _____

3. Set the cross products equal. $4n =$ _____

4. Solve $4n = 50$.

$n =$ _____

5. How many touchdowns should the Cougars score in a 10-game season?   _____ touchdowns

The Rodriguez family is taking a 385 mile trip. After 3 hours they traveled a distance of 165 miles. At this rate, how many total hours will they need to travel to complete their trip? Find out by answering 6 to 11.

6. Write a proportion. Use h to represent the hours needed to complete the trip.

Distance traveled → $\dfrac{\boxed{}}{\boxed{}} = \dfrac{\boxed{}}{h}$ ← Total Distance

Hours traveled → ← Total hours

7. What is one cross product?   _____

8. What is the other cross product?   _____

© Pearson Education, Inc.

Solving Proportions Using Cross Products (continued)

9. Write an equation using the cross products.   _____

10. Solve $165h = 1,155$.

$$h = \text{_____}$$

11. How long will it take to complete the trip?   _____

Write the cross products for each proportion.

12. $\dfrac{5}{10} = \dfrac{12}{n}$ **13.** $\dfrac{1}{12} = \dfrac{n}{9}$ **14.** $\dfrac{n}{15} = \dfrac{10}{6}$

_____   _____   _____

Find the missing number in each proportion.

15. $\dfrac{6}{8} = \dfrac{n}{20}$ **16.** $\dfrac{n}{5} = \dfrac{27}{45}$ **17.** $\dfrac{9}{8} = \dfrac{81}{n}$ **18.** $\dfrac{5}{n} = \dfrac{10}{12}$

_____   _____   _____   _____

19. $\dfrac{6}{7} = \dfrac{n}{56}$ **20.** $\dfrac{n}{12} = \dfrac{3}{36}$ **21.** $\dfrac{66}{n} = \dfrac{11}{12}$ **22.** $\dfrac{1.5}{6} = \dfrac{10}{n}$

_____   _____   _____   _____

23. $\dfrac{n}{5} = \dfrac{11}{2.2}$ **24.** $\dfrac{20}{18} = \dfrac{30}{n}$ **25.** $\dfrac{3}{2} = \dfrac{n}{6}$ **26.** $\dfrac{25}{n} = \dfrac{15}{12}$

_____   _____   _____   _____

27. Five bags of rice weigh 70 ounces. How much do
four bags of rice weigh?   _____

28. If 15 pieces of gum cost $0.90, how much do 12 pieces
of gum cost?   _____

29. A babysitter earns $51 for working 8.5 hours. How much
does the sitter earn for working 40 hours?   _____

30. Reasoning When solving a proportion involving the lengths and
widths of two rectangles, does it matter whether you put length or
width in the top of the ratio?

© Pearson Education, Inc.

Similar Figures and Proportions

Similar figures have the same shape, but not necessarily the same size. The lengths of the sides of similar figures are proportional.

In the trapezoids below, $\frac{12}{15} = \frac{24}{30}$.

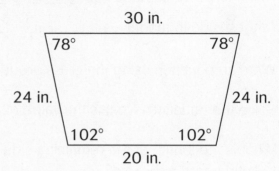

15 in.

78°   78°

12 in.   12 in.

102° 102°

10 in.

30 in.

78°   78°

24 in.   24 in.

102°   102°

20 in.

1. Complete the proportion for the trapezoids above.

$$\frac{10}{12} = \frac{\Box}{24}$$

Mrs. King enlarged the trapezoid shown below for a bulletin board display so the longest side is 16 inches. The enlarged shape is similar to the shape shown. Find the lengths of the remaining sides of the bulletin board trapezoid by answering 2 to 10.

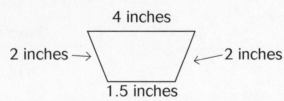

4 inches

2 inches →   ← 2 inches

1.5 inches

2. Write a proportion to find the legs of the trapezoid. Use n to represent the length of the legs of the trapezoid on the bulletin board.

legs in model → $\dfrac{2 \text{ in.}}{\boxed{} \text{ in.}} = \dfrac{n \text{ in.}}{\boxed{} \text{ in.}}$ ← legs on bulletin board

longest side in model →   ← longest side on bulletin board

3. Write an equation using the cross products.   _____

4. Solve $4n = 32$. What is the value of n? $n =$ _____

5. What is the length of the legs of the bulletin board trapezoid?   _____

© Pearson Education, Inc.

Similar Figures and Proportions (continued)

6. Write a proportion to find the remaining side. Use b to represent the length of the remaining side of the bulletin board trapezoid.

remaining side in model → $\dfrac{1.5 \text{ in.}}{\boxed{}\text{ in.}} = \dfrac{b \text{ in.}}{\boxed{}\text{ in.}}$ ← remaining side on bulletin board

longest side in model → ← longest side on bulletin board

7. Write an equation using the cross products. _____

8. Solve the equation. What is the value of b? $b =$ _____

9. What is the length of the remaining side of the bulletin board trapezoid? _____

10. Fill in the measurements for the bulletin board trapezoid:

$\boxed{}$ inches

$\boxed{}$ inches →

$\boxed{}$ inches ←

$\boxed{}$ inches

The figures shown below are similar. Find the missing sides. Show the proportion you use and the equation using the cross products.

11.

8 feet

10 feet   10 feet

8 feet

2 feet

$\boxed{}$ feet $\boxed{}$ feet

$\boxed{}$ feet

Proportion: _____

Equation: _____

12.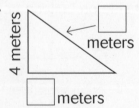

4 meters

$\boxed{}$ meters

$\boxed{}$ meters

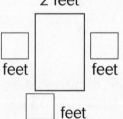

12 meters

15 meters

9 meters

Proportion: _____

Equation: _____

Proportion: _____

Equation: _____

13. Reasoning Is it possible to find two squares that are not similar? Explain.

© Pearson Education, Inc.

Name _____

Maps and Scale Drawings

Materials centimeter ruler

In a scale drawing, the dimensions of an object are reduced or enlarged by the same scale. The dimensions of the scale drawing and the original figure are proportional and therefore, similar. A map is typically a scale drawing.

1. What is the relationship between a scale
   drawing and the original figure?   _____

The scale drawing or map of the island shown

has a scale of $\frac{1 \text{ centimeter}}{300 \text{ meters}}$. Answer 2 to 9 to find the

actual length of the island.

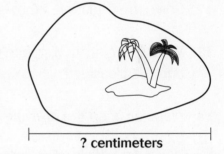

2. What distance on the map represents 300 meters?

   _____   ? **centimeters**

3. Use a centimeter ruler to measure the length
   of the island.

   What is the length of the island in the drawing?   _____

4. Write a proportion that can be used to find the actual
   length of the island. Let x equal the actual length.

   $$\frac{1 \text{ cm}}{300 \text{ m}} = \frac{\boxed{} \text{ cm}}{x \text{ m}} \quad \begin{array}{l} \leftarrow \text{ length in drawing} \\ \leftarrow \text{ actual length} \end{array}$$

5. What is one cross product in the proportion?   _____

6. What is the other cross product?   _____

7. Write an equation using the cross products.   _____

8. Solve the equation. What is the value of x?   _____

9. What is the actual length of the island?   _____

© Pearson Education, Inc.

Maps and Scale Drawings (continued)

A buried treasure is located 900 meters from the tree on the island.
Answer 10 to 14 to find the scale distance between the tree and
the treasure.

10. Write a proportion that can be used to find the scale
distance between the tree and the treasure. Let d
equal the scale distance.   _____

11. Write an equation using the cross products.   _____

12. Solve the equation. What is the value of d?   _____

13. What is the scale distance between the tree
and the treasure?   _____

14. Place an X on the drawing that could represent the location of the treasure.

If the scale is $\frac{1 \text{ inch}}{12 \text{ feet}}$, what is the actual length for each scale length?

15. $4\frac{1}{2}$ inches   **16.** 5 inches   **17.** 3 inches

_____   _____   _____

If the scale is $\frac{1 \text{ inch}}{30 \text{ feet}}$, what is the scale length for each actual length?

18. 60 feet   **19.** 150 feet   **20.** 75 feet

_____   _____   _____

21. A scale drawing of a house shows a scale of $\frac{1 \text{ inch}}{3 \text{ feet}}$.

The drawing shows a room which is 5 inches long.
How long is the actual room?   _____

22. A treasure map shows a scale of $\frac{1 \text{ inch}}{40 \text{ feet}}$.

If the map shows the treasure to be located 2 inches
from a large rock, how many feet in actual distance
is the treasure from the rock?   _____

23. Reasoning How is a scale similar to a rate?

© Pearson Education, Inc.

Name _____

Understanding Percent

Rhonda has made the pattern shown with black, gray and white tiles.
Use the pattern to answer 1 to 12.

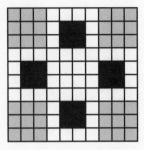

1. What is the total number of tiles in the pattern? _____

2. How many of the tiles are black? _____

3. What is the ratio of black tiles to total number of tiles? _____

4. Write the ratio of black tiles to total
number of tiles in simplest form. _____

Percent mean "per hundred." The percent of black tiles means the
number of black tiles per one hundred tiles.

5. How many tiles are black out of 100? _____

So, 16% of the tiles are black.

6. How many of the tiles are gray? _____

7. What is the ratio of gray tiles to total
number of tiles in simplest form? _____

8. What percent of the tiles are gray? _____

9. How many of the tiles are white? _____

10. What is the ratio of white tiles to total
number of tiles in simplest form? _____

11. What percent of the tiles are white? _____

© Pearson Education, Inc.

Understanding Percent (continued)

12. Reasoning What percent of the tiles are either black, gray or white?

Write each ratio as a percent.

13. $\frac{13}{100}$

14. 87 out of 100

15. $\frac{29}{100}$

_____   _____   _____

Tell what percent of each grid is shaded. Then write the ratio in simplest form.

16.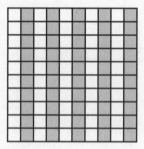

17.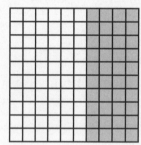

18.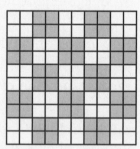

_____   _____   _____

19.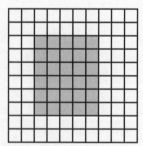

20.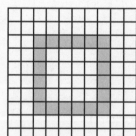

21.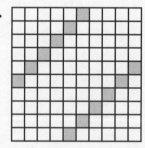

_____   _____   _____

22. There are 100 students in the 5th grade. Of those, 43 of them are in the school band. What percent of 5th grade students are in band?

_____

© Pearson Education, Inc.

Name _____

Relating Percents, Decimals, and Fractions

The hundred grid below represents the number of students out of 100 surveyed that ride the bus to school. Write this number as a percent, a decimal, and a fraction in simplest form by answering 1 to 7.

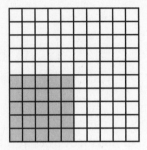

1. How many students were surveyed?   _____

2. How many students ride the bus out of 100?   _____

3. What percent of the students surveyed ride the bus? _____

4. Write a decimal to represent the shaded
part of the hundred grid.   _____

5. What fraction of the hundred grid is shaded?   _____

6. Write the fraction from item 5 in simplest form.   _____

7. The percent, decimal, and fraction forms are all
equal. Use one of each form to fill in the blanks.   _____ = _____ = _____

The same survey of 100 students found that 32% walk to school. Write this percent as a decimal and a fraction in simplest form by answering 8 to 10.

8. To change a percent to a decimal, remove the percent
sign and move the decimal point two places to the left.
What decimal is equal to 32%?   _____

9. To change a percent to a fraction, remove the percent
sign and write the number over a denominator of 100.
What fraction is equal to 32%?   _____

10. Write the fraction from item 9 in simplest form.   _____

© Pearson Education, Inc.

Name _____

Relating Percents, Decimals, and Fractions (continued)

Write each expression in two other ways.

11. 19%　　　　**12.** $\frac{23}{100}$　　　　**13.** 0.7　　　　**14.** 11%

_____　_____　_____　_____

15. 2%　　　　**16.** $\frac{9}{100}$　　　　**17.** 0.13　　　　**18.** 25%

_____　_____　_____　_____

Write each percent as a decimal and as a fraction in simplest form.

19. 60%　　　　**20.** 5%　　　　**21.** 16%　　　　**22.** 45%

_____　_____　_____　_____

Express each shaded part as a decimal, as a percent, and as a fraction in simplest form.

23. 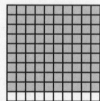　　　**24.** 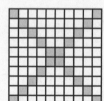　　　**25.**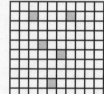

_____　　_____　　_____

26. In Mrs. Hughes's class $\frac{3}{5}$ of the students voted to have tacos

at their end of the year party. What percentage of students
voted for tacos?　　　　　　　　_____

27. Reasoning When dividing a number by 100, the decimal point is
moved two places to the left. How does this relate to the conversion
of a percent into a decimal?

© Pearson Education, Inc.

Percents Greater than 100 or Less Than 1

Shea bought a pair of shoes at a discount store. She found the same
shoes at a department store where the price was 120% the price
at the discount store. Use the diagram and answer 1 to 7 to write a
decimal and a fraction to represent 120%.

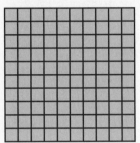 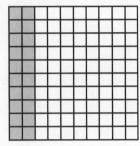

1. To change a percent to a fraction, remove the
percent sign and write the number over a
denominator of 100. What is 120% in fraction form? _____

2. Is the fraction that represents 120% proper or improper? _____

3. What is 120% written as an improper fraction in simplest form? _____

4. Since 120% is greater than 100%, should a decimal
that represents 120% be greater than or less than 1? _____

5. To change a percent to a decimal, remove the
percent sign and move the decimal point two
places to the left. What is 120% in decimal form? _____

6. Is the decimal you wrote for 120% greater than 1? _____

7. Is 120% written as an improper fraction greater than 1? _____

A report states that a company's revenue increased $\frac{1}{4}$% during

the prior year. Use the diagram to write a decimal and a fraction to

represent $\frac{1}{4}$%.

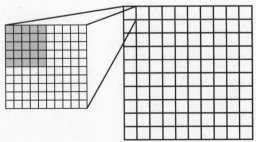

© Pearson Education, Inc.

Percents Greater than 100 or Less than 1 (continued)

8. What is the decimal equivalent of $\frac{1}{4}$? _____

9. Write $\frac{1}{4}$% as a decimal percent. _____

10. To change a percent to a decimal, remove the percent sign and move the decimal point two places to the left. What is 0.25% in decimal form? _____

11. What is 0.25% = 0.0025 as a fraction? _____

12. What is the fraction in simplest form? _____

Express each shaded part as a decimal, a percent and a fraction in simplest form.

13.
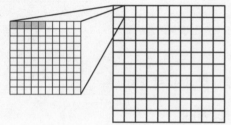

14.
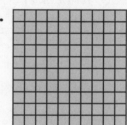

Write each percent as a fraction and a decimal. Write fractions in simplest form.

15. 150%

16. $\frac{3}{4}$%

17. 240%

_____   _____   _____

18. 0.3%

19. 310%

20. 115%

_____   _____   _____

21. Reasoning When is the fraction equivalent to a percent an improper fraction? Explain.

© Pearson Education, Inc.

Estimating Percent of a Number

Benchmark percents can be used to estimate the percent of a number.

1. Fill in the table of benchmark percents and simplified fraction equivalents.

Percent	10%	25%	$33\frac{1}{3}\%$	50%	$66\frac{2}{3}\%$	75%
Fraction	$\frac{1}{10}$		$\frac{1}{3}$		$\frac{2}{3}$	

The circle graph shows the types of tickets sold at a museum during a week. A total of 212 tickets sold during that week.

Estimate the number of adult tickets sold by answering 2 to 6.

Museum Tickets Sold

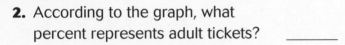

Child 31%   Adult 48%   Senior 21%

2. According to the graph, what percent represents adult tickets? _____

3. What benchmark percent is closest to 48%? _____

4. What fraction is equal to 50%? _____

5. What is $\frac{1}{2} \times 212$? _____

6. About how many adult tickets were sold? _____

Estimate the number of child tickets by answering 7 to 12.

7. According to the graph, what percent represents child tickets?_____

8. What benchmark percent is the closest to 31%? _____

9. What fraction is equal to $33\frac{1}{3}\%$? _____

10. What is 212 rounded to the nearest compatible number, that is, to the nearest number that is easy to divide by 3? _____

11. What is $\frac{1}{3} \times 210$? _____

12. About how many child tickets were sold? _____

© Pearson Education, Inc.

Estimating Percent of a Number (continued)

Estimate the number of senior tickets sold by answering 13 to 18.

13. According to the graph, what percent represents senior tickets? _____

14. What benchmark percent is the closest to 21%? _____

15. What fraction is equal to 25%? _____

16. What is 212 rounded to the nearest hundred? _____

17. What is $\frac{1}{4} \times 200$? _____

18. About how many senior tickets were sold? _____

Estimate.

19. 13% of 34   **20.** 37% of 58   **21.** 68% of $32

_____   _____   _____

22. 72% of $18.03   **23.** 31% of 94   **24.** 27% of 59

_____   _____   _____

25. 51% of 795   **26.** 48% of 8   **27.** 12% of 230

_____   _____   _____

Use this information for Exercise 28 and 29.

A store is offering a discount of 22% on all its items for customers who own a special discount card.

28. Jackson uses his discount card to buy a sweater that originally cost $29. Estimate his discount. _____

29. Patricia uses her discount card to buy a pair of shoes that cost $52 and a pair of jeans that cost $39. Estimate her discount on the jeans. _____

30. **Reasoning** Does an estimate 29% of 43 as $\frac{1}{4}$ of 40 give an overestimate or an underestimate? Explain.

© Pearson Education, Inc.

Math Diagnosis and Intervention System

Intervention Lesson   **H82**

Finding the Percent of a Whole Number

Of the students in the fifth grade, 65% signed up to participate in the band. If there are 120 students in the fifth grade, find the number that signed up to participate by answering 1 to 4.

1. What is 65% written in decimal form?   _____

2. To find 65% of 120, multiply the decimal form by 120.
Write an expression that can be used to find 65% of 120.   _____

3. What is 0.65 × 120?   _____

4. How many students signed up to participate in band?   _____ students

Of the 78 students who signed up to participate in band, about 15% chose to play the clarinet. Find the number of students that chose to play the clarinet by answering 5 to 9.

5. What is 15% written in decimal form?   _____

6. To find 15% of 78, multiply the decimal form by 78.
Write an expression that can be used to find 15% of 78.   _____

7. What is 0.15 × 78?   _____

8. Because 15% of 78 is a number of students,
the final answer should be a whole number.
What is 11.7 rounded to the nearest whole number?   _____

9. How many students chose to play the clarinet?   _____ students

Of the 12 clarinet players, 25% are girls. Find the number of girls that play the clarinet by answering 10 to 12.

10. To find 25% of 12, multiply the decimal form by 12.
Write an expression that can be used to find 25% of 12.   _____

11. What is 0.25 × 12?   _____

12. How many clarinet players are girls?   _____ girls

© Pearson Education, Inc.

Finding the Percent of a Whole Number (continued)

Find each amount.

13. 40% of 15

14. 5% of 60

15. 67% of 20

_____

_____

_____

16. 76% of 80

17. 30% of 400

18. 53% of 120

_____

_____

_____

19. 80% of 45

20. 30% of 79

21. 2% of 50

_____

_____

_____

22. 75% of 150

23. 10% of 6

24. 19% of 40

_____

_____

_____

25. 5% of 99

26. 25% of 260

27. 48% of 65

_____

_____

_____

28. 71% of 90

29. 49% of 200

30. 55% of 24

_____

_____

_____

31. 80% of 50

32. 30% of 400

33. 18% of 75

_____

_____

_____

34. A store offers a 25% discount on all purchases. If you buy
an item costing $30, how much is the discount?   _____

35. **Reasoning** Since 10% of $45 is $4.50, how can you use the result to
find 20% of $45?

© Pearson Education, Inc.

Tips and Sales Tax

Ivan was charged $27 for a haircut. The sales tax is 7.5% and Ivan
tipped 15% on the amount after tax. What is the total amount Ivan paid
for his haircut?

Find the cost with sales tax by answering 1 to 5.

1. What is 7.5% written in decimal form?   _____

2. To find 7.5% of $27, multiply the decimal form by 27.
Write an expression that can be used to find 7.5% of 27.   _____

3. What is 0.075 × 27?   _____

4. Sales tax is always rounded up to the nearest cent.
What is the amount of sales tax? $_____

5. What is the cost of the haircut with tax? $_____

Find the amount of the tip by answering 6 to 10.

6. What is 15% written in decimal form?   _____

7. To find 15% of $29.03, multiply the decimal form
by 29.03. Write an expression that can be used to
find 15% of 29.03.   _____

8. What is 0.15 × 29.03?   _____

9. What is the tip amount rounded to the nearest dollar? $_____

10. What is the cost of the haircut with tax and a 15% tip? $_____

11. If Ivan decided to tip 20% rather than 15%,
what would be the total cost of his haircut? $_____

12. Reasoning Will the tip amount be more or less if it is figured on the
amount before tax rather than the amount after tax? Explain.

© Pearson Education, Inc.

Tips and Sales Tax (continued)

Find the sales tax and the total cost. Round the sales tax to the nearest cent.

13. cost: $65
rate of sales tax: 6%

_____

14. cost: $18
rate of sales tax: 7%

_____

15. cost: $24.50
rate of sales tax: 8%

_____

16. cost: $10.85
rate of sales tax: 4.5%

_____

Find the amount of tip and the total cost. Round the tip amount to the nearest dollar.

17. cost: $15.75
rate of tip: 15%

_____

18. cost: $72
rate of tip: 10%

_____

19. cost: $41.80
rate of tip: 20%

_____

20. cost: $6.25
rate of tip: 10%

_____

21. In one city, the sales is 8%. If you buy an item costing $40, how
much sales tax would you pay?   _____

22. A restaurant requires diners to leave a 15% tip for the waiters.
If the cost of the meal is $35, how much should the tip be?   _____

Use the following information for Exercises 23 to 25.

Jose and George spend $18.50 at a restaurant for two meals. The sales
tax rate is 5%. They want to leave a 15% tip, to the nearest dollar.

23. What is the cost of the meal with tax?   _____

24. How much tip should they leave?   _____

25. What is the total cost with sales tax and tip?   _____

© Pearson Education, Inc.

Computing Discounts

A clothing store has all its merchandise on sale at a 15% discount.
If Pilar chooses a shirt that regularly costs $18.50, how much is
the sale price?

Find the discount and sale price by answering 1 to 5.

1. What is 15% written in decimal form?   _____

2. To find 15% of $18.50, multiply the decimal form by 18.5.
Write an expression that can be used to find 15% of 18.5.   _____

3. What is 0.15 × 18.5?   _____

4. Round the discount to the nearest cent.
What is the amount of discount? $_____

5. Sale price = Regular price − Discount
What is the sale price? $_____

Teachers get a 30% discount on books at a local book store. A teacher
buys a book regularly priced at $24.49. What is the teacher's price?

Find the teacher's price by answering 6 to 12.

6. What is 30% written in decimal form?   _____

7. To find 30% of $24.49, multiply the decimal form by 24.49.
Write an expression that can be used to find 30% of 24.49.   _____

8. What is 0.3 × 24.49?   _____

9. Round the discount to the nearest cent.
What is the amount of discount? $_____

10. Sale price = Regular price − Discount
What is the sale price? $_____

11. The teacher pays 100% − 30% = 70%.
Find 70% of $24.49, rounded to the nearest cent. $_____

12. **Reasoning** Is 70% of $24.49 to the nearest cent the same
as the sale price you found by subtracting the discount?   _____

© Pearson Education, Inc.

Computing Discounts (continued)

Find the discount and the sale price.

13. regular price: $35
rate of discount: 10%

_____

14. regular price: $24.50
rate of discount: 15%

_____

15. regular price: $72
rate of discount: 25%

_____

16. regular price: $60
rate of discount: 30%

_____

17. regular price: $90
rate of discount: 40%

_____

18. regular price: $46.80
rate of discount: 50%

_____

19. William bought two CDs on sale at a 15% discount. One CD cost
$15.99 and the other CD cost $14.99. How much did he pay for
both CDs after the discount?   _____

Use the following for Exercises 20–23.

Mary bought a new television for $250. The television was on sale at a
10% discount. The sales tax rate was 6%.

20. What was the discount?   _____

21. What was the sale price?   _____

22. What is the amount of tax?   _____

23. What is the total cost of the television?   _____

24. **Reasoning** If an item has a discount of 20%, what percent of the
original price will the customer pay? How can this be used to find
the discounted price?

© Pearson Education, Inc.